# Fundamentals of Nuclear Magnetic Resonance

# Fundamentals of Nuclear Magnetic Resonance

**Jacek W. Hennel**

*The Niewodniczański Institute of Nuclear Physics,*
*31-342 Kraków, Radzikowskiego 152, Poland*

**and**

**Jacek Klinowski**

*Department of Chemistry, University of Cambridge,*
*Lensfield Road, Cambridge CB2 1EW, UK*

Longman Scientific & Technical

**Longman Scientific & Technical**
Longman Group UK Limited
Longman House, Burnt Mill, Harlow,
Essex, CM20 2JE, England
*and Associated Companies throughout the world.*

*Copublished in the United States with John Wiley & Sons, Inc., 605 Third Avenue, New York , NY 10158*



First edition 1993

ISBN 0 582 06703 0

**British Library Cataloguing in Publication Data**
A catalogue record for this book is available from the British Library

**Library of Congress Cataloging-in-Publication Data**
A catalog record for this book is available from the Library of Congress

Printed in Hong Kong
WP/01

# Contents

# Preface

The aim of this book is to explain the physical and mathematical basis of nuclear magnetic resonance (NMR) *simply but exactly*. We would like the reader to be able to grasp the fundamental concepts to the extent which will enable him or her to understand the phenomenon, the reasons for and the significance of the various spectral effects and be able to read original research papers.

The mathematics required for reading the text is taught at university courses in natural and technical sciences during the first two years. We assume that the reader is already familiar with calculus, matrix algebra, vectors and complex numbers. Even so, a survey of these subjects is provided.

It is not possible to understand NMR fully without quantum mechanics. Aware of the fact that many readers may have problems in this area, we have included in the opening chapter a condensed account of quantum mechanics at a level sufficient to follow the rest of the book. We are convinced that the effort invested in proper understanding of NMR will turn out to be worth while. As a reward, instead of grappling with unfamiliar rules and equations, the reader will find that the study of NMR is a genuine intellectual adventure. This applies in particular to those who need to be in close contact with NMR for professional reasons.

NMR was discovered in 1945, independently by Bloch, Hansen and Packard at Stanford and by Purcell, Torrey and Pound at Harvard. Chemical applications of the effect began when it was shown in 1950 that the precise frequency of the radiation absorbed by a sample placed in a magnetic field depends on the chemical environment of the nuclei. Several years later commercial spectrometers became available, capable of measuring high-resolution $^1H$ spectra in solutions. The introduction of Fourier transform techniques in 1966 with Fourier algorithms which run on small computers, and the subsequent development of high-field superconducting magnets, meant that other nuclei could also be observed both in solution and in the solid state. Virtually every chemical element can now be studied by NMR. Together with X-ray and neutron diffraction, the technique has become the main tool for the study of the structure and properties of condensed matter.

Scientists come to NMR by two different routes. The effect was discovered by physicists and has always been of interest to them as a physical phenomenon.

They formulated and solved the various problems using rigorous terminology and the appropriate mathematical formalism. It was the physicists who were largely responsible for the development of solid-state NMR, which has greatly enhanced our knowledge of a wide range of materials in chemistry (crystal structure, catalysts, polymers, liquid crystals), physics (molecular motion in condensed matter), biology (action of drugs, membranes), medicine (NMR imaging), geology (minerals, coal and oil shales) and in technology of glass, cements and ceramics. However, the main users of NMR are organic chemists, who became captivated by the manifest power of the technique for structural elucidation.

As a result, the many books on NMR written over the years belong to one of two categories. One approach is to treat NMR as a purely physical effect, and to describe it using the theory of angular momentum, the tensor formalism and the density operator. These texts are too advanced for beginners, who are left in need of further reading in various areas of mathematics and physics. By contrast, books in the second category use a descriptive and essentially intuitive approach, stressing the chemical interpretation of the spectra, largely (or completely) dispensing with mathematics. Chemists are interested in the interpretation of spectra, and would like the various techniques which they use to be described by reference to simple models. However, modern NMR techniques quite simply cannot be appreciated by those who lack the necessary training and are unequipped to tackle original research papers. Although readers can often grasp the gist of the work, only very few are able to understand the physical reality. This volume is intended to remedy the problem.

NMR rarely calls on really sophisticated concepts of higher mathematics: most mathematics it uses is circa 200 years old. We aim to introduce *ideas* rather than *techniques*. An eminently successful example of this approach is R.P. Feynman's *Lectures on Physics,* the celebrated text which assumes little prior knowledge from the reader and is still able to explain, with remarkable clarity, the whole of modern experimental physics, including many supposedly elementary concepts. Our book is addressed to everyone who is seriously interested in NMR: undergraduate and postgraduate students, organic, inorganic and physical chemists, physicists, earth scientists, mineralogists, those interested in fuels, polymers, wood, the structure of molecules in solution and the solid and those who wish to become involved in NMR imaging. We are not concerned with giving the reader advice on how to do any particular NMR experiment, but on the science that underlies it. In other words, the book addresses just one simple question: "What is the physical basis of NMR?"

We wish the reader a pleasant journey through the fascinating realm of nuclear magnetic resonance.

We are grateful to Dr Z. Olejniczak, Dr M. Klinowska, Professor K. Zalewski, Professor R. Freeman, FRS, Mr Heyong He, Dr S. Bahçeli, Mr F. Hennel, Mr T. Skórka and Mr R. Serafin for comments on the text, and to Mr M.J. Springett for preparing the figures. Parts of the book are loosely based on *An Introduction to the Theory of NMR*, written by one of us (JWH) and published by PWN, Warsaw, in 1966.

Jacek W. Hennel
Jacek Klinowski
Cambridge, Sunday 24 May 1992

# Chapter 1. Elements of Quantum Mechanics

## 1. Operators

The concept of an operator is central to quantum mechanics and, by implication, to all branches of spectroscopy. An operator G acts on a function to give another function:

$$G\,f(x, y, z) = g(x, y, z)\,.$$

In other words, the operator G assigns function g to function f.

To define an operator we must provide instructions on how function g is derived from function f. In the case of the differential operator $\partial/\partial x$ the instruction is simple: "differentiate the function with respect to variable x"; and the function $f(x, y, z)$ gives rise to the function $g(x, y, z) = \partial f(x, y, z)/\partial x$. Clearly, the differential operator can only be applied to functions which are continuous with respect to x. A *linear* operator has the following properties:

$$G\left(f_1 + f_2\right) = G\,f_1 + G\,f_2$$

$$G\,(c\,f) = c\,G\,f$$

where c is a number. All operators used in quantum mechanics are linear. Just as with numbers, we define equality of operators, their sum, difference, the zero operator and the identity operator.

The identity operator, often denoted by $\mathbb{E}$, acts as follows

$$\mathbb{E}\,f = f\,.$$

Since multiplication by a number can be considered to be an operator (the "multiplication operator"), the identity operator is equivalent to the multiplication operator 1.

The product of operators $G_2$ and $G_1$ is formed by first acting on a function with $G_1$ and then acting with $G_2$ on the result. However, acting on the same function with the same operators in the reverse order does not necessarily give the same result: multiplication of operators is not commutative. Thus in general

$$G_2 G_1 \neq G_1 G_2 .$$

The algebra of operators is therefore different from the algebra of numbers and resembles the algebra of matrices. Indeed, we shall see that operators can be conveniently treated as matrices. The *commutator* is defined as

$$[G_1, G_2] = G_1 G_2 - G_2 G_1 .$$

When the commutator is zero we say that the two operators commute

$$[G_1, G_2] = 0 . \tag{1.1}$$

Note that both sides of (1.1) are operators, since zero can be considered as an operator which acts on any function to give zero as a result: $\mathbb{0}\, f = 0$. The zero operator and the identity operator $\mathbb{1}\, f = f$ are multiplication operators: their action consists of multiplying functions by zero and unity, respectively. Operators x and $\partial/\partial x$ do not commute since

$$\left[ \frac{\partial}{\partial x}, x \right] = \mathbb{1} . \tag{1.2}$$

This is easily verified by calculating the value of the commutator for an arbitrary function f:

$$\frac{\partial\,(x\,f)}{\partial x} - x\,\frac{\partial f}{\partial x} = f + x\,\frac{\partial f}{\partial x} - x\,\frac{\partial f}{\partial x} = f . \qquad \text{q.e.d.}$$

Quantum mechanics uses functions of the complex variable defined in multidimensional space. We shall represent these functions by Greek characters. The reader who wishes to be reminded of some relevant properties of complex numbers may consult Appendix 1 or Paliouras and Meadows (1990).

The special property of functions used in quantum mechanics is that integrals of their squares $\psi_m^* \psi_m$ and of their products $\psi_m^* \psi_n$ over all space are finite.

Integration of a product of functions involves the following definition of a Hermitian operator. Operator G is said to be Hermitian if it satisfies the equation

$$\int \psi_m^* G\, \psi_n\, dV = \left( \int \psi_n^* G\, \psi_m\, dV \right)^* \tag{1.3a}$$

where integration is over all space and the asterisk denotes the complex conjugate. We see that, when the two functions exchange places, the result is the conjugate value of the integral.

An alternative form of (1.3a) is obtained by taking the complex conjugate of each term on the right

$$\int \psi_m^* G \psi_n \, dV = \int (G \psi_m)^* \psi_n \, dV . \tag{1.3b}$$

Sometimes the action of an operator on a certain "special" function is equivalent to multiplying the function by a constant $\lambda$

$$G\psi = \lambda \psi . \tag{1.4}$$

For example, the action of the operator $\partial/\partial x$ on the function exp (ax), where a is a number, is equivalent to multiplying the function by a:

$$\frac{\partial \left[\exp(ax)\right]}{\partial x} = a \exp(ax) .$$

The function $\psi$ which satisfies condition (1.4) is known as the *eigenfunction* of the operator G, and $\lambda$ as the *eigenvalue*. The set of eigenvalues of a given operator may be continuous or may consist of discrete numbers

$$\lambda_1, \lambda_2, \lambda_3, \ldots . \tag{1.5}$$

Sometimes the number of eigenvalues of a given operator is finite. In quantum mechanics we normally deal with differential operators, for which the problem of finding eigenfunctions and the corresponding eigenvalues reduces to solving a differential equation and finding the values of $\lambda$ for which a meaningful solution exists. Eigenfunctions of special interest are those which are (a) continuous; (b) finite; (c) single-valued; (d) such that the integral $\int \varphi^* \varphi \, dV$ is finite and positive. Condition (d) implies that the eigenfunction must not be identically equal to zero. Only such eigenfunctions may play a role in quantum mechanics. Eigenfunctions which satisfy all the above conditions are said to be "well behaved".

A function $\psi_m$ is known as normalized (or "normal") when

$$\int \psi_m^* \psi_m \, dV = 1 \tag{1.6a}$$

and two functions, $\psi_m$ and $\psi_n$, are called orthogonal when

$$\int \psi_m^* \psi_n \, dV = 0 . \tag{1.6b}$$

A set of functions $\psi_m$ where m = 1, 2, 3, ... , L is known as orthonormal if all of them are normalized and each two of them are orthogonal.

Eigenfunctions and eigenvalues of Hermitian operators have two important properties: (i) the eigenvalues are real; (ii) when two well behaved eigenfunctions $\psi_m$ and $\psi_n$ have different eigenvalues, they are orthogonal.

Property (i) is proved as follows. Let $\psi$ be the eigenfunction of a Hermitian operator G, as required by (1.4). Calculate two integrals, a and b, defined as

$$a = \int \psi^* G \psi \, dV = \lambda \int \psi^* \psi \, dV$$

$$b = \int (G\psi)^* \psi \, dV = \lambda^* \int \psi^* \psi \, dV .$$

The two integrals must be equal, since G is Hermitian. At the same time, since $\psi$ is well behaved, $\int \psi^* \psi \, dV \neq 0$. It follows that $\lambda = \lambda^*$. q.e.d.

To prove property (ii) we take two eigenfunctions, $\psi_1$ and $\psi_2$, of a Hermitian operator G, so that $G\psi_1 = \lambda_1 \psi_1$ and $G\psi_2 = \lambda_2 \psi_2$. We calculate the integrals

$$c = \int \psi_1^* G \psi_2 \, dV = \lambda_2 \int \psi_1^* \psi_2 \, dV$$

$$d = \int (G\psi_1)^* \psi_2 \, dV = \lambda_1 \int \psi_1^* \psi_2 \, dV .$$

Again, the two integrals are equal, since G is Hermitian. On the other hand, $\lambda_1 \neq \lambda_2$, which implies that $\int \psi_1^* \psi_2 \, dV = 0$. q.e.d.

The set of all linearly independent eigenfunctions[1] of an operator with the property

$$\int \psi_m^* \psi_n \, dV = \delta_{mn} \qquad (1.6c)$$

is known as the orthonormal set. $\delta_{mn}$, known as the "Kronecker delta", is defined as

$$\delta_{mn} \begin{cases} = 1 & \text{for } m = n \\ = 0 & \text{for } m \neq n \,. \end{cases}$$

The necessary and sufficient condition for two operators to have all eigenfunctions in common is that they commute.

Any function can be expanded in terms of all the eigenfunctions of an operator (see also Section 6). If the $\psi_n$ are all linearly independent eigenfunctions of an operator G, i.e. satisfy the eigenvalue equation $G\,\psi_n = \lambda_n \psi_n$, a function $\varphi$ can be expressed as the sum

$$\varphi = \sum_{n=1}^{n} c_n \psi_n$$

where the $c_n$ are numerical coefficients. Consider the effect of operator G on $\varphi$, a function which is not its eigenfunction. We have

$$G\,\varphi = G \sum_n c_n \psi_n = \sum_n c_n G\,\psi_n = \sum_n c_n \lambda_n \psi_n = \sum_n c_n' \psi_n = \varphi' \,.$$

The result is a new function, $\varphi'$.

When an eigenvalue $\lambda$ is shared by two or more linearly independent eigenfunctions, it is said to be degenerate:

$$G\,\psi_n = \lambda\,\psi_n \qquad \text{with } n = 1, 2, \ldots, k \,.$$

When the maximum number of linearly independent eigenfunctions belonging to $\lambda$ is k, we say that the eigenvalue is k-fold degenerate. This means that any additional (k + 1)th eigenfunction belonging to $\lambda$ can be represented as a linear combination of these k eigenfunctions.

---

[1] For example, three linearly independent functions are such that no linear combination $a_1 \psi_1 + a_2 \psi_2 + a_3 \psi_3 = 0$ exists (the $a_i$ are constants) other than $a_1 = a_2 = a_3 = 0$.

Any linear combination of a set of eigenfunctions belonging to a degenerate eigenvalue is also an eigenfunction belonging to the same eigenvalue. Consider $\varphi = \sum_1^k c_n \psi_n$ . We have

$$G\varphi = G\sum_1^k c_n \psi_n = \sum_1^k c_n G \psi_n = \sum_1^k c_n \lambda_n \psi_n = \lambda \sum_1^k c_n \psi_n = \lambda \varphi . \qquad \text{q.e.d.}$$

From a known set of k independent eigenfunctions $\psi_n$ belonging to a k-fold degenerate eigenvalue $\lambda$ we can form, by linear combination, any desired number of other sets $\chi_n$ (n = 1, 2, .... , k) of linearly independent eigenfunctions belonging to the same eigenvalue. All these sets contain the same information about the dynamical quantity G. Which set is obtained depends on the way the calculations have been carried out, and different authors use different sets without making an error.

Quantum mechanics often uses the so-called exponential operators. It is well known that an exponential of a number x can be expanded into a series

$$\exp x = \sum_{n=0}^{\infty} \frac{x^n}{n!} = 1 + x + \frac{x^2}{2!} + \frac{x^3}{3!} + .... \tag{1.7}$$

It is useful to define a similar function, but with an *operator* in the exponent. Let G be an operator and let a be a number. The *exponential operator* exp (a G) is defined by the following series:

$$\exp (a\,G) = \sum_{n=0}^{\infty} \frac{(a\,G)^n}{n!} .$$

Raising an operator to the power n is equivalent to the n-fold application of the operator. It follows that if a function $\varphi$ is an eigenfunction of the operator G corresponding to eigenvalue $\lambda$, then $G^n \varphi = \lambda^n \varphi$. Therefore the function $\varphi$ is also an eigenfunction of the exponential operator with eigenvalue exp (a $\lambda$), i.e.

$$\exp (a\,G)\, \varphi = \sum \frac{(a\,\lambda)^n}{n!} \varphi = \exp (a\,\lambda)\, \varphi .$$

If a is a real number and the operator G is Hermitian, the operator exp (a G) is also Hermitian, since it is easily proved that the operator $a^n G^n$ is Hermitian. If, however, a is imaginary, a = i b, where b is real, the operator exp (a G) is not Hermitian (see equation 1.3a), since

$$\int \psi_2^* \exp(i\, b\, G)\, \psi_1\, dV = \int \left[\exp(-i\, b\, G)\, \psi_2\right]^* \psi_1\, dV \tag{1.8}$$

and the sign of the term under the exponential changes. We prove (1.8) by transforming its left-hand side using the Hermiticity of $G^n$ and the relationship $(i^n)^* = (-i)^n$

$$\int \psi_2^* \sum \frac{(i\, b\, G)^n}{n!} \psi_1\, dV = \sum \frac{i^n b^n}{n!} \int (G^n \psi_2)^* \psi_1\, dV$$

$$= \int \left(\sum \frac{(-i\, b\, G)^n}{n!} \psi_2\right)^* \psi_1\, dV = \int \left[\exp(-i\, b\, G)\, \psi_2\right]^* \psi_1\, dV \,. \qquad \text{q.e.d.}$$

## 2. Expectation Values

Quantum mechanics allows us to calculate the values of measurable quantities describing microscopic systems, i.e. systems composed of particles such as electrons, atomic nuclei and nucleons. These so-called dynamical quantities appear in classical mechanics as functions of position and momentum. Examples of dynamical quantities are the energy and the momentum of a particle. Thus energy is expressed as

$$E = \frac{1}{2m}\left(p_x^2 + p_y^2 + p_z^2\right) + V(x, y, z)$$

where the $p_i$ are the coordinates of momentum **p**, and $V(x, y, z)$ is the potential energy of the particle. The angular momentum of a moving particle is given by the cross-product (see Appendix 2) of the vectors of position and momentum:

$$\mathbf{L} = \mathbf{r} \times \mathbf{p}$$

where vector **r** with coordinates $(x, y, z)$ describes the position of the particle. Position **r** and momentum **p** are further examples of dynamical quantities.

In quantum mechanics a single measurement of a dynamical quantity cannot provide complete information about the system under study. This is because when we repeat the measurement under identical conditions, we do not necessarily obtain the same result. This is an intrinsic quantum-mechanical property of the system and not the result of experimental error.

Quantum mechanics provides rules for calculating: (1) numerical values which can result from a single measurement; (2) the mean value of a large number of measurements carried out under identical conditions.

Consider rule (1). We wish to measure the dynamical quantity $G(x, y, z, p_x, p_y, p_z)$. Quantum mechanics instructs us to assign to this quantity a Hermitian operator $G_{op}$, but does not tell us explicitly how such an operator should be formed. When we introduce dynamical quantities and their corresponding operators, their commutators must satisfy certain conditions. This is the only limitation to assigning Hermitian operators to dynamical quantities. We shall not specify the conditions which must be met by commutators between the individual operators, but only give one of the possible ways of assigning operators, which meets all the requirements. This method, suggested by Schrödinger, consists of formal substitution of the following operators into G:

$$\begin{aligned}
&\text{instead of } x \text{ the operator } x;\ \text{instead of } p_x \text{ the operator } -i\hbar\frac{\partial}{\partial x}\\
&\text{instead of } y \text{ the operator } y;\ \text{instead of } p_y \text{ the operator } -i\hbar\frac{\partial}{\partial y}\\
&\text{instead of } z \text{ the operator } z;\ \text{instead of } p_z \text{ the operator } -i\hbar\frac{\partial}{\partial z}
\end{aligned}\qquad(2.1)$$

so that

$$G_{op} = G\left(x, y, z, -i\hbar\frac{\partial}{\partial x}, -i\hbar\frac{\partial}{\partial y}, -i\hbar\frac{\partial}{\partial z}\right)$$

where $\hbar$ is the Planck constant divided by $2\pi$, and the action of the operators x, y and z is to multiply by x, y and z, respectively.

Having seen how to assign operator $G_{op}$ to the dynamical quantity G we can formulate the remainder of rule (1). This says that the result of an individual measurement of the dynamical quantity G must be an eigenvalue of $G_{op}$ appearing together with a well behaved eigenfunction. Thus, if we wish to calculate values which can appear as the result of a single measurement, we must solve the eigenvalue equation[2] for the operator G

$$G\varphi = \lambda\varphi \qquad (2.2)$$

[2] Since the reader will always be aware of whether he is dealing with a dynamic quantity or its operator, in compliance with custom we shall from now on omit the subscript "op".

and discard solutions which are not well behaved. As we know, $\lambda$ can sometimes take on discrete values. This is one of the most important differences between quantum mechanics and classical mechanics. Classically, dynamical quantities can take on all values within a certain interval. In this book we deal exclusively with discrete eigenvalues. Since it is inherently impossible to predict which of the values allowed by (2.2) will appear as the result of a single measurement, such measurement does not provide complete information about the system. This information can only be obtained by performing a very large number of measurements, which allow us to establish the probability $P(\lambda_i)$ for a given eigenvalue $\lambda_i$ to occur. This probability is characteristic of the state of the system at the time the measurements were performed. We assume that all measurements are carried out under identical conditions, i.e. on the system in the same state, and we disregard the time needed for each experiment to be performed. This is equivalent to performing the same measurement on a large number of identical systems, all in the same state. If, among the results of N measurements, eigenvalue $\lambda_i$ appears $N_i$ times, the probability is

$$P(\lambda_i) = N_i/N\,.$$

In quantum mechanics the state of the system is described by the function of state $\psi$ known as the wavefunction. $\psi$ is defined in n-dimensional space, where n is the number of degrees of freedom of the system. The wavefunction must be well behaved. It cannot be unambiguously calculated from the results of measurements, but can only be determined with a certain degree of latitude if the probability density $P(\lambda_i)$ is known. Assume for the time being that the eigenvalues of operator G are non-degenerate. We then obtain the wavefunction by forming the following series of eigenfunctions of that operator:

$$\psi = \sum_i a_i\,\varphi_i \tag{2.3}$$

where coefficients $a_i$ are complex numbers, the moduli of which can be determined experimentally from

$$a_i\,a_i^* = P(\lambda_i) \tag{2.4}$$

while their phase is arbitrary. Summation is performed over the complex set of orthogonal eigenfunctions of the operator G. On the other hand, if we know the wavefunction $\psi(x, y, z)$ we can expand it into a series of eigenfunctions of operator G and thus find the probability density $P(\lambda_i)$ from (2.4). The fundamental theorem of quantum mechanics states that such an expansion is permissible.

Multiply both sides of (2.3) by $\varphi_j^*$ and integrate over all space:

$$\int \varphi_j^* \psi \, dV = \sum_i a_i \int \varphi_j^* \varphi_i \, dV .$$

The orthonormality condition (1.6c) tells us that the integral on the right-hand side is unity for $i = j$ and zero otherwise. The coefficients $a_j$ in the expansion (2.3) are thus

$$\int \varphi_j^* \psi \, dV = a_j . \tag{2.5}$$

If the operator G has degenerate eigenvalues, then the knowledge of the probability density $P(\lambda_i)$ is insufficient for forming wavefunctions, because certain additional measurements need to be performed. We will explain this in Section 3 using the operator of angular momentum as an example.

Consider the mean value of a large number of measurements (the "expectation value") defined as

$$< G > = \sum_i \lambda_i P(\lambda_i) . \tag{2.6}$$

$< G >$ can be derived from the wavefunction, since the "mean value theorem" of quantum mechanics tells us that

$$< G > = \int \psi^* G \psi \, dV . \tag{2.7}$$

To prove (2.7) we expand functions $\psi^*$ and $\psi$ as series of orthogonal eigenfunctions $\varphi_i$ of the operator G, substitute these expansions into (2.7), use the Schrödinger equation (2.2), multiply the sums, take advantage of the orthonormality of function $\varphi_i$ and finally use (2.4) to arrive at (2.6). The calculation goes as follows:

$$\int \psi^* G \psi \, dV = \int \sum_i a_i^* \varphi_i^* \sum_j a_j G \varphi_j \, dV$$

$$= \sum_i \sum_j a_i^* a_j \lambda_j \int \varphi_i^* \varphi_j \, dV = \sum_i \lambda_i a_i^* a_i = \sum_i \lambda_i P(\lambda_i) . \quad \text{q.e.d.}$$

When using (2.4) we limited ourselves to the case of an operator with non-degenerate eigenvalues. However, (2.7) applies to all Hermitian operators.

Consider the situation when the wavefunction is equal to one of the eigenfunctions of the operator G, for example $\psi = \varphi_k$. Calculating, from (2.5), the coefficients of the expansion of the function $\psi$ into a series of functions $\varphi_i$ it is easily seen that they are all zero apart from the coefficient $a_k$ appearing with function $\varphi_k$, for which $a_k = 1$. On the strength of (2.4) we have therefore

$$P(\lambda_i) = \delta_{ik}$$

which means that it is certain that a single measurement of the dynamical quantity will yield $\lambda_k$ as the result: the value of the dynamical quantity G is thus precisely determined. The question arises whether there can exist states for which the values of *two* different dynamical quantities, say $G_1$ and $G_2$, are precisely determined. A theorem about common eigenfunctions of two operators tells us that this is possible only when operators $G_1$ and $G_2$ commute.

So far we have considered the state of the system at a particular time, for example at $t = 0$. The state of the system can change in time and then the wavefunction depends not only on spatial coordinates but also on time. Laws governing time dependence of wavefunctions will be discussed in Section 5.

## 3. Angular Momentum Operator

In classical mechanics the angular momentum of a material point is defined as

$$\mathbf{L} = \mathbf{r} \times \mathbf{p} \tag{3.1}$$

where vector **r** with coordinates x, y, z determines the position of a point of mass m, and $\mathbf{p} = m\,\mathbf{v}$ is the vector of linear momentum, where $\mathbf{v} = d\mathbf{r}/dt$ is the velocity of the point. An operator may be a vector (a "vector operator") in the sense that its coordinates may be operators, and in quantum mechanics we replace vector **p** by operator **p** using the Schrödinger rules (2.1). Consider **p** in the above equation as an operator and form the cross-product (see Appendix 2)

$$\mathbf{r} \times \mathbf{p} = \begin{vmatrix} \mathbf{i} & \mathbf{j} & \mathbf{k} \\ x & y & z \\ p_x & p_y & p_z \end{vmatrix}$$

to express **L** as a linear combination of unit vectors **i, j, k** along the axes X, Y, Z of the coordinate system. We calculate the determinant

$$\mathbf{L} = \mathbf{r} \times \mathbf{p} = \mathbf{i}\,(y\,p_z - z\,p_y) + \mathbf{j}\,(z\,p_x - x\,p_z) + \mathbf{k}\,(x\,p_y - y\,p_x)$$

and thus the coordinates of operator **L**, for example $L_x$, are

$$L_x = (yp_z - zp_y) = i\hbar\,\left(z\frac{\partial}{\partial y} - y\frac{\partial}{\partial z}\right).$$

Having found the operators of the coordinates of angular momentum, we can form the operator of the square of total angular momentum $L^2 = L_x^2 + L_y^2 + L_z^2$ and calculate the following commutators:

$$\begin{aligned} [L_x, L_y] &= i\hbar L_z \\ [L_y, L_z] &= i\hbar L_x \\ [L_z, L_x] &= i\hbar L_y \end{aligned} \tag{3.2a}$$

$$\begin{aligned} [L_x, L^2] &= 0 \\ [L_y, L^2] &= 0 \\ [L_z, L^2] &= 0\,. \end{aligned} \tag{3.2b}$$

Note that operator $L^2$ commutes with all coordinates of angular momentum.

We have so far been using the Cartesian coordinate system. For convenience of calculation, this has one serious disadvantage: the length of a vector is expressed as the root of a sum of squares. It is more useful to resort to the polar[3] coordinate system, in which the length of a vector is simply one of the coordinates (see Figure 3.1). The relationship between the Cartesian and the polar coordinate systems is as follows:

$$\begin{aligned} x &= r \sin\theta\, \cos\phi \\ y &= r \sin\theta\, \sin\phi \\ z &= r \cos\theta \end{aligned} \tag{3.3}$$

[3] This coordinate system is often called "spherical". To avoid misunderstanding we prefer to call it the "polar" system, reserving the name "spherical" for the coordinate system used for the description of spherical tensors.

or by the equivalent reverse transformation

$$r = \sqrt{x^2 + y^2 + z^2}$$
$$\theta = \arccos(z/r) \tag{3.4}$$
$$\phi = \arctan(y/x)$$

with $r > 0$, $0 < \theta \le \pi$ and $0 \le \phi < 2\pi$ .

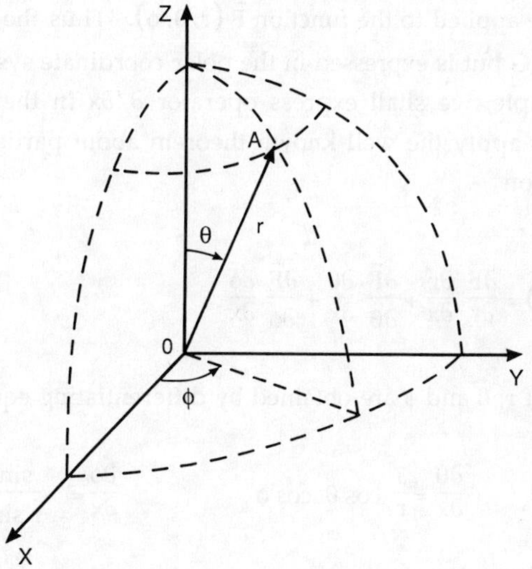


**Figure 3.1.** The polar coordinate system. Polar coordinates of point A, and of the vector **r**, are $(r, \theta, \phi)$.

The form of the operators changes upon transformation to the new coordinate system. Consider an arbitrary continuous function $F(x, y, z)$, which assigns a certain number to a point in space. If we express the position of that point in the polar system using coordinates $(r, \theta, \phi)$ we can construct a function $\bar{F}(r, \theta, \phi)$ such that

$$F(x, y, z) = \bar{F}(r, \theta, \phi)$$

where the coordinates $(x, y, z)$ and $(r, \theta, \phi)$ refer to the same point in space, i.e. are related by (3.3) and (3.4). Thus

$$\bar{F}(r, \theta, \phi) = F\left[x(r, \theta, \phi), y(r, \theta, \phi), z(r, \theta, \phi)\right].$$

Assume that we know the rules of action of operator G on functions of variables $(x, y, z)$. We seek an operator $\bar{G}$ for which

$$G\,F(x, y, z) = \bar{G}\,\bar{F}(r, \theta, \phi).$$

Operator $\bar{G}$ has the same assignment rule as operator G, but expressed in such a way that it can be applied to the function $\bar{F}(r, \theta, \phi)$. Thus the operator $\bar{G}$ is the same as operator G but is expressed in the polar coordinate system.

As an example, we shall express operator $\partial/\partial x$ in the polar coordinate system. We first apply the well known theorem about partial derivatives of a composite function

$$\frac{\partial}{\partial x}\bar{F}(r, \theta, \phi) = \frac{\partial \bar{F}}{\partial r}\frac{\partial r}{\partial x} + \frac{\partial \bar{F}}{\partial \theta}\frac{\partial \theta}{\partial x} + \frac{\partial \bar{F}}{\partial \phi}\frac{\partial \phi}{\partial x}. \tag{3.5}$$

The derivatives of r, θ and φ are obtained by differentiating equations (3.4):

$$\frac{\partial r}{\partial x} = \frac{x}{r}; \qquad \frac{\partial \theta}{\partial x} = \frac{1}{r}\cos\theta\,\cos\phi; \qquad \frac{\partial \phi}{\partial x} = -\frac{\sin\phi}{r\sin\theta}.$$

Substituting these in (3.5) we find

$$\frac{\partial \bar{F}}{\partial x} = \sin\theta\,\cos\phi\,\frac{\partial \bar{F}}{\partial r} + \frac{1}{r}\cos\theta\,\cos\phi\,\frac{\partial \bar{F}}{\partial \theta} - \frac{1}{r}\frac{\sin\phi}{\sin\theta}\frac{\partial \bar{F}}{\partial \phi}.$$

It follows that in polar coordinates the operator $\partial/\partial x$ has the form

$$\frac{\partial}{\partial x} = \sin\theta\,\cos\phi\,\frac{\partial}{\partial r} + \frac{1}{r}\cos\theta\,\cos\phi\,\frac{\partial}{\partial \theta} - \frac{1}{r}\frac{\sin\phi}{\sin\theta}\frac{\partial}{\partial \phi}.$$

Similarly, the operators of angular momentum are

$$L_x = i\hbar\left(\sin\phi\,\frac{\partial}{\partial\theta} + \cot\theta\,\cos\phi\,\frac{\partial}{\partial\phi}\right) \tag{3.6}$$

$$L_y = i\hbar\left(-\cos\phi\,\frac{\partial}{\partial\theta} + \cot\theta\,\sin\phi\,\frac{\partial}{\partial\phi}\right) \tag{3.7}$$

$$L_z = -i\hbar\,\frac{\partial}{\partial\phi} \tag{3.8}$$

$$L^2 = -\hbar^2\left[\frac{1}{\sin\theta}\,\frac{\partial}{\partial\theta}\left(\sin\theta\,\frac{\partial}{\partial\theta}\right) + \frac{1}{\sin^2\theta}\,\frac{\partial^2}{\partial\phi^2}\right]. \tag{3.9}$$

The operator in square brackets in (3.9) is known as the Legendre operator.

We now proceed to calculate the eigenvalue of the projection of angular momentum on a chosen direction in space. It is sufficient for the purpose to consider only operator $L_z$, because we can always choose the coordinate system in such a way that the Z axis lies in the desired direction. We must therefore solve the eigenvalue equation $L_z\,\psi = \lambda\,\psi$ which, according to (3.8), in polar coordinates takes the form

$$-i\hbar\,\frac{\partial}{\partial\phi}\,\psi = \lambda\,\psi\,.$$

The general solution of this differential equation is

$$\psi = A\exp\left(i\,\lambda\,\phi/\hbar\right) \tag{3.10}$$

where A is an arbitrary constant. Of the solutions of (3.10), the only single-valued ones are those where each $\phi$ and $\phi + 2\pi$ take on the same value (since for given r and $\theta$, the values of $\phi$ and $\phi + 2\pi$ correspond to the same point in space). In order for the function to be well behaved, it is therefore necessary that the ratio $\lambda/\hbar$ be a real integer so that

$$\lambda = m\,\hbar \tag{3.11}$$

where m is known as the magnetic quantum number ($m = 0, \pm 1, \pm 2, \ldots$). Substituting (3.11) into (3.10) we obtain the eigenfunction of the operator $L_z$ appearing with eigenvalue $m\hbar$

$$\psi_m = A\exp\left(i\,m\,\phi\right). \tag{3.12}$$

It is easily shown that eigenvalues given by equation (3.11) are degenerate. Consider two linearly independent functions of coordinates r and $\theta$ only, for example $f_1(r, \theta)$ and $f_2(r, \theta)$. Substituting these instead of A in equation (3.10) we obtain two linearly independent eigenfunctions corresponding to the same eigenvalue $m\hbar$.

The eigenvalues of operators $L_x$ and $L_y$ are also $m\hbar$, since, as we said, we can always choose the coordinate system in such a way that the X or Y axes lie in the desired direction. Thus the set of values which may appear as the result of a single measurement is the same for each of the three components of the total angular momentum. However, there is no common eigenfunction for operators $L_x$, $L_y$ and $L_z$, since they do not commute among themselves (see equation (3.2a)). Thus, if the value of one of them is determined, the values of the other two are indeterminate.

We shall now solve the eigenvalue equation of the operator $L^2$ of the square of angular momentum. It is convenient to do so in polar coordinates in which this operator has the form (3.9). We are seeking the solution of the following differential equation involving function $f(\theta, \phi)$:

$$-\hbar^2\left(\frac{1}{\sin\theta}\frac{\partial}{\partial\theta}\sin\theta\frac{\partial}{\partial\theta}+\frac{1}{\sin^2\theta}\frac{\partial^2}{\partial\phi^2}\right)f=\lambda f. \tag{3.13}$$

First we seek solutions in the form of the product

$$f(\theta, \phi) = \Phi(\phi)\ \Theta(\theta). \tag{3.14}$$

Substituting this value in equation (3.13) and multiplying both sides by $\sin^2\theta/f$ we obtain an equation the left-hand side of which is the sum of two terms, each dependent on a different variable. It follows that each of these terms must be a constant: if one is equal to c, the other must be - c. We then have

$$-\hbar^2\frac{\partial^2}{\partial\phi^2}\Phi(\phi) = c\ \Phi(\phi) \tag{3.15}$$

$$\frac{1}{\Theta(\theta)}\ \hbar^2\left(\sin\theta\frac{\partial}{\partial\theta}\sin\theta\frac{\partial}{\partial\theta}+\lambda\sin^2\theta\right)\Theta(\theta) = c. \tag{3.16}$$

Equation (3.15) is simply the equation for the eigenfunction of the operator $L_z^2$. Using the obvious fact that the eigenfunction of an arbitrary operator G with eigenvalue a is at the same time the eigenfunction of operator $G^2$ with eigenvalue $a^2$ we conclude that

$$\Phi(\phi) = A \exp(i\, m\, \phi) \tag{3.17}$$

$$c = m^2 \hbar^2 \tag{3.18}$$

and substitute the value of c from (3.18) into (3.16). The solution of the resulting equation is rather tedious and can be found in a textbook of quantum mechanics (see, for example, Pauling and Wilson 1935). We will only give the final result. It turns out that, after substituting the value of c from (3.18), equation (3.16) has well behaved solutions only when

$$\lambda = \hbar^2 \ell (\ell + 1) \tag{3.19}$$

where $\ell$ is a positive integer ($\ell$ = 1, 2, 3, ... ) which satisfies the condition

$$|m| \leq \ell .$$

This means that, for a given $\ell$, the quantum number m can take on $2\ell + 1$ values

$$m = -\ell, -\ell + 1, \dots, 0, \dots, \ell - 1, \ell . \tag{3.20}$$

The solutions of the differential equation (3.16) for the values of $\lambda$ and m determined by (3.19) and (3.20) are associated Legendre polynomials (Margenau and Murphy 1956, p. 132)

$$P_\ell^{|m|}(x) = \frac{1}{2^\ell \ell!} (1 - x^2)^{|m|/2} \frac{d^{|m|+\ell}}{dx^{|m|+\ell}} (x^2 - 1)^\ell$$

with $x = \cos\theta$. We thus have $\Theta(\theta) = P_\ell^{|m|}(\cos\theta)$ and, in view of (3.14) and (3.17), the required solution of (3.13) can be written as

$$f(\theta, \phi) = A\, P_\ell^{|m|}(\cos\theta) \exp(i\, m\, \phi) \tag{3.21}$$

where A is an arbitrary constant. Functions of variables $\theta$ and $\phi$, defined as

$$Y_\ell^{(m)}(\theta, \phi) = P_\ell^{|m|}(\cos\theta) \exp(i\, m\, \phi)$$

are known as unnormalized spherical harmonics. The two variables $\theta$ and $\phi$ describe a point on the surface of a sphere, and are often replaced by the single symbol $\Omega$.

It can be shown that spherical harmonics are orthogonal, i.e. that

$$\int Y_\ell^{(m)*}(\Omega)\, Y_q^{(n)}(\Omega)\, d\Omega = \begin{cases} N_\ell^{(m)} & \text{for } q = \ell \text{ and } n = m \\ 0 & \text{for all other cases.} \end{cases} \tag{3.22}$$

Integration is performed over the whole surface of a sphere of unit radius. Integral (3.22), in which $d\Omega$ is the surface element of a sphere with unit radius $d\Omega = \sin\theta\, d\theta\, d\phi$, is equivalent to the double integral

$$\int\!\!\int Y_\ell^{(m)*}(\theta, \phi)\, Y_q^{(n)}(\theta, \phi)\, \sin\theta\, d\theta\, d\phi$$

in which integration with respect to $\theta$ is between 0 and $\pi$, and integration with respect to $\phi$ between 0 and $2\pi$. The constant $N_\ell^{(m)}$ is

$$N_\ell^{(m)} = \frac{4\pi}{(2\ell + 1)} \frac{(\ell + |m|)\,!}{(\ell - |m|)\,!}\,. \tag{3.23}$$

Normalized eigenfunctions of the operator $L^2$ are found by setting $A = \left(N_\ell^{(m)}\right)^{-1/2}$ in (3.21):

$$f(\theta, \phi) = \left(N_\ell^{(m)}\right)^{-1/2} Y_\ell^{(m)}(\theta, \phi)\,. \tag{3.24}$$

This is a complete set of the orthogonal eigenfunctions of $L^2$, since it can be shown that every well behaved function $\psi(\theta, \phi)$ can be represented as a linear combination of functions (3.24)

$$\psi(\theta, \phi) = \sum_{\ell=1}^{\infty} \sum_{m=-\ell}^{+\ell} a_{m\ell} \left(N_\ell^{(m)}\right)^{-1/2} Y_\ell^{(m)}(\theta, \phi)\,. \tag{3.25}$$

We now make a digression in order to return to something which was left unexplained in Section 2. Note from (3.8) that the eigenfunctions (3.21) of operator $L^2$ are simultaneously eigenfunctions of $L_z$. Moreover, although the eigenvalues of $L^2$ and $L_z$ are degenerate, each pair of quantum numbers $\ell$ and m corresponds to precisely one normalized eigenfunction $N_\ell^{(m)}\, Y_\ell^{(m)}(\Omega)$ common to $L^2$ and $L_z$. According to (3.25) every eigenfunction of the system can be expressed as a series of such shared eigenfunctions. In the reverse situation, when we wish to construct an unknown eigenfunction, we must determine the coefficients $a_{m\ell}\, a^*_{m\ell}$. To be able to do this it is necessary to carry out numerous measurements of $L^2$ and $L_z$. If, for M such measurements, the result $L_z = m\hbar$ and $L^2 = \ell\left(\ell + 1\right)\hbar$ appears $M(\ell, m)$ times, then

$$a_{m\ell}\, a^*_{m\ell} = M(\ell, m)/M\,.$$

The measurement of only one dynamical value with degenerate eigenvalues is insufficient to determine the state of the system. In general, the wavefunction can be determined by measuring several appropriately chosen dynamical quantities. The set of these quantities is known as the complete set.

## 4. Spin Operators

For a satisfactory interpretation of atomic spectra it is necessary to assume that electrons and certain atomic nuclei have angular momentum, which is not connected with the movement of the centre of gravity of the particle in space, but constitutes its characteristic property, analogous to mass or charge. Magnetic resonance also requires the use of such a hypothesis.

To distinguish the inherent angular momentum of a particle from its orbital angular momentum, it is customary to apply the term "spin" to the former. The name suggests that the particle spins around its axis. Since electrons and atomic nuclei are charged particles, spin implies magnetic moment, which will be discussed in Section 12. It turns out that the model of a "spinning-top nucleus" or a "spinning-top electron", as developed from classical physics, leads to contradictions. Furthermore, the results of certain experiments led to the conclusion that for the electron, and some atomic nuclei, the projection of spin on a chosen direction in space is equal to the half-integer multiple of $\hbar$. This is not only in contradiction to classical mechanics, but also to quantum mechanics as described so far, in which the quantum numbers $\ell$ and m for orbital spin can only take integer values. Also the magnetic moment associated with spin cannot be interpreted classically, and for the electron it turns out to be twice as large as it should be if we were to assume that the electron rotates around its axis.

Therefore, without a classical equivalent of spin, we cannot treat it in the method prescribed by Schrödinger, i.e. by replacing dynamical quantities by operators. It follows that quantum mechanics based on rules (2.1) cannot be applied to spin, although it is a measurable quantity. This difficulty was overcome by Pauli, who gave the special form of the operator of electronic spin, and found that the eigenvalues of the coordinates are $\pm\frac{1}{2}\hbar$. We will not discuss Pauli's theory in detail, but only say that it effectively completes the treatment, although it is not logically connected with the rules of quantum mechanics as described so far. The only similarity between Pauli's spin operators and the familiar operators of orbital spin is that both groups of operators satisfy the same commutation rules (3.2a).

The combination of the quantum mechanics of dynamical quantities which have classical equivalents with Pauli's theory into a logical whole was accomplished by P.A.M. Dirac, and is described in his seminal work "The Principles of Quantum Mechanics". Dirac proved that the eigenvalues of operators associated with measurables depend exclusively on commutational rules obeyed by those operators, and not on the detailed definition of operators and the functions on which they may act. He also demonstrated that, without specifying precise definitions of the operators or functions, one can obtain eigenvalues if one assumes certain commutation rules. It turns out that both operators derived from Schrödinger's rules (2.1) or Pauli's spin operators are simply specific forms of abstract operators which appear in Dirac's theory.

We will not discuss the postulates of the algebra of operators (Rojansky 1964) but, forsaking rigorous derivation, proceed to calculate eigenvalues of the spin operator algebraically. Consider operators $I'_x$, $I'_y$ and $I'_z$ which obey the same commutation rules as the operators of orbital angular momentum (3.2a).

$$I'_x I'_y - I'_y I'_x = i\hbar I'_z$$

$$I'_y I'_z - I'_z I'_y = i\hbar I'_x \qquad (4.1)$$

$$I'_z I'_x - I'_x I'_z = i\hbar I'_y .$$

We do not describe the mode of action of these operators, but only assume that they are Hermitian. Introduce another operator defined as $I'^2 = I'^2_x + I'^2_y + I'^2_z$. Using (4.1) it is easy to show that $I'^2$ commutes with each of the three operators, and that

$$\left(I_x' + i\,I_y'\right) I_z' = \left(I_z' - \hbar\right)\left(I_x' + i\,I_y'\right) \tag{4.2a}$$

$$\left(I_x' - i\,I_y'\right) I_z' = \left(I_z' + \hbar\right)\left(I_x' - i\,I_y'\right). \tag{4.2b}$$

(Hint: when calculating the commutator $\left[I'^2, I_z'\right]$ use (4.1) to obtain terms $I_x' I_z' I_x'$ and $I_y' I_z' I_y'$. To prove (4.2), apply (4.1) to the left-hand side and compare with the right-hand side.)

Since the commutation rules do not distinguish in any way between the operators $I_x'$, $I_y'$ and $I_z'$, their eigenvalues must be the same. In order to find them, it is sufficient to consider, for example, the operator $I_z'$. Introduce function $\varphi_a$, which fulfils the conditions

$$I_z' \varphi_a = a\, \varphi_a \tag{4.3a}$$

$$I'^2 \varphi_a = b^2 \varphi_a \tag{4.3b}$$

$$\int \varphi_a^* \varphi_a \, dV = 1\,. \tag{4.3c}$$

$\varphi_a$ is therefore a normalized eigenfunction common to operators $I_z'$ and $I'^2$. We shall see later that the introduction of such a general definition of $\varphi_a$, even without specifying the space in which integration (4.3c) is performed, is quite sufficient to calculate the eigenvalues a and $b^2$.

Apply both sides of (4.2a) to function $\varphi_a$. In view of (4.3a) we have

$$I_z'\left[\left(I_x' + i\,I_y'\right)\varphi_a\right] = (a + \hbar)\left(I_x' + i\,I_y'\right)\varphi_a\,. \tag{4.4}$$

We conclude that function $\left(I_x' + i\,I_y'\right)\varphi_a$ is either a well behaved eigenfunction of operator $I_z'$ with eigenvalue $a + \hbar$, or is equal to zero (such a function does not satisfy the conditions of "good behaviour"). In the first of these cases we can write generally

$$\left(I_x' + i\,I_y'\right)\varphi_a = \hbar\, k_+ \varphi_{a+\hbar} \tag{4.5}$$

where $\varphi_{a+\hbar}$ is a normalized eigenfunction of operator $I_z'$ with eigenvalue $a + \hbar$, and $k_+$ is a dimensionless numerical coefficient.

The function $\left(I_x' + i\,I_y'\right)\varphi_a$ is at the same time an eigenfunction of operator $I'^2$, since

$$I'^2\left[\left(I_x' + i\,I_y'\right)\varphi_a\right] = \left(I_x' + i\,I_y'\right)I'^2\,\varphi_a = b^2\left[\left(I_x' + i\,I_y'\right)\varphi_a\right].$$

By multiple application of the operator $I_x' + i\,I_y'$ to function $\varphi_a$ we come to the conclusion that the possible eigenvalues of operator $I_z'$ are numbers

$$a,\ a + \hbar,\ a + 2\hbar,\ a + 3\hbar,\ \ldots \tag{4.6}$$

and that the corresponding eigenfunctions are at the same time the eigenfunctions of operator $I'^2$ with eigenvalue $b^2$. In an analogous fashion we can derive from (4.2b) the relationship

$$\left(I_x' - i\,I_y'\right)\varphi_a = \hbar\,k_-\,\varphi_{a-\hbar} \tag{4.7}$$

and include the numbers

$$a - \hbar,\ a - 2\hbar,\ a - 3\hbar,\ \ldots \tag{4.8}$$

in the set of possible eigenvalues of the operators $I_z'$ given by (4.6).

Assume that A is the largest term in the series (4.6) which fulfils the inequality $A^2 \le b^2$. It corresponds to the eigenfunction $\varphi_A$ for $I_z'$ and $I'^2$. However, the next term, $A + \hbar$, cannot correspond to any eigenfunction, which means that

$$\left(I_x' + i\,I_y'\right)\varphi_A \equiv 0\,. \tag{4.9}$$

This is because if a well behaved eigenfunction $\varphi_{A+\hbar}$ were to exist, the following relationships between expectation values would hold

$$< I'^2 > \;=\; b^2 < (A + \hbar)^2 \;=\; < I_z'^2 >$$

or

$$< I_x'^2 + I_y'^2 + I_z'^2 > \;<\; < I_z'^2 >$$

which is a contradiction. It follows that the series (4.6) stops at the value A. Multiplying (4.9) by $\left(I'_x - i\, I'_y\right)$ we obtain

$$\left(I'_x - i\, I'_y\right)\left(I'_x + i\, I'_y\right)\varphi_A = \left[I'^2_x + I'^2_y + i\left(I'_x I'_y - I'_y I'_x\right)\right]\varphi_A$$

$$= \left(I'^2_x + I'^2_y - \hbar I'_z\right)\varphi_A = \left(I'^2 - I'^2_z - \hbar I'_z\right)\varphi_A$$

$$= \left(b^2 - A^2 - \hbar A\right)\varphi_A = 0\,.$$

Since $\varphi_A$ is not identically equal to zero, then

$$b^2 = A\,(A + \hbar) \tag{4.10}$$

which, after the substitution $\ell = A/\hbar$, is identical to (3.19).

In a similar way we can show that the series (4.8) stops at - A. It follows that the full list of eigenvalues of operator $I'_z$ which can appear together with eigenvalue $b^2$ of the operator $I'^2$ is

$$-A,\ -A + \hbar,\ \dots,\ A - \hbar,\ A\,. \tag{4.11}$$

The difference between A and - A is therefore an integer multiple of $\hbar$. Thus $2A = n\hbar$, or

$$A = \frac{1}{2}\, n\hbar$$

with n = 0, 1, 2, ... .

From our general considerations, based on the commutation rules (4.1), we have arrived at the conclusion that the maximum projection of angular momentum on any given direction in space can take integer or half-integer values.

The theory of orbital angular momentum is a special case of our present considerations in which n is even and $A = \ell\,\hbar$ where $\ell$ is an integer. On the other hand, the spin of the electron represents the case with n = 1 and $A/\hbar = 1/2$. For permanent nuclei, n takes on values from 0 to 14, depending on the nuclear species.

Operator $I = I'/\hbar$ is usually introduced for simplicity. This is because both the eigenvalues m of the coordinates $I_x$, $I_y$, $I_z$, and of the square $I^2 = I_x^2 + I_y^2 + I_z^2$, are dimensionless numbers. Dividing the terms of the series (4.11) by $\hbar$ we get

$$m = -I, -I+1, \ldots, I-1, I \tag{4.12}$$

where $I = A/\hbar$, the maximum value of the quantum number m, is known as the *spin quantum number*. The eigenvalue $I(I+1)$ of the operator $I^2$ is found by dividing (4.10) by $\hbar^2$. We see therefore that the quantum number I plays a similar role in the theory of spin to that of $\ell$ in the theory of orbital angular momentum. The difference is that, unlike $\ell$, I may assume both integer and half-integer values.

An atomic nucleus cannot change its spin quantum number I except as the result of a nuclear reaction or a radioactive process. Energy changes accompanying such processes are of the order of $10^{-14}$ J, while in NMR energy changes are of the order of $10^{-26}$ J. We can therefore consider spin quantum number as a constant characteristic for a given nuclear species (see Tables 14.1-14.3). Using the terminology of quantum mechanics we say that each wavefunction $\psi$ describing a spin is an eigenfunction of the operator $I^2$ with eigenvalue $I(I+1)$, where I is a number characteristic for a given nucleus.

We now proceed to calculate the factor $k_+$ in (4.5), which can be written as

$$\left(I_x + i\,I_y\right) \varphi_m = k_+ \,\varphi_{m+1} \tag{4.13}$$

where the $\varphi_m$ are normalized eigenfunctions of operators $I_z$ and $I^2$ with eigenvalues m and I, $(m < I)$. By squaring both sides of (4.13) and integrating over all space we find

$$k_+^2 = \int \left[\left(I_x + i\,I_y\right) \varphi_m\right]^* \left(I_x + i\,I_y\right) \varphi_m \, dV .$$

After performing the multiplication within the integral, we write it as a sum of four terms. We then transform each of these terms using the Hermiticity of operators $I_x$ and $I_y$. For example

$$\int \left(I_x \varphi_m\right)^* I_x \varphi_m \, dV = \int \left(I_x^2 \varphi_m\right)^* \varphi_m \, dV = \left\langle I_x^2 \right\rangle.$$

Proceeding in this way we find

$$k_+^2 = \left\langle I_x^2 \right\rangle + \left\langle I_y^2 \right\rangle + \left\langle I_z^2 \right\rangle - m^2 - m .$$

Note that $\left\langle I_z^2 \right\rangle = m^2$. The sum of the first three terms is of course equal to $I(I+1)$, so that

$$k_+^2 = I\left(I+1\right) - m^2 - m = \left(I-m\right)\left(I+m+1\right)$$

and

$$k_+ = \sqrt{\left(I-m\right)\left(I+m+1\right)}\,. \tag{4.14}$$

Proceeding in the same way we find

$$k_- = \sqrt{\left(I+m\right)\left(I-m+1\right)}\,. \tag{4.15}$$

Note that for $I = 1/2$, $k_+ = k_- = 1$. The "raising" and "lowering" operators

$$I_+ = I_x + i\,I_y \qquad \text{and} \qquad I_- = I_x - i\,I_y \tag{4.16}$$

are not Hermitian. They are, however, useful because their properties are particularly easy to remember. These properties, easily derived from (4.13), (4.7) and (4.9) are as follows:

$$\begin{aligned}
&I_+\,\varphi_m = \varphi_{m+1}\sqrt{\left(I-m\right)\left(I+m+1\right)} && \text{for } m < I\\
&I_+\,\varphi_m = 0 && \text{for } m = I\\
&I_-\,\varphi_m = \varphi_{m-1}\sqrt{\left(I+m\right)\left(I-m+1\right)} && \text{for } m > -I\\
&I_-\,\varphi_m = 0 && \text{for } m = -I\,.
\end{aligned} \tag{4.17}$$

Together with the relationships

$$I_z\,\varphi_m = m\,\varphi_m \tag{4.18}$$

$$I^2\,\varphi_m = I\,(I+1)\,\varphi_m \tag{4.19}$$

derived earlier, rules (4.17) completely describe the properties of operators $I_x$, $I_y$, $I_z$ and $I^2$.

## 5. Time Dependence of Wavefunctions

The time dependence of the wavefunction $\Phi$ is described by the equation

$$\mathcal{H}\,\Phi(t) = i\hbar \frac{\partial}{\partial t}\Phi(t)\,. \tag{5.1}$$

Of course, $\Phi$ may also depend on the coordinates x, y and z, but this is not explicitly written out for simplicity. Equation (5.1) is known as the time-dependent Schrödinger equation and $\mathcal{H}$ is the energy operator, also known as the Hamiltonian. The meaning of the above equation, which is one of the postulates of quantum mechanics, is as follows: if at time $t = 0$ the state of the system was described by the function $\Phi(0)$, then the later (and earlier) states of the system are determined by the function $\Phi(t)$, which is the solution of (5.1). Consider two specific cases.

**Case A.** At $t = 0$ the wavefunction $\Phi(t)$ is the eigenfunction of the Hamiltonian with the eigenvalue $E_n$, so that

$$\begin{aligned} &\Phi(0) = \varphi_n = \Phi_n \\ &\mathcal{H}\,\varphi_n = E_n\,\varphi_n\,. \end{aligned} \tag{5.2}$$

The solution of (5.1) with the initial condition (5.2) is

$$\Phi_n(t) = \varphi_n \exp\left(-i\,E_n\,t/\hbar\right). \tag{5.3}$$

Equation (5.3) is a wavefunction describing the entire history of the system in the time interval from $-\infty$ to $+\infty$. It can easily be shown that the solution (5.3) is the eigenfunction of the Hamiltonian for the eigenvalue $E_n$ for all values of t. It follows that if the system is in the eigenstate of the Hamiltonian, its energy does not change. This is why the eigenstates of the Hamiltonian are known as stationary states. This conclusion is not true, however, if the Hamiltonian is time-dependent, because there is the possibility of a transition from one stationary state to another. Such transitions will be discussed in Section 9.

The function $\Phi_n(t)$ is sometimes called the "time-dependent eigenfunction" as distinct from $\varphi_n$, which is time-independent. It must be borne in mind that both functions correspond to the same eigenvalue $E_n$.

**Case B.** At $t = 0$ the wavefunction is not the eigenfunction of the Hamiltonian. Denote it by $\Psi(0)$ and expand it as a series of eigenfunctions of the Hamiltonian

$$\Psi(0) = \sum_n a_n \varphi_n . \tag{5.4}$$

A postulate of quantum mechanics states that such an expansion is possible. The coefficients $a_n$ are numerical constants, which are calculated as explained in Section 1:

$$a_n = \int \varphi_n^* \, \Psi(0) \, dV .$$

We use these coefficients to form a linear combination of time-dependent eigenfunctions of the Hamiltonian

$$\Psi(t) = \sum_n a_n \Phi_n(t) . \tag{5.5}$$

To show that function (5.5) satisfies the differential equation (5.1) with the initial condition (5.4) we substitute (5.3) into (5.5). We conclude that the time-dependent Schrödinger equation allows us to deduce the entire past and future history of the system described by the function $\Psi(t)$.

The wavefunction can also be represented in an alternative way to (5.5) as

$$\Psi(t) = \sum_n a_n(t) \varphi_n \tag{5.6}$$

where

$$a_n(t) = a_n(0) \exp\left(- i \hbar E_n t\right) . \tag{5.7}$$

Equations (5.5) and (5.6) describe two ways of expressing the wavefunction. The former describes the so-called Heisenberg method, in which time dependence resides in the wavefunction; the latter describes the Schrödinger method, in which time dependence resides in the coefficients $a_n(t)$.

## 6. Hilbert Space

This section deals with the principles of the matrix method of quantum mechanics, and is essential for a full understanding of the rest of the book. We assume that the reader is familiar with elementary matrix algebra.

The matrix method relies on the representation of wavefunctions by a series of numbers, known as coefficients of expansion, and is closely analogous to the representation of vectors in analytical geometry by their coordinates in the Cartesian coordinate system.

In quantum mechanics a wavefunction $\Psi$ is expressed by a linear combination of linearly independent functions $\varphi_n$

$$\Psi = \sum_{n=1}^{L} a_n \varphi_n . \tag{6.1}$$

Thus a wavefunction is expressed in terms of the coefficients of expansion $a_1, a_2, \dots, a_L$, which are also known as coordinates. We may therefore treat the wavefunction as a vector, and write these coefficients as a vertical matrix

$$[\Psi] = \begin{bmatrix} a_1 \\ a_2 \\ \cdot \\ \cdot \\ \cdot \\ a_L \end{bmatrix} \tag{6.2}$$

So, to each wavefunction $\Psi$ there corresponds a unique single-column matrix $[\Psi]$ known as the representation of the wavefunction. Unlike the coordinates of a vector, which are real numbers, the coordinates of a wavefunction may be complex. We limit ourselves to the case in which the number of linearly independent functions $\varphi_n$ needed for the expansion of $\Psi$ is finite. The set of numbered functions $\varphi_1, \varphi_2, \dots, \varphi_L$ is known as a *complete set* or *basis,* provided that every wavefunction describing the state of a given quantum system can be expressed as a linear combination of these functions. The set of functions $\varphi_1, \varphi_2, \dots, \varphi_L$ spans the L-dimensional space known as *Hilbert space*.

In this book we shall use exclusively basis functions which are time-independent. When a time-dependent function is expanded into a series of time-independent functions, the coefficients of the expansion become time-dependent.

Linear independence of basis functions $\varphi_n$ means that none of them can be expressed as a linear combination of L - 1 remaining functions. From L linearly independent, but not necessarily orthogonal, functions we can form L orthogonal linear combinations. Orthogonality (1.6b) is a special case of linear independence. It is always possible to convert a non-orthonormal basis into an orthonormal one by a suitable transformation (for this procedure see Heine 1960). We shall use only orthonormal bases, because this leads to a significant simplification of the calculations. In the orthonormal basis $\varphi_n$ the coefficients of expansion $a_k$ can be expressed by the integrals

$$a_k = \int \varphi_k^* \Psi \, dV \tag{6.3}$$

which is proved by substituting into (6.3) the function $\Psi$ written in the form (6.1) and performing the integration.

The question of finding a complete basis is vital. We are assisted in this task by the postulate of quantum mechanics which states that a complete basis may be formed by the set of all eigenfunctions of any Hermitian operator related to a dynamical quantity measurable in the given quantum system. If the eigenvalues of this operator are not degenerate, the basis thus obtained is orthogonal. This is because, as we remember from Section 1, eigenfunctions of the same Hermitian operator corresponding to different eigenvalues are mutually orthogonal. To obtain the orthonormal basis, it only remains to normalize the eigenfunctions by multiplying each of them by a suitable number. The dimension of a basis appropriate for a system composed of N identical spins I is $L = (2I + 1)^N$ because, as is explained in Section 15, this is the number of linearly independent eigenfunctions of the Zeeman Hamiltonian.

In quantum mechanics a scalar product of two functions is defined as follows:

$$\left(\Psi^{(1)}, \Psi^{(2)}\right) = \int \Psi^{(1)*} \Psi^{(2)} \, dV . \tag{6.4}$$

The product is not commutative because $\left(\Psi^{(1)}, \Psi^{(2)}\right) = \left(\Psi^{(2)}, \Psi^{(1)}\right)^*$. Expanding functions $\Psi^{(1)}$ and $\Psi^{(2)}$ in an orthonormal basis $\varphi_n$

$$\Psi^{(1)} = \sum_1^L a_n^{(1)} \varphi_n$$

$$\Psi^{(2)} = \sum_1^L a_m^{(2)} \varphi_m$$

and substituting in (6.4) we obtain the expression for the scalar product in terms of the coefficients of expansion

$$\left(\Psi^{(1)}, \Psi^{(2)}\right) = a_1^{(1)*} a_1^{(2)} + a_2^{(1)*} a_2^{(2)} + \dots + a_L^{(1)*} a_L^{(2)} .$$

The form of the scalar product of functions is identical to that of the scalar product of vectors in analytical geometry.

The product can be expressed as the product of two matrices. To demonstrate this, we define a horizontal matrix $[\Psi]^\dagger$

$$[\Psi]^\dagger = \begin{bmatrix} a_1^* & a_2^* & \dots & a_L^* \end{bmatrix}$$

known as the Hermitian adjoint of matrix $[\Psi]$. Using the rules of matrix multiplication we obtain

$$\left(\Psi^{(1)}, \Psi^{(2)}\right) = \left[\Psi^{(1)}\right]^\dagger \left[\Psi^{(2)}\right] = \begin{bmatrix} a_1^{(1)*} & a_2^{(1)*} & \dots\dots & a_L^{(1)*} \end{bmatrix} \begin{bmatrix} a_1^{(2)} \\ a_2^{(2)} \\ \dots\dots \\ a_L^{(2)} \end{bmatrix}$$

$$= a_1^{(1)*} a_1^{(2)} + a_2^{(1)*} a_2^{(2)} + \dots + a_L^{(1)*} a_L^{(2)} . \qquad \text{q.e.d.}$$

In the so-called "Dirac notation", a vertical single-column matrix is denoted by a special set of brackets $| \ \rangle$ called a "ket", which contains information necessary to identify the wavefunction in question. There are no firm and fast rules as to how this should be done, and often a wavefunction is simply denoted by a number

$$\left[\Psi^{(1)}\right] = |1\rangle \quad \text{and} \quad \left[\Psi^{(2)}\right] = |2\rangle . \tag{6.5}$$

Similarly, a horizontal single-row matrix is denoted by another set of brackets $\langle \ |$ called a "bra"

$$\left[\Psi^{(1)}\right]^\dagger = \langle 1| \quad \text{and} \quad \left[\Psi^{(2)}\right]^\dagger = \langle 2| . \tag{6.6}$$

In this notation the scalar product becomes a "bra-ket"

$$\left(\Psi^{(1)}, \Psi^{(2)}\right) = \langle 1|2\rangle$$

or, according to (6.4)

$$\int \Psi^{(1)*}\,\Psi^{(2)}\,dV = \langle 1|2\rangle\,.$$

It is also common to write

$$\Psi^{(1)} = |1\rangle \qquad \text{and} \qquad \Psi^{(1)*} = \langle 1|\,.$$

The latter usage is strictly speaking incorrect, as it is incompatible with the definitions (6.5) and (6.6). Nevertheless, it is often used as it is convenient and does not cause confusion.

In Dirac's notation we have

$$\langle m|n\rangle = (\langle n|m\rangle)^*\,.$$

Because a complete basis may be constructed using different operators, it is possible to have more than one such basis. Two complete bases must be related via a linear transformation, because the functions of one basis, say $\varphi_k$, may be expressed as a linear combination of functions, $\chi_i$, of the other basis

$$\varphi_k = \sum_{i=1}^{N} s_{ik}\,\chi_i \tag{6.7a}$$

$$\chi_i = \sum_{\ell=1}^{N} s_{i\ell}^{-}\,\varphi_\ell\,. \tag{6.7b}$$

The coefficients of expansion $s_{ik}$ form the matrix $\{S\}$ and the coefficients $s_{i\ell}^{-}$ the matrix $\{S^-\}$.

By substituting one of equations (6.5) into the other, we show that

$$\sum_\ell s_{i\ell}\,s_{\ell j}^{-} = \delta_{ij}$$

which means that the matrices $\{S\}$ and $\{S^-\}$ are reciprocal with respect to one another, so that

$$\{S\}\{S^-\} = \{1\}$$

where $\{1\}$ is a unit matrix. We similarly prove that $\{S^-\}\{S\} = \{1\}$.

We will now consider how the representation of a function changes on changing the basis. Expand an arbitrary function $\Psi$ in the basis $\varphi_k$

$$\Psi = \sum_k p_k \varphi_k \tag{6.8}$$

and in the basis $\chi_i$

$$\Psi = \sum_i r_i \chi_i . \tag{6.9}$$

We denote representations in these bases by $[p]$ and $[r]$, respectively.

Substituting (6.7a) into (6.8) we obtain

$$\Psi = \sum_i \Big( \sum_k s_{ik} p_k \Big) \chi_i . \tag{6.10}$$

Comparing (6.10) and (6.9) we conclude that

$$r_i = \sum_k s_{ik} p_k \tag{6.11}$$

which is written in matrix notation as $[r] = \{S\}[p]$ or $[p] = \{S^-\}[r]$. We see therefore that coordinates of the same function in two different bases are linked by the same linear transformation (6.7) which connects the bases.

A transformation which does not change the scalar product is known as a unitary transformation. The necessary and sufficient condition for a transformation S to be unitary is that

$$\bar{s}_{ij} = s^*_{ji} . \tag{6.12}$$

This can be proved by calculating the scalar product of the two functions before and after transformation. We leave this calculation to the reader.

Since the condition of orthonormality of the basis (6.2) has the form of a scalar product, the unitary transformation $\{c\}$ transforms a given orthonormal basis into another orthonormal basis. The reverse statement, that two orthonormal bases are related through a unitary transformation, is also true.

We conclude that the scalar product is invariant with respect to orthonormal transformation.

Just as in a given orthonormal basis $\varphi_1, \varphi_2, \dots, \varphi_L$, the function $\Psi$ is represented in the form of a vertical matrix $[\Psi]$, the operator G can be represented in the form of a square matrix $\{G\}$ with elements

$$G_{k\ell} = \int \varphi_k^* G\, \varphi_\ell\, dV \tag{6.13}$$

or, in Dirac's notation,

$$G_{k\ell} = \langle k|G|\ell\rangle$$

with $k, \ell = 1, 2, \dots, L$. It is often said that this matrix element of G "links" the wavefunctions $\varphi_k$ and $\varphi_\ell$. Matrix $\{G\}$ is known as the representation of operator G in the basis $\varphi_n$. The advantage of the above definition is that we can now represent the action of the operator G on function $\Psi$ as a matrix product calculated according to the rules of matrix algebra (multiplication from the left of a square matrix of dimension $L \times L$ by a column matrix of L elements gives a column matrix of the same dimension)

$$\{G\}\,[\Psi] = [\chi]\,.$$

We prove this by calculating the elements of the matrix $[\chi]$ in two different ways:

(i) Using equation (6.3):

$$[G\Psi]_k = \int \varphi_k^* G\, \Psi\, dV = \int \varphi_k^* G \sum_i a_i\, \varphi_i\, dV = \sum G_{ki}\, a_i$$

where $[G\Psi]_k$ is the k-th element of the column matrix $[G\Psi]$.

(ii) Using the rules of matrix multiplication:

$$\big[\{G\}\,[\Psi]\big]_k = \sum_i G_{ki}\, a_i\,.$$

We have shown that, in an orthonormal basis, matrix multiplication $\{G\}[\Psi]$ is equivalent to the action of the operator G on the function $\Psi$.

Note that the identity operator E, corresponding to multiplication by 1, is represented by the unit matrix $\{1\}$, i.e. an $L \times L$ matrix the only non-zero elements of which are the diagonal elements, all equal to 1. In other words, $E_{ij} = \delta_{ij}$.

In the special case, when the operator acts on one of the basis functions we obtain a matrix element

$$[P\,\varphi_s]_k = \int \varphi_k^* P\,\varphi_s\,dV = p_{ks} \tag{6.14}$$

(note the order of the subscripts s and k).

We will now consider how the representation of the operator G changes upon a unitary change of the basis. Consider two orthonormal bases, "old" $\varphi_n$ and "new" $\chi_n$ with $n = 1, 2, \ldots, L$, related by the unitary transformation S. Denote the representation of the operator G in the old basis by $\{G\}$ and in the new basis by $\{G'\}$. We derive the relationship between these matrices by substituting into (6.13) the expansion (6.7a)

$$G_{k\ell} = \int \left(\sum_i s_{ik}^* \chi_i^*\right) G \left(\sum_j s_{j\ell}\,\chi_j\right) dV\,.$$

We transform this expression taking into account that $G'_{ij} = \int \chi_i^* G\,\chi_j\,dV$ and that, because the transformation is unitary, $s_{ik}^* = \bar{s}_{ki}$. We find that

$$G_{k\ell} = \sum_{ij} \bar{s}_{ki}\,G'_{ij}\,s_{j\ell}$$

which in matrix notation takes the form

$$\{G\} = \{S^-\}\{G'\}\{S\}\,. \tag{6.15a}$$

Multiplying both sides from the left by $\{S\}$ and from the right by $\{S^-\}$ we obtain the desired relationship

$$\{G'\} = \{S\}\{G\}\{S^-\}\,. \tag{6.15b}$$

The product of operators is equivalent to the product of their representations:

$$\{GP\} = \{G\}\{P\}\,.$$

We prove this by calculating matrix elements using (6.13) and (6.14):

$$\{GP\}_{rs} = \int \varphi_r^* G P \varphi_s \, dV = \int \varphi_r^* G \sum_k p_{ks} \varphi_k \, dV$$

$$= \sum_k g_{rk} p_{ks} = \{\{G\}\{P\}\}_{rs} . \qquad \text{q.e.d.}$$

We will now show that matrix manipulation of representations enables us to find the eigenvalues and eigenfunctions of the operator G. We will conduct our calculations in an orthonormal basis. Assume that G has L eigenfunctions. Denote the $\ell$th eigenfunction, with coordinates $x_1^{(\ell)}, x_2^{(\ell)}, \ldots, x_L^{(\ell)}$ and eigenvalue $\lambda^{(\ell)}$, by $\chi^{(\ell)}$. Assume that $\chi^{(\ell)}$ is normalized, i.e. that

$$\sum_{i=1}^{L} \left| x_i^{(\ell)} \right|^2 = 1 . \tag{6.16}$$

As an eigenfunction, $\chi^{(\ell)}$ satisfies the equation $G \chi^{(\ell)} = \lambda^{(\ell)} \chi^{(\ell)}$, which, expressed using representations, takes the form $\{G\}\left[\chi^{(\ell)}\right] = \lambda^{(\ell)}\left[\chi^{(\ell)}\right]$. Written in terms of matrix elements, this equality of two single-column matrices gives the following set of homogeneous linear equations with unknowns $x_1^{(\ell)}, x_2^{(\ell)}, \ldots, x_L^{(\ell)}$:

$$\begin{aligned}
\left[g_{11} - \lambda^{(\ell)}\right] x_1^{(\ell)} + g_{12}\, x_2^{(\ell)} + \ \ldots\ + g_{1L}\, x_L^{(\ell)} &= 0 \\
g_{21}\, x_1^{(\ell)} + \left[g_{22} - \lambda^{(\ell)}\right] x_2^{(\ell)} + \ \ldots\ + g_{2L}\, x_L^{(\ell)} &= 0 \\
\ldots \qquad\qquad\qquad &= 0 \\
g_{L1}\, x_1^{(\ell)} + g_{L2}\, x_2^{(\ell)} + \ldots + \left[g_{LL} - \lambda^{(\ell)}\right] x_L^{(\ell)} &= 0 .
\end{aligned} \tag{6.17}$$

We discard zero as a solution because it contradicts condition (6.16). For a non-zero solution to exist, it is necessary that the determinant of the set of equations be zero:

$$\begin{vmatrix} g_{11}-\lambda & g_{12} & \dots & g_{1L} \\ g_{21} & g_{22}-\lambda & \dots & g_{2L} \\ \dots & \dots & \dots & \dots \\ g_{L1} & g_{L2} & \dots & g_{LL}-\lambda \end{vmatrix} = 0 \,. \tag{6.18}$$

This equation of the Lth order with the unknown $\lambda$, and L solutions $\lambda^{(1)}, \lambda^{(2)}, \dots, \lambda^{(L)}$ is called the "characteristic equation of the matrix". The solutions are the eigenvalues of the operator G. If some of them are identical, then they are degenerate.

The procedure for obtaining the eigenvalues and eigenfunctions of the operator G is as follows:

1. Establish an arbitrary orthonormal basis.
2. Calculate matrix elements $G_{k\ell}$ in that basis.
3. Find the eigenvalues by solving the characteristic equation (6.18).
4. Substitute one of the solutions, for example $\lambda^{(\ell)}$ into equation (6.17) and solve it for the unknowns $x_1^{(\ell)}, x_2^{(\ell)}, \dots, x_L^{(\ell)}$ which are the coordinates of the function $\chi^{(\ell)}$. We know that, since its determinant is zero, equation (6.17) can give only the ratios of the unknowns, i.e. numbers $k\,x_1^{(\ell)}$, $k\,x_2^{(\ell)}$, ..., $k\,x_L^{(\ell)}$, where k can be chosen at will with the exception of $k = 0$. We find k from the condition of orthonormality (6.16), and then calculate the exact coordinates of the required eigenfunction.
5. Repeat step 4 for each of the remaining eigenvalues $\lambda$.

The above procedure is known as diagonalization of the matrix, because it leads to the eigenfunctions of G and because the representation of each operator G in the basis of its own eigenfunctions is diagonal, i.e. $g_{k\ell} = 0$ for $k \neq \ell$. The diagonal elements are in such a case equal to the eigenvalues, i.e. $g_{kk} = \lambda^{(k)}$. The most difficult step in this procedure is the solution of the characteristic equation, especially when $L > 3$. The solution of the set of equations (6.17) is also rather tedious. If the symmetry properties of the operator G are known, group theory provides a more direct route to the eigenfunctions. A very simple application of the above-described procedure in two-dimensional Hilbert space is described in Section 45.

# 7. Statistical Treatment of Measurables

This section is concerned with the calculation of dynamical quantities in the entire sample, just as they are measured experimentally. The calculation of the expectation values for the whole sample treated as a single quantum system is not feasible in practice, because of the enormous number of spins involved. Fortunately, it often happens that the nuclear spins in the sample are arranged in identical groups (for example, in identical molecules). Such a group containing only several spins may be approximately treated as an isolated quantum system, and handled according to the rules of quantum mechanics. The expectation values found for such an isolated system may be subsequently averaged over all systems, yielding the expectation value for the whole sample. The sample treated as a collection of identical quantum systems is known as an ensemble. We assume that all the systems have the same structure and obey the same laws of motion, although at any given moment they may find themselves at different stages of such motion.

By considering the individual systems as isolated from their surroundings we are making an approximation, which consists of neglecting interactions between spins belonging to different systems. However, the error involved is often small, in view of the large distances between the individual systems in comparison with the dimensions of the system itself. As an example, consider a hydrated crystalline compound such as barium chlorate, $BaClO_3 \cdot H_2O$. The $^1H$ NMR spectrum of this crystal can be successfully calculated by assuming that the pair of protons in the $H_2O$ molecule forms an isolated system. The proton-proton distance in $H_2O$ is $1.62 \times 10^{-10}$ m, while the distance between the neighbouring water molecules in the chlorate is $4.77 \times 10^{-10}$ m. This is a very large difference if one considers that the interaction between two magnetic dipoles is inversely proportional to the cube of the distance between them.

In cases where spin-spin interactions do not affect the quantity we wish to calculate, we can consider a single spin as an isolated quantum system. This is done when calculating the magnetization at thermodynamic equilibrium.

Treating a small group of spins as a quantum system reduces the dimension, L, of the Hilbert space needed for the matrix representation of operators and wavefunctions. The dimension of Hilbert space is equal to the number of linearly independent eigenfunctions of the Hamiltonian describing the energy of the system. For example, in the case of a system composed of a single spin of quantum number I we have $L = 2I + 1$. In general, the dimension of Hilbert space for a system composed of N identical spins I is $L = (2I + 1)^N$. An example of how linearly independent eigenfunctions of the Hamiltonian for a system composed of two spins with I = 1/2 can be constructed is given in Section 15.

Consider first a quantum system at time t at a state described by the wavefunction Ψ (t). We substitute an expansion (5.6) of this function into a series of eigenfunctions $\varphi_n$ of the Hamiltonian into expression (2.7) for the expectation value of the operator G

$$<G> = \int \sum_n a_n^*(t)\, \varphi_n^*\, G \sum_m a_m(t)\, \varphi_m\, dV = \sum_m \sum_n a_n^*(t)\, a_m(t)\, G_{nm}\, dV$$

where the sums run from 1 to L. As was said earlier, we must now average this value over the whole ensemble. The averaging does not apply to the elements $G_{nm}$, which are the same throughout the ensemble. Only the products $a_n^*(t)\, a_m(t)$ may be different for the individual systems, because at any given moment the different systems may be at different stages of motion. It follows that the mean of the expectation value $\langle\langle G \rangle\rangle$ takes the following form:

$$\langle\langle G \rangle\rangle = \overline{<G>} = \sum_m \sum_n \overline{a_n^*(t)\, a_m(t)}\; G_{nm}$$

where the bar indicates averaging over the whole ensemble.

Introducing, by definition, the concept of a *density matrix* with elements

$$\rho_{mn}(t) = \overline{a_n^*(t)\, a_m(t)} \qquad (7.1)$$

we may write

$$\langle\langle G \rangle\rangle = \sum_m \sum_n \rho_{mn}(t)\, G_{nm} = \sum_m \{\rho\, G\}_{mm} = \mathrm{Tr}\,\{\rho\, G\}. \qquad (7.2)$$

If the number of systems in the ensemble (i.e. in the sample) is N, the result of measuring the dynamical quantity G is $N\langle\langle G \rangle\rangle$. Note that the density matrix is Hermitian, and that Tr ρ = 1, which follows from (2.4), because $\Sigma\, P(\lambda_i) = \Sigma\, a_i^*\, a_i = 1$.

The density matrix has been defined in terms of the coefficients $a_n$ of a wavefunction Ψ represented in the orthonormal basis of the eigenfunctions of the Hamiltonian (the "eigenbasis"). What will happen to the density matrix on replacing this basis by another orthonormal basis? Denote the coordinates of the wavefunction Ψ in the new basis by $r_i$. In accordance with (6.11) the coordinates of the same function in two different bases are related by

$$r_i = \sum_k s_{ik}\, a_k \tag{7.3}$$

which is equivalent to

$$a_i = \sum_k s^-_{ik}\, r_k \tag{7.4}$$

where the matrix $\{S\}$ with elements $s_{ik}$ is the matrix linking the two bases according to (6.7a) and $s^-_{ik}$ are the elements of the matrix $\{S^-\}$ reciprocal with respect to $\{S\}$.

Substituting (7.4) into (7.1) we obtain

$$\rho_{mn} = \overline{\left(\sum_k s^{-*}_{nk}\, r^*_k\right)\left(\sum_\ell s^-_{m\ell}\, r_\ell\right)} = \sum_{k\ell} s^-_{m\ell}\, \rho'_{\ell k}\, s_{kn}$$

where $\rho'_{\ell k} = \overline{r^*_k r_\ell}$. In the matrix form this relationship is written as

$$\{\rho\} = \{S^-\}\{\rho'\}\{S\}.$$

Multiplying both sides of the above from the left by $\{S\}$ and from the right by $\{S^-\}$ we obtain

$$\rho' = S\, \rho\, S^- . \tag{7.5}$$

We have omitted the braces $\{\ \}$, as it is clear that S, $S^-$, ρ and ρ' are all matrices. Comparing (7.5) with (6.15b), we conclude that the density matrix transforms just like any linear operator. We can thus consider the density matrix as the matrix representation of an operator, which we will call the density operator.

It remains to show that the density matrix in the new basis gives the same mean expectation value, since this must be independent of the basis in which it is calculated. Considering that the representation of the operator G in the new basis is the matrix $G' = S\, G\, S^-$ we calculate

$$\mathrm{Tr}\, \rho' G' = \mathrm{Tr}\, S\, \rho\, S^- S\, G\, S^- = \mathrm{Tr}\, S\, \rho\, G\, S^- = \mathrm{Tr}\, \rho\, G . \qquad \text{q.e.d.}$$

In the last step of the above calculation we have used Theorem 1 of Appendix 3 about the invariance of traces with respect to a reversible transformation.

The time dependence of the density operator plays a very important role in the theory of NMR. It is easiest to calculate it in the eigenbasis of the Hamiltonian by substituting (5.7) into (7.1). We then have

$$\rho_{mn}(t) = \overline{a_n^*(0)\, a_m(0)}\, \exp\left(\frac{-i\left(E_m - E_n\right)t}{\hbar}\right) = \rho_{mn}(0)\exp\left(\frac{-i\left(E_m - E_n\right)t}{\hbar}\right). \quad (7.5a)$$

Note that in this basis only the amplitude of the matrix element $\rho_{mn}(0)$ is the result of ensemble averaging, and that it is time-independent. The amplitude of a term for which $|m - n| = p$ is known as p-quantum coherence. This is because this amplitude is the result of a coherent motion of spins with angular frequency $\omega = \left(E_m - E_n\right)/\hbar$. This frequency corresponds to a p-quantum transition between the energy levels $E_m$ and $E_n$. The role of the single-quantum coherence in the motion of magnetization is described in Section 19.

It is sometimes useful to express the time dependence of the density operator $\rho(t)$ in a form independent of the basis by using the exponential operator

$$\rho(t) = \exp\left(-i\mathcal{H}t/\hbar\right)\rho(0)\exp\left(i\mathcal{H}t/\hbar\right). \quad (7.6a)$$

To prove the correctness of this form of the density operator, we calculate its matrix elements in the eigenbasis of the Hamiltonian, using the property (1.8) of exponential operators

$$\rho_{mn} = \int \varphi_m^* \exp\left(-i\mathcal{H}t/\hbar\right)\rho(0)\exp\left(i\mathcal{H}t/\hbar\right)\varphi_n\, dV$$

$$= \int \left[\exp\left(i\mathcal{H}t/\hbar\right)\varphi_m\right]^* \rho(0)\exp\left(i\mathcal{H}t/\hbar\right)\varphi_n\, dV$$

$$= \rho_{mn}(0)\exp\left(\frac{-i\left(E_m - E_n\right)t}{\hbar}\right). \qquad \text{q.e.d.} \quad (7.6b)$$

When the Hamiltonian is time-independent, differentiation of both sides of (7.6) gives the Liouville-von Neumann equation

$$\frac{d}{dt}\rho(t) = -i\hbar^{-1}\left[\mathcal{H}, \rho(t)\right]. \quad (7.7)$$

The Liouville-von Neumann equation is to the density operator what the Schrödinger equation (5.1) is to the wavefunction: it determines its time dependence. Calculation of matrix elements of both sides of the equation in any arbitrary basis gives a system of differential equations for the matrix elements in that basis.

Most NMR experiments begin by bringing the sample to a state of thermodynamic equilibrium. The state of equilibrium is thus the starting point for further evolution of the system during the course of the experiment. As we have seen, for the determination of the density operator as a function of time, it is necessary to know its initial value. It follows that we need to find the form of this operator at the state of thermodynamic equilibrium.

Thermodynamic equilibrium is achieved by leaving the sample for a sufficiently long time under conditions invariant with respect to the magnetic field, temperature, pressure, etc. In this state all dynamical quantities measured for the whole ensemble are time-independent. In other words, in the state of thermodynamic equilibrium, mean expectation values of all Hermitian operators must be time-independent. The density matrix must therefore also be constant. In particular, the off-diagonal elements of the density matrix in the eigenbasis of the Hamiltonian must all be zero. If even one pair of off-diagonal elements $\rho_{mn}$ and $\rho_{nm}$ were to be non-zero, it would be possible to construct a Hermitian operator Q whose expectation value Tr $\rho$ Q would be time-dependent.

The diagonal elements of the density matrix in the eigenbasis of the Hamiltonian are the products $a_n a_n^*$. We know from Section 3 that such a product is equal to the probability of the system finding itself in a state of energy $E_n$. At thermodynamic equilibrium this probability is given by Boltzmann's law as

$$a_n a_n^* = z^{-1} \exp\left(-E_n/kT\right)$$

where k = 1.380 658 (12) × $10^{-23}$ J $K^{-1}$ is Boltzmann's constant, T is the absolute temperature and z is another constant, independent of n, which can be found from the condition

$$\sum a_n a_n^* = 1 \,. \tag{7.8}$$

To summarize, we have found that at thermodynamic equilibrium the form of the density matrix represented in the eigenbasis of the Hamiltonian is as follows

$$\{\rho_\infty\} = z^{-1}\begin{Bmatrix} \exp(-E_1/kT) & & & \\ & \exp(-E_2/kT) & & \\ & & \ddots & \\ & & & \exp(-E_L/kT) \end{Bmatrix} \tag{7.9}$$

where the off-diagonal terms (not shown) are all zero. It can be demonstrated that this matrix is the representation of the exponential operator

$$\rho_\infty = z^{-1}\exp\left(-\mathcal{H}/kT\right). \tag{7.10}$$

Accordingly, $\rho_\infty$ is known as the "equilibrium density operator".

At accessible magnetic fields we always have $E_n << kT$, with the exception of the case when the temperature of the sample is extremely low $\left(T < 10^{-3}\ K\right)$. We can thus assume, to a very good approximation, that

$$\rho_{nn} = \exp\left(\frac{-E_n}{kT}\right) = 1 - \frac{E_n}{kT}$$

(the "high-temperature approximation", see Section 16). With this approximation (7.10) takes the form

$$\rho_\infty = z^{-1}\left(1 - \frac{\mathcal{H}}{kT}\right). \tag{7.11}$$

The constant z is calculated from the condition $\mathrm{Tr}\,\rho_\infty = 1$

$$z = \mathrm{Tr}\left(1 - \frac{\mathcal{H}}{kT}\right) = \mathrm{Tr}\,\{1\} = L$$

because $\mathrm{Tr}\,\mathcal{H} = 0$ for all spin interactions (see Appendix 3). L is the dimension of Hilbert space.

In the theory of NMR we are normally interested in the expectation values of traceless operators. If $\mathrm{Tr}\,G = 0$, then using (7.11) we have

$$\langle\langle G \rangle\rangle = \mathrm{Tr}\,\rho_\infty G = z^{-1}\,\mathrm{Tr}\left(G - \mathcal{H}G/kT\right) = \left(z\,kT\right)^{-1}\mathrm{Tr}\,\mathcal{H}G\,.$$

When calculating the expectation values of such operators it is convenient to use the matrix σ, which we shall call the effective density matrix

$$\sigma = \rho - z^{-1}\{1\}$$

since $\mathrm{Tr}\,\rho\,G = \mathrm{Tr}\,\sigma\,G$.
At thermodynamic equilibrium $\sigma$ has a fairly simple form:

$$\sigma_\infty = \frac{-\mathcal{H}}{\mathrm{Tr}\{1\}kT}. \tag{7.12}$$

## 8. Stationary Perturbation Theory

We shall now describe a method of calculating eigenvalues and eigenfunctions, known as the stationary (time-independent) perturbation theory. The theory is explained in an abbreviated manner, adapted for use in later sections. A more complete description of the perturbation theory may be found in textbooks on quantum mechanics, such as Rojansky (1964) and Pauling and Wilson (1935).

In many physical problems, particularly those concerning NMR, the Hamiltonian $\mathcal{H}$ of the system under consideration can be written as the sum of two components

$$\mathcal{H} = \mathcal{H}_0 + \mathcal{H}_1$$

where the eigenfunctions and the eigenvalues of $\mathcal{H}_0$ are known. We say that $\mathcal{H}_0$ is the "unperturbed" Hamiltonian, while $\mathcal{H}_1$ takes account of the perturbation. This terminology suggests that $\mathcal{H}_0$ describes the main part of the energy of the system, to which $\mathcal{H}_1$ is only a small addition. A very good example of such a situation is the system of several spins in a molecule interacting with a strong external magnetic field and, at the same time, undergoing mutual dipolar interactions. If the intensity of the magnetic field in which the sample is immersed is several tesla, the energy of dipolar interactions is at least 1000 times smaller than the Zeeman energy. All the same, it is the smaller interaction which is responsible for the structure of the spectrum, and cannot therefore be neglected.

We wish to find the eigenfunctions and eigenvalues of the total Hamiltonian $\mathcal{H} = \mathcal{H}_0 + \mathcal{H}_1$. This may not be easy, particularly when the number of spins, N, in the system is large. We shall see in Section 15 that the dimension of Hilbert space in which the problem has to be solved is $(2I + 1)^N$.

**Case 1.** Consider first a situation in which the perturbation commutes with the unperturbed Hamiltonian

$$[\mathcal{H}_0, \mathcal{H}_1] = 0 .$$

We thus have

$$\mathcal{H}_0 \mathcal{H}_1 \varphi = \mathcal{H}_1 \mathcal{H}_0 \varphi = \lambda_0 \mathcal{H}_1 \varphi \tag{8.1}$$

where $\varphi$ is the eigenfunction of $\mathcal{H}_0$

$$\mathcal{H}_0 \varphi = \lambda_0 \varphi .$$

We see therefore that the function $\mathcal{H}_1 \varphi$ is also an eigenfunction of $\mathcal{H}_0$ with the same eigenvalue $\lambda_0$. It follows that, if the value of $\lambda_0$ is non-degenerate, $\varphi$ and $\mathcal{H}_1 \varphi$ must be linearly dependent. There must therefore exist a number $\lambda_1$ such that

$$\mathcal{H}_1 \varphi = \lambda_1 \varphi .$$

The required eigenfunction of the Hamiltonian $\mathcal{H}$ is $\varphi$, because

$$\mathcal{H} \varphi = (\mathcal{H}_0 + \mathcal{H}_1) \varphi = (\lambda_0 + \lambda_1) \varphi .$$

If we now assume that the eigenvalue $\lambda_0$ is k-fold degenerate, and denote the corresponding eigenfunctions by $\varphi_i$ ($i = 1, 2, \ldots, k$), it follows from (8.1) that the function $\mathcal{H}_1 \varphi_i$ is also an eigenfunction of $\mathcal{H}_0$ with the same eigenvalue $\lambda_0$. Since k is the maximum number of independent eigenfunctions belonging to $\lambda_0$, the eigenfunction $\mathcal{H}_1 \varphi_i$ must be a linear combination of functions $\varphi_i$

$$\mathcal{H}_1 \varphi_i = \sum_j c_{ij} \varphi_j$$

where the $c_{ij}$ are the appropriate numerical coefficients. We see therefore that the eigenfunctions of $\mathcal{H}_0$ are not necessarily eigenfunctions of $\mathcal{H}_1$, and the matrix $\mathcal{H}_1$ is not diagonal, although $\mathcal{H}_0$ and $\mathcal{H}_1$ commute. However, the only off-diagonal elements of $\mathcal{H}_1$ are those which "link" functions belonging to the degenerate eigenvalue.

Inversely, if the only off-diagonal elements of $\mathcal{H}_1$ are those linking functions belonging to a degenerate eigenvalue of $\mathcal{H}$, the two Hamiltonians commute. This is because by diagonalizing the matrix $\{ c_{ij} \}$ using the procedure described in Section 6, we arrive at a new set of eigenfunctions $\chi_i$ such that

$$\mathcal{H}_1 \chi_i = \lambda_i \chi_i .$$

As linear combinations of eigenfunctions $\varphi_i$, eigenfunctions $\chi_i$ are eigenfunctions of the Hamiltonian $\mathcal{H}_0$. Moreover, as eigenfunctions of both $\mathcal{H}_0$ and $\mathcal{H}_1$, the $\chi_i$ are also the required eigenfunctions of the total Hamiltonian $\mathcal{H}$

$$\mathcal{H} \chi_i = \left(\mathcal{H}_0 + \mathcal{H}_1\right) \chi_i = \left(\lambda_0 + \lambda_1\right) \chi_i .$$

The functions $\chi_i$ are known as "correct zeroth-order wavefunctions". Note that, from an infinite number of sets of linearly independent eigenfunctions of the Hamiltonian $\mathcal{H}$ belonging to a degenerate eigenvalue $\lambda_0$ (compare Section 1), the perturbation selects precisely one set $\chi_1, \chi_2, \dots \chi_k$. It is so provided that all the eigenvalues of the perturbation are different. If they are not, degeneracy is not completely lifted and a certain arbitrary element remains.

To summarize the results for case 1, the decomposition of the Hamiltonian into two commuting parts, the eigenfunctions and eigenvalues of one of which, $\mathcal{H}_0$, are known, allows us to find the eigenfunctions and the eigenvalues of the total Hamiltonian.

(i) Eigenfunctions belonging to non-degenerate eigenvalues of $\mathcal{H}_0$ are also eigenvalues of the total Hamiltonian.

(ii) If degenerate eigenvalues of $\mathcal{H}_0$ exist, the remaining eigenfunctions of the total Hamiltonian are obtained by diagonalizing the perturbation in Hilbert spaces corresponding to the various degenerate eigenvalues of $\mathcal{H}_0$. In this way we do not evade the necessity of carrying out the diagonalization, but we reduce it to a lower-dimensional space.

**Case 2.** Consider now the situation when $\left[\mathcal{H}_0, \mathcal{H}_1\right] \neq 0$. In this case we represent $\mathcal{H}_1$ in the eigenbasis of $\mathcal{H}_0$ and decompose the thus-created matrix $\mathcal{H}_1$ into a sum of two matrices

$$\mathcal{H}_1 = \mathcal{H}_1' + \mathcal{H}_1''$$

in such a way that matrix $\mathcal{H}_1''$ contains all non-diagonal elements except those which "link" functions belonging to the same degenerate value of $\mathcal{H}_0$. All remaining matrix elements are left in the matrix $\mathcal{H}_1'$. As a result, Hamiltonians $\mathcal{H}_0$ and $\mathcal{H}_1'$ commute. $\mathcal{H}_1'$ is known as the secular and $\mathcal{H}_1''$ the non-secular part of the perturbation.

Case 2 can be reduced to case 1 by neglecting the non-secular part of the perturbation. It turns out that this procedure, known as "truncation", leads to a negligibly small error when the perturbation is small in comparison with the unperturbed Hamiltonian. The perturbation Hamiltonian which remains after its non-secular part has been discarded is known as the truncated Hamiltonian.

In order to estimate the magnitude of the error caused by the truncation we will use the following Hamiltonian in two-dimensional space:

$$\mathcal{H} = \mathcal{H}_0 + \mathcal{H}_1' + \mathcal{H}_1''$$

with

$$\{\mathcal{H}_0 + \mathcal{H}_1'\} = \begin{Bmatrix} \lambda_1 & 0 \\ 0 & \lambda_2 \end{Bmatrix}; \quad \{\mathcal{H}_1''\} = \begin{Bmatrix} 0 & a \\ a^* & 0 \end{Bmatrix}; \quad \{\mathcal{H}\} = \begin{Bmatrix} \lambda_1 & a \\ a^* & \lambda_2 \end{Bmatrix}. \quad (8.4)$$

The non-diagonal elements are complex conjugates, because the operators are Hermitian. The eigenvalues of $\mathcal{H}$ are obtained from the secular equation

$$\begin{vmatrix} \lambda_1 - x & a \\ a^* & \lambda_2 - x \end{vmatrix} = 0$$

with solutions

$$x = \frac{1}{2}\left[(\lambda_1 + \lambda_2) \pm (\lambda_1 - \lambda_2)\sqrt{1 + 4\,a\,a^*\,(\lambda_1 - \lambda_2)^{-2}}\,\right].$$

When the non-secular part is so small that $4\,a\,a^* << (\lambda_1 - \lambda_2)^2$, we can use the approximation $\sqrt{1 - 2\delta} \cong 1 - \delta$ (correct for $\delta << 1$) to obtain

$$x_1 = \lambda_1 + \frac{a\,a^*}{\lambda_1 - \lambda_2}$$

$$x_2 = \lambda_2 - \frac{a\,a^*}{\lambda_1 - \lambda_2}.$$

We are interested in the difference between the two eigenvalues, as this is what determines the position of lines in the spectrum. We find

$$\frac{x_1 - x_2}{\lambda_1 - \lambda_2} = 1 + \frac{2\,a\,a^*}{(\lambda_1 - \lambda_2)^2}.$$

We see therefore that in the case of a perturbation which is much smaller, for example 1000 times, than the unperturbed Hamiltonian $\mathcal{H}_0$, discarding the non-diagonal terms (truncation) leads to an error of the order of $10^{-6}$, while discarding the diagonal terms produces an error of the order of $10^{-3}$. Discarding the diagonal terms would remove information about the structure of the spectrum (we know that the Zeeman Hamiltonian alone gives a single unsplit line) while discarding the non-diagonal elements merely removes details which, in any case, cannot be observed because of the limited accuracy of the experiment.

Excessive accuracy in a theory may make comparison with experiments difficult. The removal of unobservable details is thus an important advantage of perturbation theory. The simplification of the calculations alone is not very important in an era of generally accessible computers.

## 9. Time-Dependent Perturbation Theory

### A. Transitions between energy states

We shall now describe, in an approximate fashion, the time behaviour of a system under the influence of a time-dependent perturbation. Time-dependent perturbation theory is used when the Hamiltonian of the system can be represented as a sum $\mathcal{H} = \mathcal{H}_0 + \mathcal{H}'$ of terms with the following properties: (i) $\mathcal{H}_0$ is a time-independent operator for which both the time-independent and the time-dependent Schrödinger equations can be solved exactly; (ii) the eigenvalues of $\mathcal{H}'$ are much smaller than those of $\mathcal{H}_0$ and are time-dependent. The problem of finding the time-dependent eigenfunction of the unperturbed Hamiltonian $\mathcal{H}_0$ consists of solving the time-dependent Schrödinger equation for $\mathcal{H}_0$ alone

$$\mathcal{H}_0 \Phi_{on}(t) = i \hbar \frac{\partial}{\partial t} \Phi_{on}(t) \tag{9.1}$$

with the initial condition

$$\Phi_{on}(0) = \varphi_{on} \tag{9.2}$$

where $\varphi_{on}$ is the normalized eigenfunction of $\mathcal{H}_0$ with eigenvalue $E_n$. It follows from Section 5 that the desired solution is the function

$$\Phi_{on}(t) = \varphi_{on} \exp\left(-i E_n t/\hbar\right) . \tag{9.3}$$

The functions $\Phi_{on}$ are mutually orthonormal, since the functions $\varphi_n$ are orthonormal for all n.

The search for the solution of the time-dependent Schrödinger equation containing the full Hamiltonian of the system, that is the equation

$$\left(\mathcal{H}_o + \mathcal{H}'\right) \Phi (t) = i \hbar \frac{\partial}{\partial t} \Phi (t) \tag{9.4}$$

proceeds as follows. Let $\Phi (t)$ be the solution of (9.4). For an arbitrarily chosen time $t = t'$ we may represent the function $\Phi (t')$ by a series of solutions of the "unperturbed" equation

$$\Phi (t') = \sum_n a_n \Phi_{on} (t') .$$

At another time t" the coefficients $a_n$ in the series may be different, so that in general they must be treated as functions of time. We may therefore write for all t

$$\Phi (t) = \sum_n a_n (t) \Phi_{on} (t) . \tag{9.5}$$

Treating functions $\Phi_{on} (t)$ as known (since we have assumed that the solution of the unperturbed problem is available) we see that the solution reduces to finding the coefficients $a_n (t)$. In order to calculate them, we substitute (9.5) in (9.4) and use (9.1) to obtain

$$\sum_n a_n (t) \mathcal{H}' (t) \Phi_{on} (t) = i \hbar \sum_n \dot{a}_n (t) \Phi_{on} (t)$$

where the dot in $\dot{a}_n (t)$ denotes differentiation with respect to time. Multiplying both sides by $\Phi^*_{om} (t)$, integrating over dV and using orthonormality of $\Phi_{on} (t)$ we find

$$\dot{a}_m (t) = \frac{1}{i\hbar} \sum_n a_n (t) \int \Phi^*_{om} (t) \mathcal{H}' (t) \Phi_{on} (t) \, dV$$

or, using (9.3)

$$\dot{a}_m(t) = \frac{1}{i\hbar}\sum_n a_n(t) \int \varphi_{om}^* \mathcal{H}'(t)\, \varphi_{on}\, dV \exp\left(-i\,\omega_{nm} t\right) \tag{9.6}$$

where $\omega_{nm} = \left(E_n - E_m\right)/\hbar$. Equations (9.6) represent a set of differential equations with unknowns $a_n(t)$.

Assume that at $t = 0$ the system was in a state described by function $\varphi_{o\ell}$ with energy $E_\ell$. Thus at $t = 0$ the coefficients of the expansion are

$$\begin{aligned} &a_n(0) = 0 \quad \text{for } n \neq \ell \\ &a_\ell(0) = 1\,. \end{aligned} \tag{9.7}$$

These are the initial conditions with which the set of equations (9.6) must be solved. We will do it approximately. Consider a very short time interval beginning at $t = 0$ and assume that during this interval the values of coefficients $a_n(t)$ "do not have the time" to change very much. In other words, assume that equations (9.7) are valid not only at $t = 0$ but during the entire time interval under consideration. Having made this assumption we can substitute (9.7) in the right-hand side of equations (9.6), which then take a much simpler form

$$\dot{a}_m(t) = \frac{1}{i\hbar}\int \varphi_{om}^* \mathcal{H}'(t)\, \varphi_{ol}\, dV \exp\left(-i\,\omega_{\ell m} t\right).$$

The above differential equations are no longer simultaneous but independent. Their solutions with initial conditions (9.7) are as follows:

$$a_{\ell m}(t) = \frac{1}{i\hbar}\int_0^t \int \varphi_{om}^* \mathcal{H}'(t')\, \varphi_{o\ell}\, dV \exp\left(-i\,\omega_{\ell m} t'\right) dt'\,.$$

After introducing the notation

$$\langle m \,|\, \mathcal{H}'(t') \,|\, \ell \rangle = \int \varphi_{om}^* \mathcal{H}'(t')\, \varphi_{o\ell}\, dV$$

the solution takes the form

$$a_{\ell m}(t) = \frac{1}{i\hbar}\int_0^t \langle m \,|\, \mathcal{H}'(t') \,|\, \ell \rangle \exp\left(-i\,\omega_{\ell m} t'\right) dt'\,. \tag{9.8}$$

The subscript $\ell$ in $a_{\ell m}$ (t) signifies that at time t = 0 the system was in the state $\varphi_{o\ell}$. Introducing the coefficients $a_{\ell m}$ (t) into (9.5) we arrive at the approximate solution of the perturbation problem

$$\Phi(t) = \sum_m a_{\ell m}(t)\,\Phi_{om}(t) = \sum_m a_{\ell m}(t) \exp\left(-i\,\hbar^{-1} E_m t\right) \varphi_{om} \tag{9.9}$$

which describes the evolution of the system since t = 0. In view of (2.4) the probability of finding the system at time t in the state $\varphi_{om}$ is $P(m) = a^*_{\ell m} a_{\ell m}$. Since we have assumed that at t = 0 the system was in the state $\varphi_{o\ell}$, P (m) is also the probability of transition of the system from the energy eigenstate $\ell$ to eigenstate m during time t. We will denote this probability by $W_{\ell m}$

$$W_{\ell m} = a^*_{\ell m} a_{\ell m}. \tag{9.10}$$

Note that, since $\mathcal{H}'(t)$ is Hermitian, $a^*_{\ell m} = a_{m\ell}$ and $W_{\ell m} = W_{m\ell}$. The assumptions we have made in deriving (9.8) limit its application to cases for which $W_{\ell m} << 1$.

**B. The general case**

We shall now calculate the probability of transition between states which are not necessarily eigenfunctions of energy. This calculation will be useful for the evaluation of spin-spin relaxation times (Section 57) and may be omitted on first reading.

Consider a dynamical quantity G and its operator G and assume that at time t = 0 the state of the system is described by one of the eigenfunctions of this operator

$$\psi_1, \psi_2, \psi_3, \ldots$$

for example, by function $\psi_n$ with eigenvalue $g_n$. If the wavefunction of the system is $\Psi_n$ (t) we can write

$$\Psi_n(0) = \psi_n. \tag{9.11}$$

After time t we carry out a single measurement of quantity G. What is the probability, $U_{n\ell}$ (t), of getting $g_\ell$ as a result of this measurement? $U_{n\ell}$ (t) is known as the probability of transition of the system from state n to state $\ell$ after time t.

Calculate first the function $\Psi_n(t)$ by solving the time-dependent Schrödinger equation

$$\left[\mathcal{H}_o + \mathcal{H}'(t)\right] \Psi_n(t) = i\hbar \frac{\partial}{\partial t} \Psi_n(t) \tag{9.12}$$

with (9.11) as the initial condition. Knowing $\Psi_n(t)$ we can then use (2.4) to calculate the probability of finding the system in state $\psi_\ell$

$$U_{n\ell}(t) = P(g_\ell) = A^*_\ell(t)\, A_\ell(t) \tag{9.13}$$

where the $A_\ell$ are coefficients of expansion of $\Psi_n(t)$ into functions $\psi_i$, calculated according to (2.5) as

$$A_\ell(t) = \int \psi^*_\ell \Psi_n(t)\, dV\,. \tag{9.14}$$

We shall call function $\psi_\ell$ the "final state function".

We will show that the required solution of (9.12) with condition (9.11) is the function

$$\Psi_n(t) = \sum_i b_{ni}\, \Phi_i(t) \tag{9.15}$$

where the $b_{ni}$ are constants, and functions $\Phi_i(t)$ are the solutions of the same equation for initial conditions $\Phi_i(0) = \varphi_{oi}$. Indeed, function (9.15), as a linear combination of solutions, is a solution of (9.12) and furthermore fulfils the condition (9.11), provided the coefficients $b_{ni}$ are chosen so that

$$\psi_n = \sum_i b_{ni}\, \varphi_{oi}\,. \qquad \text{q.e.d.} \tag{9.16}$$

Using (9.9)

$$\Phi_i(t) = \sum_j a_{ij}\, \Phi_{oj}(t) = \sum_j a_{ij}\, \varphi_{oj} \exp\left(-i\,\omega_j\, t\right)$$

we can express $\Psi_n(t)$ by eigenfunctions $\Phi_{oj}(t)$ of the unperturbed part of the Hamiltonian

$$\Psi_n(t) = \sum_{i,j} b_{ni}\, a_{ij} \exp\left(-i\,\omega_j t\right) \varphi_{oj}\,. \tag{9.17}$$

Also the final state function $\psi_\ell$ may be represented using $\varphi_{oj}$ by substituting $\ell$ instead of n in equation (9.16):

$$\psi_\ell = \sum_i b_{\ell i}\, \varphi_{oi}\,. \tag{9.18}$$

We substitute (9.17) and (9.18) in (9.14) and, bearing in mind the orthonormality of $\varphi_{oi}$, we find

$$A_\ell(t) = \int \psi_\ell^* \Psi_n(t)\, dV = \sum_{i,j} b_{\ell j}^*\, b_{ni}\, a_{ij} \exp\left(-i\,\omega_j t\right). \tag{9.19}$$

The required probability of transition from state n to state $\ell$ during time t is

$$U_{n\ell}(t) = A_\ell^* A_\ell$$

$$= \left(\sum_{i,j} b_{\ell j}\, b_{ni}^*\, a_{ij}^* \exp\left(i\,\omega_j t\right)\right)\left(\sum_{p,q} b_{\ell q}^*\, b_{np}\, a_{pq} \exp\left(-i\,\omega_q t\right)\right). \tag{9.20}$$

Formula (9.20) is useful for the calculation of the spin-spin relaxation time. In that particular case its form becomes much simpler: most terms have a mean value of zero and can be discarded.

## 10. Units and Dimensions

The form of all physical laws must be independent of the system of units in which they are formulated. However, the numerical values of the various quantities, as well as the values of the constants, do depend on the units used. This book uses the SI unit system, and in this section we compare SI units with units belonging to other systems which the reader may encounter in the literature on NMR. This is important, since the multitude of units used by various authors often poses serious difficulties to a student.

For example, the magnitude Q of an electric charge expressed in coulombs is related to the magnitude Q' of the same charge expressed in electrostatic units by

$$\frac{1}{10} Q = \frac{1}{c} Q' \qquad (10.1)$$

where c = 299 792 458 m $s^{-1}$ is the speed of light in vacuum[4] .

The magnetic field is described by two vectors: magnetic field intensity **H** and magnetic induction **B**. The definition of H is based on the generation of a magnetic field by an electric current. According to this definition, the magnetic field intensity generated inside an elongated coil of length $\ell$ (in metres) and n turns through which passes a current of intensity I (in amperes) is

$$H = n I/\ell . \qquad (10.2)$$

Equation (10.2) gives the magnitude of **H**. The unit of H is therefore A $m^{-1}$. The vector **H** is collinear with the axis of the coil, and its direction is determined using the "right-hand rule". According to this, when we place the right hand on the coil in such a way that the index finger points in the direction of flow of positive charges in the turns of the coil under the palm, the thumb points in the direction of **H**.

The magnetic induction, **B**, is defined by reference to the generation of electrical potential U in a conductor placed in a changing magnetic field. The unit of magnetic induction is V s $m^{-2}$. According to Faraday's law

$$U = -\frac{d\,(B\,S\,n)}{dt} \qquad (10.3)$$

the voltage U is generated by the change of magnetic induction B on the terminals of a coil of cross-section S (in $m^2$) and n turns with the axis aligned with the direction of the magnetic field. In the SI system, the unit of B is defined in such a way that U is expressed in volts: 1 tesla (T) = 1 V s $m^{-2}$.

The relationship between **H** and **B** in vacuum is

$$B = \mu_o H$$

where

$$\mu_o = 4\pi \times 10^{-7} \frac{V\,s\,m}{m^2\,A} = 4\pi \times 10^{-7}\ H\ m^{-1}$$

4 All the numerical values quoted in this book are taken from "Quantities, Units and Symbols in Physical Chemistry", sponsored by the International Union of Pure and Applied Chemistry, prepared for publication by I. Mills, T. Cvitas, N. Kallay, K. Homann and K. Kuchitsu, and published by Blackwell Scientific Publications, Oxford (1988). Whenever appropriate, numerical values quoted are followed, in parentheses, by the standard deviation uncertainty in the least significant digits.

is a constant, known as the permeability of vacuum, and henry $(\mathrm{H} = \mathrm{V\,s\,A^{-1}})$ is a unit of self-induction. The value of $\mu_o$ does not come from experiment, but from the definition of the ampere.

In older NMR literature **B** is often expressed in secondary units of 1 gauss ($1\ \mathrm{G} = 10^{-4}\ \mathrm{T}$) and H in secondary units of 1 oersted $(1\ \mathrm{Oe} = 10^3/4\pi\ \mathrm{A\,m^{-1}})$. The advantage of these units is that it is easy to remember the relationship $\mu_o = 1\ \mathrm{G\,Oe^{-1}}$. This means that in vacuum a field of intensity of 1 oersted corresponds to a magnetic induction of 1 gauss. Unfortunately, the use of these units complicates many equations in electromagnetism. In consequence, in the SI system gauss and oersted have been replaced by tesla and $\mathrm{A\,m^{-1}}$.

The units generally used in all the equations in this book are listed below. The exceptional use of other units is clearly pointed out in the text.

| | |
|---|---|
| length | metre (m) |
| mass | kilogram (kg) |
| time | second (s) |
| force | newton (N) |
| energy | joule (J) |
| electric charge | coulomb (C) |
| electric current | ampere (A) $(1\ \mathrm{A} = 1\ \mathrm{C\,s^{-1}})$ |
| electric potential | volt (V) |
| magnetic field intensity | $\mathrm{A\,m^{-1}}$ |
| magnetic induction | tesla (T) |
| temperature | kelvin (K) |
| amount of substance | mole (mol) |
| viscosity | pascal second $(1\ \mathrm{Pa\,s} = 10\ \mathrm{poise})$ |

For readers who are used to other units we give some conversion factors:

1 newton = $10^5$ dyne
1 joule = $10^7$ erg
1 $\mathrm{A\,m^{-1}} = 4\pi \times 10^{-3}$ oersted
1 tesla = $10^4$ gauss = weber $\mathrm{m^{-2}}$

Faraday's law (10.3) implies that in SI units the force acting on a linear piece of wire carrying a current of intensity I and perpendicular to the vector **B** is

$$F = I\,B\,\ell\,. \tag{10.4}$$

Equation (10.4) gives only the magnitude of the force, the direction of which is described by the more general formula

$$\mathbf{F} = \ell\, \mathbf{I} \times \mathbf{B}$$

where the vector **I** is parallel to the conducting wire and its direction is that of the direction of flow of positive charges. The definition of the cross-product of vectors is given in Appendix 2.

# Chapter 2. Magnetic Properties of the Nucleus

## 11. Dipole Magnetic Moment

Consider a magnetic needle (Figure 11.1) placed in a homogeneous magnetic field **B**. When a torque **T** acts on the needle, vector **M'** defined as

$$\mathbf{T} = \mathbf{M'} \times \mathbf{B} \tag{11.1}$$

is known as its dipole magnetic moment. When torque is expressed in units of N m ≡ J and **B** in tesla (T), the unit of magnetic moment is J $T^{-1}$.

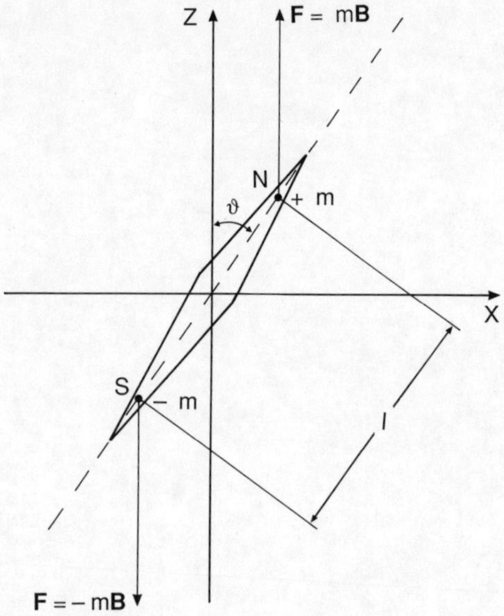


**Figure 11.1.** Action of the magnetic field on a magnetized needle. The vector of magnetic induction **B** coincides with the Z axis.

The above definition could well serve as a basis for further considerations. We shall, however, introduce another definition, which, although less rigorous, conveys better the physical sense of the problem.

Assume that the magnetic poles of the needle contain "magnetic charges" + m (at the N pole) and - m (at the S pole) separated by distance $\ell$ (see Figure 11.1). When the magnetic field **B** is directed along the Z axis, two antiparallel forces **F** = m **B** act on the poles. The magnitude of the total torque is

$$T = B \ell m \sin \vartheta . \tag{11.2}$$

According to the generally accepted definition, **T** is perpendicular to the plane of the drawing and directed towards the reader.

The vector of length $m\ell$, reaching from the point of suspension of the needle towards the positive pole, is the dipole magnetic moment **M'** of the needle. Taking into account the directions of vectors **T, M'** and **B** and the formula (11.2), it is easy to see that (11.1) is satisfied.

The torque acts on a magnetic dipole to align the magnetic moment vector with the vector of magnetic field **B**. Work is performed in the process, and thus the potential energy of the magnetic moment depends on the angle $\vartheta$ formed by the magnetic moment and the magnetic field. We can determine the value of energy in any position by reference to an arbitrary position. Assume that E = 0 for $\vartheta = \pi/2$. Since the length of the path traversed by a single magnetic charge along the lines of the field is $\frac{1}{2} \ell B \cos \vartheta$, work performed by the magnetic moment from this starting point is

$$E = 2 m \frac{1}{2} \ell B \cos \vartheta = \mathbf{M'} \cdot \mathbf{B}$$

It follows that the energy of the system is

$$E = - \mathbf{M'} \cdot \mathbf{B} . \tag{11.3}$$

We note that NMR literature sometimes uses equations based on a different definition of the magnetic moment from that given in (11.1). This alternative definition is

$$\mathbf{T} = \mathbf{M'^*} \times \mathbf{H} . \tag{11.4}$$

The relationship between magnetic moment **M'** defined by (11.1) and magnetic moment **M'*** defined by (11.4) is

$$\mathbf{M'^*} = \mu_0 \mathbf{M'} .$$

In the SI system of units $\mu_0 = 4\pi \times 10^{-7}$ H m$^{-1}$, and therefore the units and numerical values of **M'*** and **M'** differ. It is important to remember this when using equations containing the magnetic moment. The form of many equations depends on which of the two definitions has been adopted. For example, in the convention (11.4) equation (11.3) must be replaced by $E = - \mathbf{M}'^* \cdot \mathbf{H}$. All equations containing the magnetic moment in this book are based on the definition (11.1).

## 12. Magnetic Moment of a Conducting Loop

Consider a direct electric current **I** flowing through a rectangular wire loop with sides of lengths a and b (Figure 12.1). The loop is placed in the magnetic field **B** directed along the Z axis, in such a way that a is parallel to X and b is parallel to the ZY plane. A line normal to the plane of the loop forms the angle $\vartheta$ ($\leq \pi/2$) with Z. To calculate the torque acting on the loop, so as to turn it around X, it is sufficient to consider forces acting on the two sides of length a, since forces acting on the remaining two sides cancel each other.

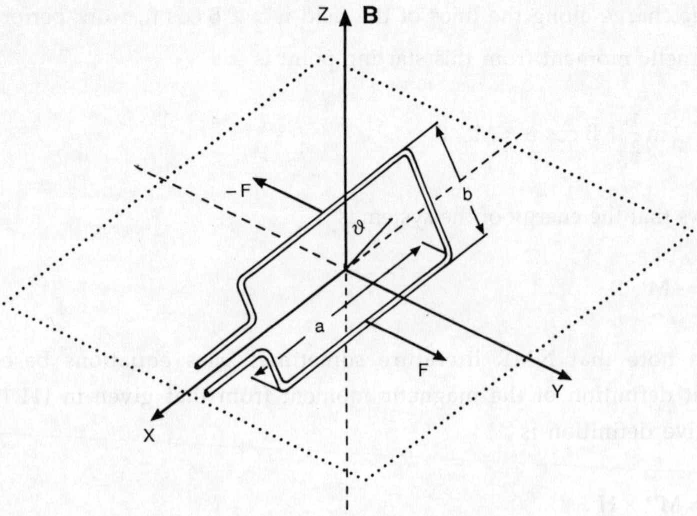


**Figure 12.1.** The action of the magnetic field on a conducting rectangular loop.

The force acting on the entire side of length a of the loop is given by (10.4) as

$$F = B\, I\, a\,.$$

A force of equal magnitude but opposite direction is acting on the other side of length a. The torque acting on the loop so as to rotate it around X is therefore

$$T = F\, b \sin \vartheta = B\, I\, a\, b \sin \vartheta$$

while from (11.1) it follows that

$$T = B\, M' \sin \vartheta.$$

By equating the last two expressions we derive the magnitude of the magnetic moment of the loop

$$M' = I\, S \tag{12.1}$$

where S = a b is the area of the loop. **M'** is perpendicular to the plane of the loop and has the same direction as the magnetic field **H** produced by the loop (the "right-hand rule", see Section 10).

By dividing the loop into a large number of rectangular loops, we can prove that equation (12.1) is valid for a loop of any shape. Such a division is possible because currents in each side common for two elementary rectangular loops cancel one another.

The magnetic moment of a coil is the sum of the magnetic moments of its turns. Treating each turn as a closed loop we obtain for an elongated coil of length $\ell$, cross-sectional area S and n turns

$$M' = n\, S\, I = H\, V \tag{12.2}$$

where $H = n\, I/\ell$ is the magnetic field intensity inside the coil (10.2) and V is the volume of the coil.

## 13. Orbital and Intrinsic Magnetic Moments of the Electron

An electron circulating at a constant linear velocity v around a circular orbit of radius r may be considered as a loop carrying electric current. Applying (12.1) we obtain for the magnetic moment of the orbit

$$M' = I\, S = -\frac{e\, v}{2\pi r}\, \pi\, r^2 = -\frac{1}{2}\, e\, v\, r$$

where $v/2\pi r$ is the period of revolution and $-e = 1.602\ 177\ 33\ (49) \times 10^{-19}$ C is the electronic charge.

Consider now the angular momentum **K** of the orbiting electron

$$\mathbf{K} = m_e \mathbf{v} \times \mathbf{r}$$

where $m_e$ is the mass of the electron. Since both **M'** and **K** are perpendicular to the plane of the orbit, we may write

$$\mathbf{M'} = \gamma \mathbf{K} \tag{13.1}$$

where

$$\gamma = -\frac{e}{2m_e}. \tag{13.2}$$

This illustrates the general law that a rotating electrically charged body possesses a magnetic moment proportional to its angular momentum. The proportionality constant $\gamma$ is known as the gyromagnetic ratio and depends on the sign, the size and the distribution of the charge within the body. The unit of $\gamma$ is $T^{-1}\ s^{-1}$.

Uhlenbeck and Goudsmit showed in 1925 that for a satisfactory interpretation of atomic spectra it is necessary to assume that the electron itself, independently of whether or not it moves around an orbit, has its own angular momentum, known as the electron spin and associated intrinsic magnetic moment which is proportional to this angular momentum. In order to apply (13.2) to the relationship between the intrinsic angular momentum of the electron and its intrinsic magnetic moment, an additional dimensionless coefficient, known as the Landé factor, is introduced into (13.2) so that $\gamma$ becomes

$$\gamma = g\frac{-e}{2\ m_e}. \tag{13.3}$$

Experiments show that $g = 2.002\ 319\ 304\ 386\ (20)$. A different value for the Landé factor is obtained by taking into account both the motion of the electron around an orbit and its intrinsic spin. It is customary to write (13.1) in the form

$$\mathbf{M'} = -\frac{g\ \mu_B\ \mathbf{K}}{\hbar} \tag{13.4}$$

where $\mu_B = e\hbar / 2\,m_e = 9.274\,0154\,(31) \times 10^{-24}\,J\,T^{-1}$, known as the Bohr magneton, is often used as a unit of magnetic momentum. The last formula is often written with e in electrostatic units of charge. In this case it differs by the factor of 10/c in accordance with (10.1).

Comparing (13.1) and (13.4) we obtain a formula often used in the literature on electron spin resonance

$$\gamma\hbar = -g\,\mu_B\,.$$

## 14. Magnetic Moment of the Nucleus

Studies of the ultra fine structure of atomic spectra have shown that an atomic nucleus, like the electron, may possess its own angular momentum known as the nuclear spin, and its own associated intrinsic magnetic moment. Historically speaking, the concept of nuclear magnetic moment is earlier than that of electron spin. It was introduced by Pauli in 1924, several months before Uhlenbeck and Goudsmit's hypothesis of the existence of the electron spin. Different atomic nuclei can have different values of angular momentum, including zero. Since nuclei with zero angular momentum do not undergo nuclear magnetic resonance, we shall not consider them further.

The proportionality between the magnetic moment and the angular momentum, derived in the previous section for the electron, is also applicable to the nuclear angular momentum **K** and the dipole moment of the nucleus $\mu$, so that

$$\mu = \gamma\mathbf{K}\,. \tag{14.1}$$

The nuclear gyromagnetic ratio $\gamma$, characteristic for a given nucleus, is often expressed as

$$\gamma = g_n \frac{e}{2\,m_p} \tag{14.2}$$

where e is the charge of the proton and $g_n$ is the Landé factor for the nucleus. Equation (14.2) has no further justification apart from being analogous to (13.3). Despite this, the values of $g_n$ are, just as for the electron, of the order of unity. We see therefore that the unsophisticated theory of coefficient $\gamma$ described in Section 13 can serve as a qualitative description of the atomic nucleus. It does not, however, apply to the neutron, which, despite its lack of electrical charge, does have a magnetic moment (see Table 14.2). The conclusion from the theory that nuclear magnetic moments should be ca. 2000 times smaller than the magnetic moment of the electron (since $m_p/m_e = 1836$) is confirmed experimentally.

Treating orbital momentum as a quantum operator **I'** = $\hbar$ **I**, we can replace (14.1), which relates physical quantities, by an operator equation

$$\mu = \gamma \hbar \mathbf{I} .$$

The vector **I** is an operator in the sense that its coordinates $I_x$, $I_y$ and $I_z$ are operators.

We see that the operator $\mu$ of the dipole magnetic moment differs by a factor $\gamma \hbar$ from the spin operator **I**. This makes it very easy to use. Consider, for example, the eigenvalue of the z component of this operator

$$\mu_z \varphi = \lambda \varphi .$$

Putting $\mu_z = \gamma \hbar I_z$ we find that the operators $\mu_z$ and $I_z$ have common eigenfunctions and that the eigenvalues of $\mu_z$ are

$$\lambda_m = \gamma \hbar m$$

where m is the eigenvalue of $I_z$. We know from Section 4 that the quantum number m can take on integer or half-integer values in intervals of 1 from a certain minimum value - I to a maximum value of + I. It follows that the eigenvalues of $\mu_z$ are

$$-\gamma \hbar I, -\gamma \hbar (I-1), \ldots, \gamma \hbar (I-1), \gamma \hbar I .$$

Invoking the physical interpretation of eigenvalues discussed in Section 2, we see that these are the only possible values of the z component of the nuclear magnetic moment. In order to determine them, we need to know two quantities characteristic for each type of nucleus: the gyromagnetic ratio $\gamma$ and the dimensionless quantity I, known as the spin quantum number. The quantum number I may take on only positive integer or half-integer values or can be zero. It is linked to the eigenvalue of the square of the operator **I** (i.e. operator $I_x^2 + I_y^2 + I_z^2$) which is equal to I (I + 1). Stable nuclei do not change their angular momentum and therefore I is a quantity characteristic for each type of nucleus. The total quantum spin number of a nucleus is made up of the spins of the individual nucleons. Nucleons of opposite spin can pair, but only with nucleons of the same kind (i.e. protons with protons and neutrons with neutrons). When there is an odd number of either protons or neutrons non-zero total spin results, although its actual value depends upon orbital-type internuclear interactions.

The properties of stable nuclei with $I \neq 0$ are given in Tables 14.1-14.3. We see that the electron, the proton and the neutron (an uncharged composite particle) all have $I = 1/2$. The spin quantum number of naturally occurring isotopes varies between 0 and 7 (for $^{176}Lu$) although unstable isotopes may have I of up to 8. Table 14.1 gives the nuclear structure of the naturally occurring isotopes of the first 15 elements in the Periodic Table. We see that $^{16}O$ and $^{28}Si$, the main isotopes of two of the most abundant elements, both have $I = 0$.

The most important conclusions from Tables 14.1-14.3 are as follows. Firstly, nuclei with an even number of both protons and neutrons have $I = 0$. When the number of protons and the number of neutrons are both odd, the nucleus has an integer spin quantum number. Since this is relatively unlikely to occur, there are only seven permanent nuclei with integer spin quantum number: $^{2}H$, $^{6}Li$, $^{10}B$, $^{14}N$, $^{50}V$, $^{138}La$ and $^{176}Lu$. Secondly, 88 nuclei (i.e. 74% of nuclei with spin) have $I > 1/2$. These are known as quadrupolar nuclei. Thirdly, there are 31 permanent nuclei with $I = 1/2$.

The maximum eigenvalue, $\mu$, of the operator $\mu_z$ can be described in a number of ways

$$\mu = (\mu_z)_{max} = \gamma I \hbar = g_n I e \hbar / 2 m_p = g_n I \mu_N = \mu' \mu_N$$

where $\mu' = g_n I$ and $\mu_N = e \hbar / 2 m_p c$. The constant $\mu_N = 5.050\,7866\,(17) \times 10^{-27}$ J $T^{-1}$ is known as the nuclear magneton. We may consider the dimensionless quantity $\mu'$ as the numerical value of $\mu$ expressed in units of the nuclear magneton. $\mu'$ is often described as the "magnetic moment of the nucleus". Knowing $\mu'$ and the spin quantum number I we can calculate the gyromagnetic ratio of a given nucleus from

$$\gamma = \frac{\mu' \mu_N}{I \hbar} = 4.789\,415\,459 \times 10^{7} \frac{\mu'}{I} \qquad (14.3)$$

where $\hbar = 1.054\,572\,66\,(33) \times 10^{-34}$ J s is the Planck constant divided by $2\pi$, and the unit of $\gamma$ is $T^{-1}$ $s^{-1}$.

**Table 14.1.** Nuclear properties of isotopes of the first 15 elements in the Periodic Table.

| Isotope | Natural abundance, (%) | Protons | Neutrons | I |
|---|---|---|---|---|
| $^{1}H$ | 99.985 | 1 | 0 | 1/2 |
| $^{2}H$ | 0.015 | 1 | 1 | 1 |
| $^{3}H$ | traces | 1 | 2 | 1/2 |
| $^{3}He$ | 0.000138 | 2 | 1 | 1/2 |
| $^{4}He$ | 99.999862 | 2 | 2 | 0 |
| $^{6}Li$ | 7.5 | 3 | 3 | 1 |
| $^{7}Li$ | 92.5 | 3 | 4 | 3/2 |
| $^{9}Be$ | 100 | 4 | 5 | 3/2 |
| $^{10}B$ | 19.9 | 5 | 5 | 3 |
| $^{11}B$ | 80.1 | 5 | 6 | 3/2 |
| $^{12}C$ | 98.90 | 6 | 6 | 0 |
| $^{13}C$ | 1.10 | 6 | 7 | 1/2 |
| $^{14}N$ | 99.634 | 7 | 7 | 1 |
| $^{15}N$ | 0.366 | 7 | 8 | 1/2 |
| $^{16}O$ | 99.762 | 8 | 8 | 0 |
| $^{17}O$ | 0.038 | 8 | 9 | 5/2 |
| $^{18}O$ | 0.200 | 8 | 10 | 0 |
| $^{19}F$ | 100 | 9 | 10 | 1/2 |
| $^{20}Ne$ | 90.48 | 10 | 10 | 0 |
| $^{21}Ne$ | 0.27 | 10 | 11 | 3/2 |
| $^{22}Ne$ | 9.25 | 10 | 12 | 0 |
| $^{23}Na$ | 100 | 11 | 12 | 3/2 |
| $^{24}Mg$ | 78.99 | 12 | 12 | 0 |
| $^{25}Mg$ | 10.00 | 12 | 13 | 5/2 |
| $^{26}Mg$ | 11.01 | 12 | 14 | 0 |
| $^{27}Al$ | 100 | 13 | 14 | 5/2 |
| $^{28}Si$ | 92.23 | 14 | 14 | 0 |
| $^{29}Si$ | 4.67 | 14 | 15 | 1/2 |
| $^{30}Si$ | 3.10 | 14 | 16 | 0 |
| $^{31}P$ | 100 | 15 | 16 | 1/2 |

**Table 14.2.** NMR properties of nuclides with I = 1/2.

| Nuclide | Natural abundance (%) | Magnetic moment, ($\mu' = \mu/\mu_N$) | Gyromagnetic ratio, $\gamma$ ($10^7$ $T^{-1}$ $s^{-1}$) | Resonance frequency (MHz*) |
|---|---|---|---|---|
| neutron | - | -1.913 043 | -18.324 72 | 68.498 |
| $^{1}H$ | 99.985 | 2.792 845 6 | 26.752 196 | 100.000 |
| $^{3}H$ | traces | 2.978 960 | 28.534 95 | 106.664 |
| $^{3}He$ | 0.000138 | -2.127 624 | -20.380 15 | 76.181 |
| $^{13}C$ | 1.10 | 0.702 411 | 6.728 28 | 25.150 |
| $^{15}N$ | 0.366 | -0.283 189 2 | -2.712 621 | 10.140 |
| $^{19}F$ | 100 | 2.628 867 | 25.181 47 | 94.129 |
| $^{29}Si$ | 4.67 | -0.555 29 | -5.319 0 | 19.883 |
| $^{31}P$ | 100 | 1.131 60 | 10.839 4 | 40.518 |
| $^{57}Fe$ | 2.2 | 0.090 622 94 | 0.868 061 8 | 3.245 |
| $^{77}Se$ | 7.6 | 0.535 06 | 5.125 2 | 19.158 |
| $^{89}Y$ | 100 | -0.137 415 3 | -1.316 278 | 4.920 |
| $^{103}Rh$ | 100 | -0.088 40 | -0.846 8 | 3.165 |
| $^{107}Ag$ | 51.839 | -0.113 570 | -1.087 87 | 4.067 |
| $^{109}Ag$ | 48.161 | -0.130 690 5 | -1.251 862 | 4.680 |
| $^{111}Cd$ | 12.80 | -0.594 885 7 | -5.698 310 | 21.300 |
| $^{113}Cd$ | 12.22 | -0.622 300 5 | -5.960 911 | 22.282 |
| $^{115}Sn$ | 0.36 | -0.918 84 | -8.801 4 | 32.900 |
| $^{117}Sn$ | 7.68 | -1.001 05 | -9.588 89 | 35.843 |
| $^{119}Sn$ | 8.58 | -1.047 29 | -10.031 8 | 37.499 |
| $^{123}Te$ | 0.908 | -0.736 79 | -7.057 6 | 26.381 |
| $^{125}Te$ | 7.14 | -0.888 28 | -8.508 7 | 31.806 |
| $^{129}Xe$ | 26.4 | -0.777 977 | -7.452 11 | 27.856 |
| $^{169}Tm$ | 100 | -0.231 6 | -2.218 | 8.293 |
| $^{171}Yb$ | 14.3 | 0.493 67 | 4.728 8 | 17.676 |
| $^{183}W$ | 14.3 | 0.117 784 7 | 1.128 240 | 4.217 |
| $^{187}Os$ | 1.6 | 0.064 651 85 | 0.619 289 1 | 2.315 |
| $^{195}Pt$ | 33.8 | 0.609 50 | 5.838 3 | 21.824 |
| $^{199}Hg$ | 16.84 | 0.505 885 2 | 4.845 789 | 18.114 |
| $^{203}Tl$ | 29.524 | 1.622 257 | 15.539 33 | 58.086 |
| $^{205}Tl$ | 70.476 | 1.638 213 5 | 15.692 170 | 58.658 |
| $^{207}Pb$ | 22.1 | 0.582 19 | 5.576 7 | 20.846 |

* For a magnetic field of 2.34866 T in which $^{1}H$ resonates at 100.000 MHz.

**Table 14.3.** NMR properties of nuclei with I > 1/2.

| Nucleus | Spin | Natural abundance (%) | Magnetic moment, ($\mu' = \mu/\mu_N$) | Gyromagnetic ratio, $\gamma$ ($10^7$ $T^{-1}$ $s^{-1}$) | Quadrupolar moment (Q $fm^{-2}$) | Resonance frequency (MHz*) |
|---|---|---|---|---|---|---|
| $^{2}H$ | 1 | 0.015 | 0.857 437 6 | 4.106 625 | 0.287 5 | 15.351 |
| $^{6}Li$ | 1 | 7.42 | 0.822 046 7 | 3.937 123 | -0.064 5 | 14.717 |
| $^{7}Li$ | 3/2 | 92.58 | 3.256 424 | 10.397 58 | -3.66 | 38.866 |
| $^{9}Be$ | 3/2 | 100 | -1.177 9 | -3.761 0 | 5.3 | 14.059 |
| $^{10}B$ | 3 | 19.58 | 1.800 65 | 2.874 69 | 8.473 | 10.746 |
| $^{11}B$ | 3/2 | 80.42 | 2.688 637 | 8.584 666 | 4.065 | 32.090 |
| $^{14}N$ | 1 | 99.63 | 0.403 760 7 | 1.933 778 | 1.56 | 7.229 |
| $^{17}O$ | 5/2 | 0.037 | -1.893 80 | -3.628 08 | -2.578 | 13.562 |
| $^{21}Ne$ | 3/2 | 0.257 | -0.661 796 | -2.113 08 | 10.30 | 7.899 |
| $^{23}Na$ | 3/2 | 100 | 2.217 520 | 7.080 416 | 10.2 | 26.467 |
| $^{25}Mg$ | 5/2 | 10.13 | -0.855 46 | -1.638 9 | 22 | 6.126 |
| $^{27}Al$ | 5/2 | 100 | 3.641 504 | 6.976 270 | 14.0 | 26.077 |
| $^{33}S$ | 3/2 | 0.76 | 0.643 821 | 2.055 68 | -6.4 | 7.684 |
| $^{35}Cl$ | 3/2 | 75.53 | 0.821 873 6 | 2.624 196 | -8.249 | 9.809 |
| $^{37}Cl$ | 3/2 | 24.47 | 0.684 123 0 | 2.184 366 | -6.493 | 8.165 |
| $^{39}K$ | 3/2 | 93.1 | 0.391 465 8 | 1.249 928 | 4.9 | 4.672 |
| $^{41}K$ | 3/2 | 6.88 | 0.214 896 9 | 0.686 153 7 | 6.0 | 2.565 |
| $^{43}Ca$ | 7/2 | 0.145 | -1.317 27 | -1.802 56 | -5 | 6.738 |
| $^{45}Sc$ | 7/2 | 100 | 4.756 483 | 6.508 792 | -22 | 24.330 |
| $^{47}Ti$ | 5/2 | 7.28 | -0.788 48 | -1.510 5 | 29 | 5.646 |
| $^{49}Ti$ | 7/2 | 5.51 | -1.104 17 | -1.510 95 | 24 | 5.648 |
| $^{50}V$ | 6 | 0.24 | 3.347 45 | 2.672 05 | 7 | 9.988 |
| $^{51}V$ | 7/2 | 99.76 | 5.151 4 | 7.049 2 | -5.2 | 26.350 |
| $^{53}Cr$ | 3/2 | 9.55 | -0.474 54 | -1.515 2 | 2.2 | 5.664 |
| $^{55}Mn$ | 5/2 | 100 | 3.453 2 | 6.615 5 | 40 | 24.729 |
| $^{59}Co$ | 7/2 | 100 | 4.627 | 6.332 | 40.4 | 23.668 |
| $^{61}Ni$ | 3/2 | 1.19 | -0.750 02 | -2.394 8 | 16.2 | 8.952 |
| $^{63}Cu$ | 3/2 | 69.09 | 2.223 3 | 7.098 9 | -20.9 | 26.536 |
| $^{65}Cu$ | 3/2 | 30.91 | 2.381 7 | 7.604 6 | -19.5 | 28.426 |
| $^{67}Zn$ | 5/2 | 4.11 | 0.875 479 | 1.677 21 | 15.0 | 6.269 |
| $^{69}Ga$ | 3/2 | 60.4 | 2.016 59 | 6.438 86 | 16.8 | 24.069 |
| $^{71}Ga$ | 3/2 | 39.6 | 2.562 27 | 8.181 18 | 10.6 | 30.581 |
| $^{73}Ge$ | 9/2 | 7.76 | -0.879 466 9 | -0.936 029 4 | -17.3 | 3.499 |
| $^{79}Br$ | 3/2 | 50.54 | 2.106 399 | 6.725 613 | 29.3 | 25.140 |
| $^{81}Br$ | 3/2 | 49.46 | 2.270 560 | 7.249 770 | 27 | 27.100 |
| $^{83}Kr$ | 9/2 | 11.55 | -0.970 669 | -1.033 10 | 27.0 | 3.862 |
| $^{85}Rb$ | 5/2 | 72.15 | 1.353 03 | 2.592 09 | 27.4 | 9.689 |
| $^{87}Rb$ | 3/2 | 27.85 | 2.751 24 | 8.784 55 | 13.2 | 32.837 |
| $^{87}Sr$ | 9/2 | 7.02 | -1.092 83 | -1.163 11 | 16 | 4.348 |
| $^{91}Zr$ | 5/2 | 11.23 | -1.303 62 | -2.497 43 | -21 | 9.335 |
| $^{93}Nb$ | 9/2 | 100 | 6.170 5 | 6.567 4 | -37 | 24.549 |
| $^{95}Mo$ | 5/2 | 15.72 | -0.914 2 | -1.751 | -1.9 | 6.547 |
| $^{97}Mo$ | 5/2 | 9.46 | -0.933 5 | -1.788 | -10.2 | 6.685 |

**Table 14.3.** continued

| Nucleus | Spin | Natural abundance (%) | Magnetic moment, ($\mu' = \mu/\mu_N$) | Gyromagnetic ratio, $\gamma$ ($10^7$ $T^{-1}$ $s^{-1}$) | Quadrupolar moment (Q $fm^{-2}$) | Resonance frequency (MHz*) |
|---|---|---|---|---|---|---|
| $^{99}Ru$ | 5/2 | 12.72 | -0.641 3 | -1.229 | 7.7 | 4.592 |
| $^{101}Ru$ | 5/2 | 17.07 | -0.718 9 | -1.377 | 44 | 5.148 |
| $^{105}Pd$ | 5/2 | 22.23 | -0.642 | -1.23 | 80 | 4.598 |
| $^{113}In$ | 9/2 | 4.28 | 5.528 9 | 5.884 5 | 84.6 | 21.996 |
| $^{115}In$ | 9/2 | 95.72 | 5.540 8 | 5.897 2 | 86.1 | 22.044 |
| $^{121}Sb$ | 5/2 | 57.25 | 3.363 4 | 6.443 5 | -20 | 24.086 |
| $^{123}Sb$ | 7/2 | 42.75 | 2.549 8 | 3.489 2 | -26 | 13.043 |
| $^{127}I$ | 5/2 | 100 | 2.813 28 | 5.389 59 | -78.9 | 20.146 |
| $^{131}Xe$ | 3/2 | 21.18 | 0.691 861 | 2.209 07 | -12.0 | 8.258 |
| $^{133}Cs$ | 7/2 | 100 | 2.582 024 | 3.533 253 | -0.3 | 13.207 |
| $^{135}Ba$ | 3/2 | 6.59 | 0.837 943 | 2.675 50 | 18 | 10.001 |
| $^{137}Ba$ | 3/2 | 11.32 | 0.937 365 | 2.992 95 | 28 | 11.188 |
| $^{138}La$ | 5 | 0.089 | 3.713 9 | 3.557 5 | 52 | 13.298 |
| $^{139}La$ | 7/2 | 99.911 | 2.783 2 | 3.808 5 | 22 | 14.236 |
| $^{141}Pr$ | 5/2 | 100 | 4.136 | 7.924 | -5.89 | 29.619 |
| $^{143}Nd$ | 7/2 | 12.17 | -1.065 | -1.457 | -48.4 | 5.448 |
| $^{145}Nd$ | 7/2 | 8.3 | -0.656 | -0.898 | -25.3 | 3.356 |
| $^{147}Sm$ | 7/2 | 14.97 | -0.814 9 | -1.115 | -18 | 4.168 |
| $^{149}Sm$ | 7/2 | 13.83 | -0.671 8 | -0.919 3 | 5.3 | 3.436 |
| $^{151}Eu$ | 5/2 | 47.82 | 3.471 8 | 6.651 2 | 116 | 24.862 |
| $^{153}Eu$ | 5/2 | 52.18 | 1.533 1 | 2.937 1 | 294 | 10.979 |
| $^{155}Gd$ | 3/2 | 14.73 | -0.259 1 | -0.827 3 | 159 | 3.092 |
| $^{157}Gd$ | 3/2 | 15.68 | -0.339 9 | -1.085 | 203 | 4.057 |
| $^{161}Dy$ | 5/2 | 18.88 | -0.480 6 | 0.920 7 | 244 | 3.442 |
| $^{163}Dy$ | 5/2 | 24.97 | 0.672 6 | 1.289 | 257 | 4.817 |
| $^{165}Ho$ | 7/2 | 100 | 4.173 | 5.710 | 274 | 21.345 |
| $^{167}Er$ | 7/2 | 22.94 | -0.566 5 | -0.775 2 | 282 7 | 2.898 |
| $^{173}Yb$ | 5/2 | 16.13 | -0.679 89 | -1.302 5 | $28\underline{0}$ | 4.869 |
| $^{175}Lu$ | 7/2 | 97.42 | 2.232 7 | 3.055 2 | 569 | 11.421 |
| $^{176}Lu$ | 7 | 2.59 | 3.19 | 2.18 | $81\underline{0}$ | 8.159 |
| $^{177}Hf$ | 7/2 | 18.50 | 0.793 6 | 1.086 | $45\underline{0}$ | 4.059 |
| $^{179}Hf$ | 9/2 | 3.75 | -0.640 9 | -0.682 1 | $51\underline{0}$ | 2.550 |
| $^{181}Ta$ | 7/2 | 99.988 | 2.371 | 3.244 | $39\underline{0}$ | 12.128 |
| $^{185}Re$ | 5/2 | 37.07 | 3.187 1 | 6.105 7 | 236 | 22.823 |
| $^{187}Re$ | 5/2 | 62.93 | 3.219 7 | 6.168 2 | 224 | 23.057 |
| $^{189}Os$ | 3/2 | 16.1 | 0.659 933 | 2.107 13 | 91 | 7.877 |
| $^{191}Ir$ | 3/2 | 37.3 | 0.146 2 | 0.466 8 | 78 | 1.745 |
| $^{193}Ir$ | 3/2 | 62.7 | 0.159 2 | 0.508 3 | 70 | 1.900 |
| $^{197}Au$ | 3/2 | 100 | 0.148 159 | 0.473 063 | 54.7 | 1.768 |
| $^{201}Hg$ | 3/2 | 13.22 | -0.560 255 | -1.788 86 | 45.5 | 6.687 |
| $^{209}Bi$ | 9/2 | 100 | 4.110 6 | 4.375 0 | -46 | 16.354 |
| $^{235}U$ | 7/2 | 0.72 | -0.35 | -0.48 | 455 | 1.79 |

* For a magnetic field of 2.34866 T in which $^{1}H$ resonates at 100.000 MHz.

## 15. Zeeman Energy Eigenfunctions

Consider a nucleus with a magnetic moment $\mu$ placed in a constant magnetic field of induction $\mathbf{B}_0$. Magnetic field distinguishes a certain direction in space, and it is convenient to choose the laboratory coordinate system in such a way that the Z axis coincides with $\mathbf{B}_0$.

In this situation the expression (11.3) for the energy of a nuclear magnetic moment $\mu$ interacting with a magnetic field is

$$E = - \mu \cdot \mathbf{B}_0 = - B_0 \mu_z = - B_0 \gamma \hbar I_z$$

where the dot in $- \mu \cdot \mathbf{B}_0$ denotes the scalar product of vectors (see Appendix 2). Following the rules of construction of operators (see Section 2), we convert this classical formula for energy into an expression for the operator of energy (the Hamiltonian) by treating the coordinate $I_z$ of the spin as an operator

$$\mathcal{H}_Z = - \mu \cdot \mathbf{B}_0 = - \mathbf{B}_0 \cdot \mathbf{I} \gamma \hbar \tag{15.1a}$$

or, when $\mathbf{B}_0$ is aligned with the Z axis

$$\mathcal{H}_Z = - B_0 \gamma \hbar I_z = \hbar \omega_0 I_z \tag{15.1b}$$

where $\omega_0 = - \gamma B_0$. Because of the similarity of the situation in hand and the levels in the Zeeman effect, the operator $\mathcal{H}_Z$ is known as the "Zeeman Hamiltonian". Since $\mathcal{H}_Z$ and $I_z$ are proportional to each other, they have the same eigenfunctions. The eigenvalues of $\mathcal{H}_Z$ are

$$E(m) = - B_0 \gamma \hbar m \tag{15.2}$$

and may be interpreted as the allowed values of energy for a free nucleus with spin quantum number I and gyromagnetic ratio $\gamma$ in the magnetic field $\mathbf{B}_0$. There are 2I + 1 such "Zeeman levels". The Zeeman energy is also called "energy of interaction of spin with the magnetic field", where the word "spin" refers not to spin itself but to a nucleus with non-zero spin and to its magnetic moment. It is in this sense that we refer to the "number of spins per unit volume of the sample" or to the "mutual interaction of spins". Similarly, instead of saying "a nucleus with spin quantum number I = 1/2" we simply say "spin 1/2".

Since the consecutive values of m differ by 1, the energy levels are equally spaced. The energy difference between the neighbouring levels is

$$\Delta E = E(m) - E(m-1) = -\gamma \hbar B_o . \tag{15.3}$$

Consider a quantum system composed of N spins interacting with the external magnetic field $\mathbf{B}_o$, but not interacting between themselves. This idealized situation, which does not occur in Nature, will be needed later on in the book as a starting point for more realistic calculations.

The Hamiltonian of the system is the sum of the Zeeman energies of the individual spins:

$$\mathcal{H}_Z = -\hbar B_o \sum_{i=1}^{N} \gamma_i I_z^{(i)} = \hbar \sum_{i=1}^{N} \omega_i I_z^{(i)} \tag{15.4}$$

where $\omega_i = -\gamma_i B_o$ and $I_z^{(i)}$ the operator of the z component of the ith spin. We wish to find the eigenfunctions and eigenvalues of the Hamiltonian $\mathcal{H}_Z$. To simplify the calculations, we assume for the time being that N = 2. We must thus solve the equation

$$\hbar \left(\omega_1 I_z^{(1)} + \omega_2 I_z^{(2)}\right) \varphi = \lambda \varphi . \tag{15.5}$$

We will show that the solutions are the products

$$\varphi = \varphi_{m_1}^{(1)} \varphi_{m_2}^{(2)} . \tag{15.6}$$

The functions $\varphi_{m_1}^{(1)}$ and $\varphi_{m_2}^{(2)}$ are the eigenfunctions of the operators $I_z^{(1)}$ and $I_z^{(2)}$, respectively. We have therefore

$$I_z^{(1)} \varphi_{m_1}^{(1)} = m_1 \varphi_{m_1}^{(1)}$$

$$I_z^{(2)} \varphi_{m_2}^{(2)} = m_2 \varphi_{m_2}^{(2)} .$$

The quantum numbers can assume the values

$$m_1 = -I^{(1)}, \dots, +I^{(1)} \qquad \text{and} \qquad m_2 = -I^{(2)}, \dots, +I^{(2)}$$

where $I^{(1)}$ and $I^{(2)}$ are the spin quantum numbers.

The function $\varphi^{(1)}_{m_1}$ is defined in the space $V^{(1)}$ of the variables of spin (1) and is not subject to the action of the operator $I^{(2)}_z$, which treats $\varphi^{(1)}_{m_1}$ as a number. For example

$$I^{(2)}_z \varphi^{(1)}_{m_1} \varphi^{(2)}_{m_2} = \varphi^{(1)}_{m_1} I^{(2)}_z \varphi^{(2)}_{m_2} = m_2 \varphi^{(1)}_{m_1} \varphi^{(2)}_{m_2} . \qquad (15.7)$$

Similarly, the operator $I^{(1)}_z$ does not affect the function $\varphi^{(2)}_{m_2}$, which is defined in the space $V^{(2)}$ of the variables of spin (2). For our purposes a more precise definition of these variables is not necessary.

We calculate

$$\hbar \left(\omega_1 I^{(1)}_z + \omega_2 I^{(2)}_z\right) \varphi^{(1)}_{m_1} \varphi^{(2)}_{m_2} = \hbar\, \omega_1 \varphi^{(2)}_{m_2} I^{(1)}_z \varphi^{(1)}_{m_1} + \hbar\, \omega_2 \varphi^{(1)}_{m_1} I^{(2)}_z \varphi^{(2)}_{m_2}$$

$$= \hbar \left(\omega_1 m_1 + \omega_2 m_2\right) \varphi^{(1)}_{m_1} \varphi^{(2)}_{m_2} . \qquad (15.8)$$

We have shown, therefore, that the products (15.6) are eigenfunctions of the Hamiltonian (15.4). It is convenient to represent these products in the Dirac notation

$$\varphi = |m_1\rangle |m_2\rangle \qquad \text{or} \qquad \varphi = |m_1\, m_2\rangle$$

where $|m_1\rangle = \varphi^{(1)}_{m_1}$ and $|m_2\rangle = \varphi^{(2)}_{m_2}$. Note that the function $\varphi$ is described by a set of numbers ($m_1\, m_2$), and therefore placing this set in Dirac's "ket" symbol removes any ambiguity. In the symbol $|m\, n\rangle$ the first of the two quantum numbers applies to the operator $I^{(1)}_z$, and the second to the operator $I^{(2)}_z$. In this notation

$$\mathcal{H}_Z |m_1\, m_2\rangle = \hbar \left(\omega_1 m_1 + \omega_2 m_2\right) |m_1\, m_2\rangle .$$

Sometimes it is convenient to number the eigenfunctions and simply give the number in Dirac's ket, instead of the set of quantum numbers $m_1\, m_2$. This notation has been used in Table 15.1.

If the spins under consideration are identical, i.e. $\gamma_1 = \gamma_2$, some of the eigenvalues are degenerate. This is clear from Table 15.1, which gives all possible eigenfunctions of $\mathcal{H}_Z$ for a system of two nuclei with $I = 1/2$.

**Table 15.1.** Eigenfunctions and eigenvalues of the Zeeman Hamiltonian for a system composed of two spins 1/2.

| Eigenfunction | Eigenvalue of $\mathcal{H}_Z$ in general | Eigenvalue of $\mathcal{H}_Z$ for $\omega_1 = \omega_2 = \omega_0$ |
|---|---|---|
| $\|1\rangle = \|+\frac{1}{2},+\frac{1}{2}\rangle = \|++\rangle$ | $\frac{1}{2}\hbar\,(\omega_1 + \omega_2)$ | $\hbar\,\omega_0$ |
| $\|2\rangle = \|+\frac{1}{2},-\frac{1}{2}\rangle = \|+-\rangle$ | $\frac{1}{2}\hbar\,(\omega_1 - \omega_2)$ | 0 |
| $\|3\rangle = \|-\frac{1}{2},+\frac{1}{2}\rangle = \|-+\rangle$ | $-\frac{1}{2}\hbar\,(\omega_1 - \omega_2)$ | 0 |
| $\|4\rangle = \|-\frac{1}{2},-\frac{1}{2}\rangle = \|--\rangle$ | $-\frac{1}{2}\hbar\,(\omega_1 + \omega_2)$ | $-\hbar\,\omega_0$ |

Table 15.1 shows that the zero level is degenerate, because it corresponds to two linearly independent eigenfunctions $\varphi_2$ and $\varphi_3$. We can therefore form two arbitrary linearly independent combinations of these functions, which will belong to the same eigenvalue (see Section 1). We shall see later in the book that it is sometimes convenient to use such combinations, because they are eigenfunctions of other important operators.

In general, if the system is composed of N identical spins, the eigenfunction of the Zeeman Hamiltonian is the product of N functions

$$\varphi = \varphi^{(1)}_{m_1}\,\varphi^{(2)}_{m_2} \ldots \varphi^{(N)}_{m_N} = |m_1\, m_2 \ldots m_N\rangle\,. \tag{15.9}$$

The number of eigenfunctions (15.9) is $(2I + 1)^N$. They are all linearly independent, and form the Hilbert space suitable for matrix representation of operators associated with physical quantities which are measured in the system. The number $(2I + 1)^N$ is therefore the dimension of the appropriate Hilbert space, denoted by L in Section 6. Note that $L = \mathrm{Tr}\,\{1\}$, where $\{1\}$ is the identity matrix which represents the identity operator in that Hilbert space.

# Chapter 3. Nuclear Paramagnetism

## 16. Magnetization at Thermodynamic Equilibrium

We shall now examine the magnetic moment of the sample caused by, at least partial, ordering of the nuclear magnetic dipoles by the external magnetic field. Consider only one type of constituent nuclei, with spin quantum number I and gyromagnetic ratio $\gamma$.

In a macroscopic sample, the number of nuclei, even of one kind only, is very large. For example, 1 $cm^3$ of water contains $6.69 \times 10^{22}$ $^1H$ nuclei with $2I + 1$ energy levels at their disposal (see (15.2)). The number N (m) of nuclei simultaneously occupying level m is known as the population of this level.

If the sample is immersed in a constant magnetic field $\mathbf{B_0}$ (we assume that $B_o \| Z$) for an extended period, it will reach a state of equilibrium, where the populations are described by Boltzmann's law. This states that the population of the level m of energy E (m) is proportional to $\exp\left[-E(m)/kT\right]$. Thus the following relationships apply:

$$
\begin{aligned}
N(m_1) &= c \exp\left[-E(m_1)/kT\right] \\
N(m_2) &= c \exp\left[-E(m_2)/kT\right] \\
&\ \vdots \\
N(m_{2I+1}) &= c \exp\left[-E(m_{2I+1})/kT\right]
\end{aligned}
\qquad (16.1)
$$

and, of course,

$$\sum N(m) = N \qquad (16.2)$$

where N is the number of nuclei of one kind in the sample, c is a proportionality constant, $k = 1.380\,658\,(12) \times 10^{-23}$ J $K^{-1}$ is Boltzmann's constant, and T is the absolute temperature of the sample. According to Boltzmann's law, at thermodynamic equilibrium the population of a higher energy level is lower than that of a lower energy level.

$\Delta E(m)$, the energy difference between the neighbouring levels, is extremely small in comparison with kT (at 293 K, $kT = 4.045 \times 10^{-21}$ J). For a proton at T = 293 K in a magnetic field of 14.093 tesla (the highest available for NMR at present) we have

$$\Delta E(m) = \gamma \hbar B_0 = 3.976 \times 10^{-25} \text{ J}.$$

As a result, at room temperature the populations of the individual levels only differ very slightly.

To estimate the actual numerical values for the distribution of spins, we calculate the ratio of the populations of neighbouring energy states:

$$\frac{N(m)}{N(m+1)} = \exp(-\zeta)$$

where

$$\zeta = \frac{E(m+1) - E(m)}{kT} = \frac{\gamma \hbar B}{kT}.$$

For T = 293 K (room temperature), B = 1 tesla and $\gamma = 26.75 \times 10^7 \text{ T}^{-1} \text{ s}^{-1}$ (the gyromagnetic ratio of $^1$H), we have $\zeta = 7 \times 10^{-6}$. Since the exponent is so small, we can assume approximately that

$$\frac{N(m)}{N(m+1)} = 1 - \zeta = 0.999\,993. \qquad (16.3a)$$

Clearly, the population difference is very small indeed: for 1000 000 spins at level N (m + 1) there are 1000 007 spins at level N (m). Even so, it is this minuscule population difference, of just seven nuclei in a million, which produces the net magnetic moment **M'** of the sample and makes the NMR experiment possible.

The approximation made in (16.3a) is known as the "high-temperature approximation". Despite its name, it is correct for a very wide range of temperatures, including very low temperatures. For example, for protons in a field of B = 1 tesla and at T = 0.1 K, $\zeta = 0.02$, while for B = 8 tesla and T = 4.2 K (the boiling point of helium), $\zeta = 0.004$.

It is not only the energy differences between the levels, but also the actual values of energy for the levels, which are so small in comparison with kT. This is why the approximation

$$\exp\left(\frac{-E(m)}{kT}\right) = 1 - \frac{E(m)}{kT} \tag{16.3b}$$

carries a very small error. Also this approximation is known as the "high-temperature approximation".

The net magnetic moment is the sum of the moments of the individual nuclei, so that

$$\begin{aligned} M_z' &= \sum \mu_z = \sum_m \mu_z(m)\, N(m) \\ M_x' &= \sum \mu_x = 0 \\ M_y' &= \sum \mu_y = 0 \end{aligned} \tag{16.4}$$

where

$$\mu_z(m) = m\,\gamma\,\hbar\,.$$

$M_x'$ and $M_y'$ are both zero because, in the XY plane perpendicular to $\mathbf{B_o}$, no direction is favoured, and at equilibrium the projections of the nuclear magnetic momenta onto XY are evenly distributed and their sum is zero. Thus at equilibrium $\mathbf{M'} \,||\, \mathbf{B_o}$. Substituting (16.1) in (16.4), making the approximation (16.3b) and using the relationships

$$\sum_{m=-I}^{I} m = 0$$

$$\sum_{m=-I}^{I} m^2 = \frac{1}{3}\, I\,(I+1)\,(2I+1)$$

we find

$$\sum \mu_z = c\,\frac{\gamma^2 \hbar^2 B_o}{3kT}\, I\,(I+1)\,(2I+1)\,.$$

The proportionality coefficient c is found from (16.2) as

$$c = \frac{N}{2I+1}\,.$$

The equilibrium magnetic moment of the sample stemming from a partial ordering of nuclear magnetic moments under the influence of the applied magnetic field is thus

$$M' = \frac{\gamma^2 \hbar^2 B_0 N}{3kT} I(I+1) .$$

Let V be the volume of the sample. The net magnetic moment per unit of volume is known as *magnetization* **M**

$$M = M'/V .$$

The unit of magnetization is $J\,T^{-1}\,m^{-3}$. Since $J\,T^{-1}\,m^{-3} = (V\,A\,s)(V\,s\,m^{-2})^{-1}\,m^{-3} = A\,m^{-1}$, magnetization has the same dimension as magnetic intensity H.

Magnetization in the state of thermodynamic equilibrium is distinguished with the subscript "∞"

$$M_\infty = \frac{\gamma^2 \hbar^2 B_0 N_0}{3kT} I(I+1) \qquad \text{and} \qquad \mathbf{M}_\infty \| \mathbf{B}_0 \tag{16.5}$$

where $N_0 = N/V$ is the number of nuclei of a given kind per 1 $m^3$ of the sample. Note that the vector of equilibrium magnetization $\mathbf{M}_\infty$ has the same direction as the magnetic field, irrespective of the sign of $\gamma$. In the SI system of units, 1 $m^3$ must be used as the unit of volume, even though in laboratory practice the volume of a sample rarely exceeds several $cm^3$. Equation (16.5) is known as the Langevin-Curie formula.

When $\mathbf{M} \| \mathbf{H}$, the proportionality constant between these two vectors is known as magnetic susceptibility $\chi$. In the special case of thermodynamic equilibrium we have

$$M = \chi_\infty H \tag{16.6}$$

where

$$\chi_\infty = \frac{\gamma^2 \hbar^2 \mu_0 N_0}{3kT} I(I+1) . \tag{16.7}$$

Since **M** and **H** have the same dimension, $\chi$ is dimensionless.

The Langevin-Curie formula can be derived more elegantly using the density operator (see Section 7). If the effective density operator $\sigma_\infty$ at thermodynamic equilibrium is given by (7.12), with $\mathcal{H} = \mathcal{H}_Z + \mathcal{H}_L$, with $\mathcal{H}_Z$ as the Zeeman Hamiltonian (15.1), describing the energy of spin interaction with the external magnetic field **B**, and $\mathcal{H}_L$ describing all intermolecular interactions, we have:

$$M_Z = N_0 \langle\langle \mu_z \rangle\rangle = N_0 \operatorname{Tr}\{\mu_Z \sigma_\infty\} = \frac{N_0 \gamma \hbar}{\operatorname{Tr}\{1\} kT} \operatorname{Tr}\{I_Z \mathcal{H}_Z\}.$$

Because $\operatorname{Tr}\{I_Z \mathcal{H}_L\} = 0$, internuclear interactions do not contribute to the magnetization and can be neglected. We are therefore allowed to decompose the sample into quantum systems each containing a single spin, where $\operatorname{Tr}\{1\} = 2I + 1$ and $\operatorname{Tr}\{I_Z^2\} = I(I+1)(2I+1)/3$. Substituting these values into the last expression, we obtain the Langevin-Curie formula in the form of (16.5). Application of the same procedure to the remaining coordinates gives expressions containing $\operatorname{Tr}\{I_x I_z\} = 0$ or $\operatorname{Tr}\{I_y I_z\} = 0$, leading to $M_x = M_y = 0$. The calculation of traces is explained in Appendix 3.

## 17. Magnetic Induction in the Interior of a Magnetized Sample

Consider a sample which has acquired magnetization **M** in an applied magnetic field **H.** In consequence, an additional magnetic field is present in the interior of the sample. This extra field comes from the elementary magnetic dipoles, which have become partially ordered through the action of the field **H.**

Imagine that the sample fills an elongated coil, and that the action of field **H** generated by the current **I** gave rise to magnetization **M.** The magnetic moment of the entire sample is then

$$\mathbf{M'} = \mathbf{M}\, V \tag{17.1}$$

where V is the volume of the coil. On the other hand, the magnetic moment of an empty coil is given by (12.2) as

$$\mathbf{M'} = \mathbf{H}\, V.$$

The sum of the two moments is the magnetic moment of a coil filled with the sample

$$\mathbf{M'} = (\mathbf{H} + \mathbf{M})\, V. \tag{17.2}$$

A comparison of (17.2) and (17.1) shows that a coil filled with the sample behaves like an empty coil, but one in which current **I'** (different from **I**) gave rise to a magnetic field intensity **H** + **M** and to the associated magnetic induction

$$B_{int} = \mu_0 (H + M) = \mu_0 (1 + \chi) H \tag{17.3}$$

where $\chi = M/H$. Equation (17.2) gives the value of magnetic induction inside a magnetized body. We see that the extra magnetic field is $\chi$ **H** and that the extra magnetic induction is $\mu_0 \chi$ **H**.

## 18. Complex Coefficient of Magnetic Susceptibility

The relationship between the magnetization **M** of the sample and the applied magnetic field **H** was derived on the assumption that the field does not change with time and that it acts on the sample long enough for the state of equilibrium to be established. Consider now the case when the direction of the magnetic field is constant, and its intensity is a sinusoidal function of time with amplitude $2H_1$

$$H = 2 H_1 \cos(\omega t) . \tag{18.1}$$

This could, for example, be the field inside a coil carrying an alternating current. Such an oscillating field causes magnetization which also has a sinusoidal time dependence but is shifted in phase:

$$M = \Gamma 2 H_1 \cos(\omega t + \varphi) . \tag{18.2}$$

Note that the relationship between **M** and **H** is now described by two constants, $\Gamma$ and $\varphi$, which are independent of one another. These constants generally depend on the frequency.

It turns out to be possible (and very useful) to express (18.2) in a way which is formally identical to (16.6). However, the relationship will be one between complex numbers. Expressing (18.1) and (18.2) in complex notation

$$H = 2 H_1 \exp(i \omega t)$$

$$M = \Gamma 2 H_1 \exp(i \omega t) \exp(i \varphi)$$

it follows that

$$M = \Gamma H \exp(i\varphi) .$$

By definition $\chi = \Gamma \exp(i\varphi)$, so that we can write the above expression as

$$M = \chi H \tag{18.3}$$

which is formally identical to (16.6), derived for a constant magnetic field.

Express the complex quantity $\chi$ in the form

$$\chi = \chi' + i\chi'' \tag{18.4}$$

and consider the meaning of the real part $\chi'$ and the imaginary part $\chi''$. To this end imagine a long coil filled with the sample and connected to a source of alternating current with frequency $\omega/2\pi$. As before, the length, cross-section and the number of turns are $\ell$, S and n, respectively. The voltage generated by self-induction at the ends of the coil is given by Faraday's law

$$U = -S n \frac{d}{dt} B_{int} = -S n^2 \ell^{-1} \mu_0 (1 + \chi) \frac{dI}{dt} .$$

Since generally $U = -L\, dI/dt$ (see (10.3) or Grant and Phillips 1979; Horowitz and Hill 1989), where L is the coefficient of self-induction, we obtain

$$L = k(1 + \chi)$$

where $k = \mu_0 S n^2 \ell^{-1}$ is a real constant. Calculate the complex inductance of the coil, expressing $\chi$ in the form (18.4)

$$i\omega L = i\omega k(1 + \chi') - \omega k \chi'' .$$

We see that complex inductance is not purely imaginary, but composed of a real part containing $\chi'$ and an imaginary part which contains $\chi''$. It follows that $\chi''$ describes the influence of the core of the coil and, by implication, the amount of energy loss (to the core), and $\chi'$ describes the role of the core on the self-induction of the coil. This is why $\chi''$ is known as the absorption coefficient and $\chi'$ as the dispersion coefficient. The latter name comes from optics, and is used by analogy with the imaginary part of the refraction coefficient.

## 19. Larmor Precession of an Isolated Spin

Assume that a nucleus with spin quantum number I is exposed to the action of a magnetic field $\mathbf{B_o}$, the direction of which coincides with the Z axis of the familiar laboratory XYZ frame of reference. Our task is to calculate the expected values of $I_x$, $I_y$ and $I_z$. The projection of the spin vector on the XY plane is conveniently described using the complex number $< I_x > + i < I_y >$

$$< I_x > + i < I_y > = \int \Psi^* (t) \left(I_x + i\, I_y\right) \Psi (t)\, dV$$

$$< I_z > = \int \Psi^* (t)\, I_z\, \Psi (t)\, dV\,. \tag{19.1}$$

At time t = 0, the state of the nuclear spin is described by the wavefunction $\Psi$ (0), which can be expressed as a series of eigenfunctions of the operator $I_z$

$$\Psi (0) = \sum_m a_m (0)\, \varphi_m$$

where the $a_m$ (0) are the appropriate (complex) numerical coefficients, and $\varphi_m$ is the eigenfunction of the operator $I_z$, with eigenvalues m, where $- I \leq m \leq + I$. From the laws of quantum mechanics discussed in Section 5, it follows that

$$\Psi (t) = \sum_m a_m (t)\, \varphi_m \tag{19.2}$$

where

$$a_m (t) = a_m (0) \exp\left(i\, m\, \gamma\, B_o\, t\right). \tag{19.3}$$

Substituting (19.2) in (19.1), and using the rules (4.17), we find

$$< I_x > + i < I_y > = \int \left(\sum_n a_n^* (t)\, \varphi_n^*\right) I_+ \left(\sum_m a_m (t)\, \varphi_m\right) dV$$

$$= \sum_n \sum_m a_n^* (t)\, a_m (t)\, k_+ \int \varphi_n^* (t)\, \varphi_{m+1}\, dV\,.$$

From the orthogonality of the functions $\varphi_m$, it follows that only those terms of the double sum can be non-zero for which n = m + 1. Taking this into account, and substituting (19.3), we find

$$< I_x > + i < I_y > = \left( \sum a^*_{m+1}(0)\, a_m(0)\, k_+ \right) \exp\left(-i\gamma B_0 t\right). \tag{19.4}$$

The expression in the square brackets is time-independent. We see, therefore, that the projection of the spin onto the XY plane moves with angular velocity

$$\omega_0 = -\gamma B_0 \tag{19.5}$$

while $< I_z >$ is constant, since arguments similar to those given above yield

$$< I_z > = \sum_n \sum_m a^*_n(t)\, a_m(t)\, m \int \varphi^*_n \varphi_m \, dV = \sum_m m \mid a_m(0) \mid^2 .$$

We can thus say that the vector $\left(< I_x >, < I_y >, < I_z >\right)$ precesses around the direction of the magnetic field. This is known as the Larmor precession.

Equation (19.5) implies that the direction of precession forms a right-handed screw with the direction of $\mathbf{B}_0$ when $\gamma < 0$, and a left-handed screw when $\gamma > 0$. For I = 1/2 we have:

$$\Psi(t) = a_{+1/2}(t)\, \varphi_{+1/2} + a_{-1/2}(t)\, \varphi_{-1/2} \tag{19.6}$$

and

$$< I_x > + i < I_y > = a^*_{+1/2}(t)\, a_{-1/2}(t) = a^*_{+1/2}(0)\, a_{-1/2}(0) \exp\left(-i\gamma B_0 t\right)$$

$$< I_z > = \frac{1}{2}\left[ \mid a_{+1/2}(0) \mid^2 - \mid a_{-1/2}(0) \mid^2 \right]. \tag{19.7}$$

Having examined a single isolated spin, we shall now consider the assembly of spins making up the sample. The first question to address is whether the individual spins are in identical states, or whether the simultaneous presence of different states has to be considered. It is easiest to look for an answer to this question in the case of spins with quantum number I = 1/2.

A hypothesis that the state of all spins in an assembly is described by the same wavefunction, for example (19.6), would not contradict this explanation of the value of $M_z$. It would be sufficient to give the coefficients $a_{+1/2}(0)$ and $a_{-1/2}(0)$ arbitrary complex values, as long as they satisfy the relationships $|a_{+1/2}(0)|^2 = N(+1/2)/N$ and $|a_{-1/2}(0)|^2 = N(-1/2)/N$ (see Section 16). However, such a hypothesis would be incorrect. We shall demonstrate this using an example at thermodynamic equilibrium where, as we know, the coordinates of the vector of magnetization have fixed values $M_z = M_\infty$ and $M_x = M_y = 0$.

From the assumption that the coefficients $a_{+1/2}(0)$ and $a_{-1/2}(0)$ are the same for all the spins, it follows that the individual vectors

$$\gamma\hbar\left(<I_x> + i <I_y>\right)$$

are parallel and that their sum in the sample is

$$M'_x + i\,M'_y = \gamma\hbar\,N\left(<I_x> + i <I_y>\right) = N\gamma\hbar\,\overset{*}{a}_{+1/2}(t)\,a_{-1/2}(t)\,.$$

To agree with experiment, the above value should be zero. However, it would be nonsense to conclude that one of the coefficients $a_{+1/2}(t)$ and $a_{-1/2}(t)$ should be zero, since this would be equivalent to the total polarization of the sample (with only one energy level being occupied). This is impossible at thermodynamic equilibrium.

It follows that we must admit the possibility of the presence of different wavefunctions for different spins in the sample, and assume that the macroscopic magnetic moment of the sample is the sum of the expected values. Therefore, for the coordinates we have

$$M_n = \gamma\hbar\,V^{-1}\sum <I_n> = \gamma\hbar\,N_0\,\langle\langle I_n\rangle\rangle$$

where $n = x, y, z$, $\langle\langle I_n\rangle\rangle = \sum <I_n>/N$, and the summation is over all spins in the sample. We see, therefore, that macroscopic quantities describing an assembly of spins are obtained by double averaging: quantum averaging (to calculate the expectation value) and statistical averaging (over all spins). Thus, by considering nuclear spins we arrive at the same conclusion as the more general discussion of Section 7.

Using (19.7) we calculate the transverse component of the magnetization

$$M_x + i\,M_y = \gamma\,\hbar\,N_0\,\overline{a^*_{+1/2}(t)\,a_{-1/2}(t)}$$

$$= \gamma\,\hbar\,N_0\,\overline{a^*_{+1/2}(0)\,a_{-1/2}(0)}\,\exp\left(i\,\omega_0\,t\right) \qquad (19.8a)$$

where the bar means averaging over all spins.

We can arrive at the same conclusion more simply by using the density matrix formalism of (7.2)

$$M_x + i\,M_y = \gamma\,\hbar\,N_0\,\langle\langle I_+ \rangle\rangle = \gamma\,\hbar\,N_0\,\mathrm{Tr}\left(\rho\,I_+\right)$$

$$= \gamma\,\hbar\,N_0 \sum_m \sum_\ell \langle m|\rho|\ell\rangle\,\langle \ell|I_+|m\rangle$$

$$= \gamma\,\hbar\,N_0 \sum_m k_+ \left[\overline{a^*_{m+1}(0)\,a_m(0)}\right] \exp\left(i\,\omega_0\,t\right). \qquad (19.8b)$$

In the above calculation we have used the equalities

$$\langle \ell|I_+|m\rangle = k_+\,\delta_{\ell,m+1}$$

(compare (4.17)), and

$$\langle m|\rho|m+1\rangle = \overline{a^*_{m+1}(0)\,a_m(0)}\,\exp\left(i\,\omega_0\,t\right).$$

Since spin-spin interactions do not influence magnetization, we do not need to take them into account, and can consider a single spin as an isolated quantum system. Thus $m, \ell = -I, \dots, +I$. For $I = 1/2$ the expression obtained becomes (19.8a), because the sum over m contains only one non-zero term, and $k_+ = 1$. $\langle\langle M_z \rangle\rangle$ is obtained from (7.2) in a similar manner. We leave the calculation to the reader to perform.

The conclusion from (19.7) is that the vector of magnetization precesses around the Z axis, and from (19.8b) we learn that its transverse component (i.e. projection on the XY plane) depends solely on single-quantum coherences (for the definition of coherence see Section 7). However, at equilibrium all coherences vanish.

It is instructive to show that equations describing the Larmor precession of the magnetization can be derived using a classical argument. We begin with the equation

$$\mathbf{M} = \gamma \mathbf{L}.$$

We apply the theorem of the preservation of angular momentum to the resultant angular momentum of nuclear spins of one kind per unit volume of the sample

$$\frac{d}{dt}\mathbf{L} = \mathbf{T}$$

from which, on the strength of (11.1), we obtain a differential equation describing the motion of the vector **M**

$$\frac{d}{dt}\mathbf{M} = \gamma \mathbf{M} \times \mathbf{B}_0. \qquad (19.9)$$

The easiest way of solving (19.8) is to adopt a new coordinate system X'Y'Z' rotating at a constant angular velocity $\vec{\omega}$.[1] We denote this system as $\left(X'Y'Z' \mid \vec{\omega}\right)$. The velocity of an arbitrary point P with respect to the static coordinate system is

$$\mathbf{v} = \mathbf{v}_a + \vec{\omega} \times \mathbf{r} \qquad (19.10)$$

where $\mathbf{v}_a$ is the velocity of the same point in the rotating frame, and **r** is a vector connecting the common origin of the two coordinate systems with point P. Equation (19.10) is a theorem from kinematics, stating that the absolute velocity is equal to the relative velocity plus the velocity of transposition, applied to the rotating frame of reference. Treating the tip of vector **M** as point P, we may write $\mathbf{r} = \mathbf{M}$. From (19.9) we have $\mathbf{v} = \gamma\, \mathbf{M} \times \mathbf{B}_0$. Substituting these relationships into (19.10) we derive the expression for the velocity of vector **M** in the rotating frame

$$\frac{d}{dt}\mathbf{M} = \gamma \mathbf{M} \times \left( \mathbf{B}_0 + \frac{\vec{\omega}}{\gamma} \right). \qquad (19.11)$$

---

[1] We denote vectors by bold letters. For additional clarity, vectors symbolized by Greek letters have an arrow above them.

If $\vec{\omega} = -\gamma \mathbf{B}_0 = \vec{\omega}_0$, that is if the coordinate system rotates with angular velocity $\vec{\omega} = -\gamma \mathbf{B}_0$ around the direction of $\mathbf{B}_0$, vector **M** is static in this system. This is exactly equivalent to vector **M** precessing around $\mathbf{B}_0$ in the XYZ laboratory coordinate system.

In the exceptional case when $\mathbf{M} \| \mathbf{B}_0$, vector **M** is static in the XYZ frame, as is evident from equation (19.9). This occurs at equilibrium. To observe the precession of vector **M**, it must first be displaced from a position parallel to $\mathbf{B}_0$. One of the ways of doing this is via nuclear magnetic resonance.

Note the formal similarity of equations (19.9) and (19.11). It is sufficient to substitute $\mathbf{B}_{eff} = \mathbf{B}_0 + \vec{\omega}/\gamma$ in (19.11), to give it the form

$$\frac{d}{dt}\mathbf{M} = \gamma \mathbf{M} \times \mathbf{B}_{eff} .$$

The vector $\mathbf{B}_{eff}$ is known as the "effective magnetic field". It is therefore true to say that the motion of the vector of magnetization in a static coordinate frame or in a frame rotating with angular velocity $\vec{\omega}$ is a precession, with angular velocity $-\gamma \mathbf{B}_{eff}$, around the axis determined by the vector $\mathbf{B}_{eff}$.

If we choose $Z \| \mathbf{B}_0$ and $\vec{\omega} \| \mathbf{B}_0$, equation (19.11) in the rotating frame takes the following form

$$M_{x'} = |M_\perp| \cos\left[(\omega_0 - \omega)\, t\right]$$

$$M_{y'} = |M_\perp| \sin\left[(\omega_0 - \omega)\, t\right] \qquad (19.12)$$

or as a complex number

$$M_\perp = M_{x'} + i\, M_{y'} = |M_\perp| \exp\left[i\, (\omega_0 - \omega)\, t\right]$$

and

$$M_z = \text{const}$$

where $|M_\perp|$ is the length of the projection of vector **M** on the XY plane and

$$|M_\perp| = \text{const} = \sqrt{M_x^2 + M_y^2}.$$

## 20. Resonance Condition

Consider the motion of magnetization when the sample is placed in a magnetic field consisting of two components:

(i) the static field $\mathbf{B_0}$;

(ii) the field $\mathbf{B_1}$, which rotates with angular velocity $\vec{\omega}_e$, so that $\mathbf{B_1}$ is static in the rotating frame.

In this situation the effective field $\mathbf{B_{eff}}$ "seen" from the rotating system (see Section 19) is augmented by $\mathbf{B_1}$

$$\mathbf{B_{eff}} = \mathbf{B_0} + \frac{\vec{\omega}_e}{\gamma} + \mathbf{B_1} \,. \tag{20.1}$$

Precession takes place around this rotating field, so that the equation of motion of **M** in the rotating frame is still valid

$$\frac{d\mathbf{M}}{dt} = \gamma\, \mathbf{M} \times \mathbf{B_{eff}} \,. \tag{20.2}$$

If $\omega_e$ satisfies the condition

$$\vec{\omega}_e = -\gamma\, \mathbf{B_0} \tag{20.3}$$

known as the resonance condition, then $\mathbf{B_{eff}} = \mathbf{B_1}$ and the precession of **M** takes place around vector $\mathbf{B_1}$. Of course, we are referring to precession as seen in the rotating frame of reference in which $\mathbf{B_1}$ is static.

In practice, spectrometers are usually built in such a way that vector $\mathbf{B_1}$ rotates in a plane perpendicular to $\mathbf{B_0}$. Then $\vec{\omega}_e \,||\, \mathbf{B_0}$ and the vector of effective field (20.1) are composed of two mutually perpendicular parts: a vector of length $\mathbf{B_0} + \vec{\omega}_e/\gamma$ parallel to the Z axis, and a vector $\mathbf{B_1}$ lying in the XY plane.

Assume that the vector of magnetization was originally aligned in the direction of $\mathbf{B_0}$, i.e. $\mathbf{M} \,||\, Z$. As soon as the rotating field appears, magnetization begins to precess around $\mathbf{B_{eff}}$ as seen in the rotating frame. This precession takes the magnetization from the original position, and this is the more effective the closer the direction of $\mathbf{B_{eff}}$ is to the XY plane. Field $\mathbf{B_0}$ is normally several orders of magnitude more intense than field $\mathbf{B_1}$. In this situation $\mathbf{B_{eff}}$ is practically always parallel to the Z axis, with the exception of the small interval of $\vec{\omega}_e$, for which the value of $\mathbf{B_0} + \vec{\omega}_e/\gamma$ is small (see Figure 30.2). The width of this interval is of the order of 2 $B_1$, since the angle between $\mathbf{B}_{eff}$ and the Z axis is $45^0$ for $\mathbf{B}_0 + \vec{\omega}_e/\gamma = \mathbf{B}_1$. In the special case of

$$\omega_e = - \gamma B_0 \tag{20.4}$$

we have $\mathbf{B}_{eff} = \mathbf{B}_1$ and $\mathbf{B}_{eff} \perp Z$. The declination of the magnetization from its original position can then take all values from 0 to $2\pi$.

We see, therefore, that a rotating field $\mathbf{B}_1$, much weaker than $\mathbf{B}_0$, can easily change the orientation of the magnetization vector, provided that, in accordance with equation (20.4), the angular velocity of $\mathbf{B}_1$ is equal, or almost equal, to the angular frequency of Larmor precession. It is this effect which is known as nuclear magnetic resonance.

So far we have not taken into account the fact that every sample usually contains more than one kind of nucleus with non-zero spin. We now see that this precaution was unnecessary, since by acting on the sample with field $\mathbf{B}_1$ of a given angular frequency, we affect the magnetization vector of only one kind of nuclear species.

Apart from nuclear magnetic moments, the sample may contain magnetic moments of electronic origin, for example magnetic moments of incomplete orbitals of paramagnetic ions or free radicals. These magnetic moments also undergo resonance but at much larger frequencies. This effect is known as electron paramagnetic resonance (EPR).

So far we have assumed that the motion of a given spin is free from the influence of neighbouring magnetic moments. This is not always the case. The theory presented above is correct when the interactions of a given spin with the surroundings are weak, that is their energy is much smaller than the distance between the neighbouring Zeeman levels of the given nucleus. For this reason, the distinction between strong and weak interactions depends on the intensity of the magnetic field in which the experiment is carried out. The intensity of $\mathbf{B}_0$ can be as large as 10 T, for which the interactions between nuclear magnetic moments are weak. Also, the intramolecular interactions of nuclear magnetic moments with magnetic moments of electronic orbitals are usually weak. If, however, the nucleus in question and the electronic magnetic moment (for example of a paramagnetic ion) belong to the same atom or the same molecule, the coupling between them can be very strong. In such cases, the influence of the nuclear magnetic moment manifests itself as the hyperfine structure of the EPR spectrum of the ion. A nucleus can also interact with its environment via its electric quadrupole moment, which interacts with the gradient of the local electric field. Only nuclei with $I > 1/2$ may possess nuclear quadrupole moments. Strong quadrupolar interactions may weaken, or even prevent, nuclear magnetic resonance.

A rotating magnetic field can be produced by two coils perpendicular to one another, each carrying electric currents of frequency $\nu = |\omega|/2\pi$ and phase-shifted by $90^o$ with respect to one another. In general, however, NMR does not use rotating fields except for the rare occasions when we desire to measure the sign of the gyromagnetic ratio $\gamma$. This is because the NMR effect can be induced by the oscillating magnetic field of *one* coil placed in the XY plane. To explain this, we assume that the axis of the coil coincides with the X axis. The sample is placed inside the coil where, apart from the constant field $\mathbf{B_o}$, it is subjected to the oscillating field

$$\mathbf{B}_{osc} = \mathbf{i}\, 2B_1 \cos\left(\omega_e t\right)$$

where $\mathbf{i}$ is the unit vector along the X axis, $2B_1$ is the amplitude and $\omega_e$ is the angular frequency $\omega_e = 2\pi\,\nu_e$ of the alternating electric current flowing through the coil. Such a field, oscillating along the X axis (by analogy to light, known as "linearly polarized"), can be decomposed into two counter-rotating ("circularly polarized") vectors each of length $B_1$. This is shown in Figure 20.1, and follows from the Euler formula

$$\cos\left(\omega_e t\right) = \tfrac{1}{2}\left[\exp\left(i\,\omega_e t\right) + \exp\left(-\,i\,\omega_e t\right)\right].$$

If the frequency of oscillation satisfies the condition

$$2\pi\,\nu = |\gamma|\, B_o \tag{20.5}$$

then either one or the other of the component vectors has the angular velocity which fulfils the condition (20.4) of magnetic nuclear resonance. The other vector rotates in the opposite direction and has virtually no effect on the spin system (see Abragam 1983, p. 21). We shall neglect it throughout this book.

We see, therefore, that (20.5) is the condition for nuclear magnetic resonance to occur. Such a field is much easier to generate than the rotating field, but does not enable us to determine the sign of $\gamma$.

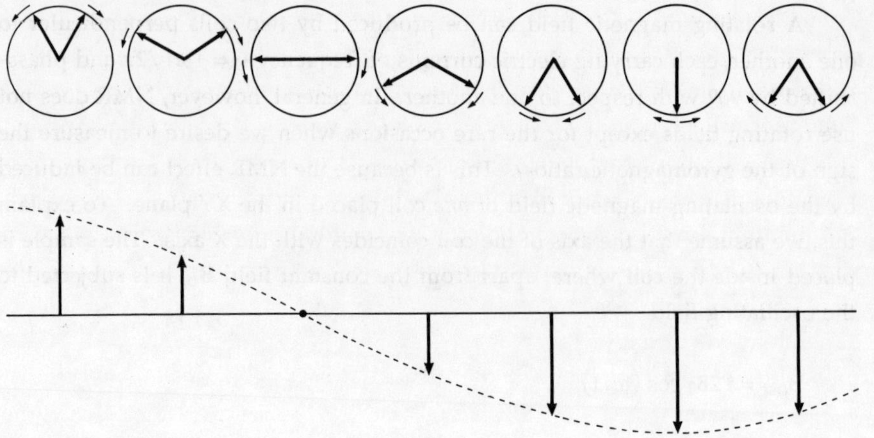

**Figure 20.1.** An oscillating vector can be decomposed into two counter-rotating vectors.

## 21. NMR as Quantized Absorption of Radiation

The phenomenon of nuclear magnetic resonance may be usefully considered from a different point of view. Assume that, before the onset of resonance, the sample is at thermodynamic equilibrium. Then the energy of interaction with field $\mathbf{B_0}$ takes the lowest possible value, $E < 0$, since the vector of magnetization is collinear with $\mathbf{B_0}$ and has the same direction. The process of the tipping of the magnetization vector must therefore involve absorption of energy.

It is easy to show that spins take energy from the oscillating field of the coil. Consider the energy difference between the neighbouring Zeeman levels ($\Delta m = \pm 1$) which, according to (15.3), is

$$\Delta E = \gamma \hbar B_0 .$$

A spin can undergo a transition from a lower to a higher energy level, which involves absorption of a quantum of radiation with a frequency

$$\nu = \frac{\Delta E}{h} = \frac{|\gamma|\, B_0}{2\pi} .$$

This result is identical to the resonance condition (20.5). We can therefore say that the phenomenon of nuclear magnetic resonance is the absorption of radiation of the appropriate resonance frequency by nuclear spins. However, this definition does not exhaust the whole of the essence of this phenomenon, because it tells us nothing about the behaviour of the projection of magnetization on the XY plane. The reason is that the energy of an individual spin is an eigenvalue of the operator $I_z$, which does not commute with operators $I_x$ and $I_y$. It follows that we cannot deduce the values of $I_x$ and $I_y$ from information about the energy state of a given spin.

We will show that nuclear resonance is strongly linked to quantum transitions of spins between neighbouring energy states, that is, states in which the quantum number m differs by $\Delta m = \pm 1$. In addition, the question arises whether it is possible to cause transitions for which $\Delta m > 1$. Of course, this would only apply to nuclei with $I > 1/2$. To answer this question, we use time-dependent perturbation theory (see Section 9), according to which the probability of transition from state m to state n is $W_{nm} = a^*_{nm}\, a_{nm}$, where the values of $a_{nm}$ are given by (9.8). In our case, the energy of perturbation is the energy of interaction between the nuclear magnetic moment $\vec{\mu}$ and the oscillating magnetic field $\mathbf{B}_{osc}$ (t), generated by the coil

$$\mathcal{H}'(t) = -\vec{\mu} \cdot \mathbf{B}_{osc}(t)\,. \tag{21.1}$$

Make the general assumption that the axis of the coil is determined by the unit vector ε. We can then write

$$\mathbf{B}_{osc}(t) = \varepsilon\, 2\, B_1 \cos\left(2\pi\, \nu\, t\right)$$

where $2\,B_1$ is the amplitude of oscillation. Substituting this expression into (21.1), and treating the coordinates of the vector $\vec{\mu}$ as operators, we have

$$\mathcal{H}'(t) = -\,2\, B_1\, \gamma\, \hbar \left(I_x\, \varepsilon_x + I_y\, \varepsilon_y + I_z\, \varepsilon_z\right) \cos\left(2\pi\, \nu\, t\right).$$

Expressing operators $I_x$ and $I_y$ by operators $I_+$ and $I_-$ (4.16), we find

$$\mathcal{H}'(t) = -\, B_1\, \gamma\, \hbar \left(I_+\, \varepsilon_- + I_-\, \varepsilon_+ + 2\, I_z\, \varepsilon_z\right) \cos\left(2\pi\, \nu\, t\right) \tag{21.2}$$

where $\varepsilon_- = \varepsilon_x - i\, \varepsilon_y$ and $\varepsilon_+ = \varepsilon_x + i\, \varepsilon_y$. Substituting (21.2) into (9.8) we see that $a_{nm}$ is proportional to

$$\langle m | I_+\, \varepsilon_- + I_-\, \varepsilon_+ + 2\, I_z\, \varepsilon_z | n \rangle\,.$$

We assumed that $m \neq n$, and it follows from the rules of operators that $\langle m|I_z|n\rangle = 0$. The remaining two terms can be non-zero only when $m - n = \pm 1$ and when, at the same time, either $\varepsilon_+$ or $\varepsilon_-$ is non-zero.

We see that the coil induces only quantum transitions with $\Delta m = \pm 1$ (this is known as the "NMR selection rule"), and that these transitions are due only to the component of $\mathbf{B}_{OSC}$ in the plane perpendicular to $\mathbf{B}_0$.

It is important to note, however, that the expression (9.10) for the transition probability is approximate, because certain simplifications were made in its derivation. It turns out that a more accurate time-dependent perturbation theory (the so-called second approximation) admits non-zero probability for transitions with $\Delta m \neq 1$. These are known as "forbidden" or "multiple-quantum" transitions. However, the probability that they occur is so small as to make them insignificant in most NMR experiments.

# Chapter 4. Motion of Magnetization

## 22. Motion of a Free Spin

When discussing the motion of the magnetization without a rotating radiofrequency field or free precession in Chapter 3, we assumed that the spins in the sample interact exclusively with the constant and homogeneous magnetic field $\mathbf{B}_0$. This assumption is correct when the sample is an atomic beam in which the individual nuclear spins can be considered to be completely isolated from their environment. However, for a sample made up of condensed matter, we must also take into account the various internal magnetic and electric fields.

The interaction of spins with internal fields may be considered to be an interaction with the environment, since the fields are generated by both electronic and nuclear magnetic moments, and by the electric charges of atoms and molecules. In gases, liquids and some solids, internal fields change randomly and very rapidly, because of the Brownian thermal motions of the molecules. Such fields cause additional motion of the magnetization, which we have not yet taken into account. This motion, known as relaxation, means that after a certain time the vector of magnetization achieves length $M_\infty$ and direction parallel to the vector $\mathbf{B}_0 \parallel Z$. It is found that, in cases where relaxation cannot be neglected, the time dependence of magnetization is still described by equations (19.12), but the quantities $M_z$ and $|M_\perp|$ must be treated as functions of time:

$$\frac{d}{dt} M_z = -\left(M_z - M_\infty\right) / T_1 \tag{22.1}$$

$$\frac{d}{dt} |M_\perp| = -|M_\perp| / T_2 \tag{22.2}$$

where $T_1$ and $T_2$ are time-independent constants. These equations describe the so-called Bloch's law of relaxation.

Let $u_c$ and $v_c$ be the derivatives $dM_{x'}/dt$ and $dM_{y'}/dt$ obtained by differentiating equations (19.12), while taking $|M_\perp|$ = const. Consider now the case when relaxation does take place, and the time dependence of $|M_\perp|$ and $M_z$ must be taken into account. Then differentiating (19.12) gives

$$\frac{d}{dt} M_{x'} = u_c - M_{x'}/T_2$$

$$\frac{d}{dt} M_{y'} = v_c - M_{y'}/T_2$$

$$\frac{d}{dt} M_z = - \left(M_z - M_\infty\right) /T_1 .$$

It follows that the velocity of the magnetization vector in the rotating frame is a superposition of the velocity of the precessional motion $(u_c, v_c, 0)$ and relaxation $\left[- M_{x'}/T_2, - M_{y'}/T_2, \left(M_\infty - M_z\right) /T_1\right]$.

Equations (22.1) and (22.2), which are identical in both the laboratory and the rotating frame, describe the approach of magnetization to the value $\mathbf{M}_\infty$ with coordinates $\left(0, 0, M_\infty\right)$. The quantities $M_z$ and $M_\perp$ are independent of one another, since (i) their initial values can be arbitrarily set by a perturbation; and (ii) their motion follows different laws. The evolution of the component $M_z$ (i.e. the component parallel to $\mathbf{B}_0$) is known as longitudinal relaxation, while the evolution of $M_\perp$ is known as transverse relaxation. Since both constants, $T_1$ and $T_2$, have the dimension of time, $T_1$ is known as the longitudinal relaxation time and $T_2$ the transverse relaxation time.

So far, we have considered the situation when the sample is placed in a homogeneous magnetic field $\mathbf{B}_0$. When $\mathbf{B}_0$ is inhomogeneous (we have in mind small changes throughout the sample, of the order of 1%) equations (22.1) and (22.2) are only approximately correct, and the value of the transverse relaxation constant $T_2$ changes. We denote the new constant by $T_2^*$.

In an inhomogeneous magnetic field, the precession of the magnetization vector proceeds at different rates in different parts of the sample. This accelerates the process of transverse relaxation, so that

$$T_2^* < T_2 .$$

From the considerations of Section 15, it follows that the energy of interaction of the assembly of spins with field $\mathbf{B}_0$ is proportional to $M_z$, and therefore that the process of longitudinal relaxation must be accompanied by an exchange of energy between the spin system and the environment. Bloembergen, Purcell and Pound (1948) showed that this exchange takes place at the expense of the kinetic energy of thermal motion of the molecules in the sample. At room temperature, however, the influence of longitudinal relaxation on the temperature of the sample is so minute as to be unmeasurable. However, at temperatures of the order of 0.01 K, the process of relaxation does cause a significant further fall in the temperature.

The assembly of the molecules in the sample treated as a reservoir of thermal energy, determined by the motion of the molecules, is referred to as "lattice". This term is applied to all three states of matter, although it originates by analogy to a crystal lattice, in which vibrations determine the thermal energy of the solid. This is why longitudinal relaxation is also known as spin-lattice relaxation, or thermal relaxation, and the constant $T_1$ as spin-lattice relaxation time.

The quantity $M_\perp$ is unrelated to the energy of the spin system, and its evolution is influenced by quantum transitions, the energy of which is transferred between spins of the same kind, leaving the total spin energy unchanged. Thus we have the terms "spin-spin relaxation" and "spin-spin relaxation time" to describe the process of transverse relaxation, and the constant $T_2$ for an ideally homogeneous magnetic field. However, the term "transverse relaxation time" is reserved for a more general concept embracing both $T_2$ and $T_2^*$.

## 23. Relaxation in Terms of Quantum Transitions

Equations (22.1) and (22.2), describing relaxation, can be interpreted in terms of quantum transitions between eigenstates of operators $I_x$, $I_y$ and $I_z$. We shall follow the train of thought of Bloembergen, Purcell and Pound (1948), the founders of the theory of nuclear relaxation. Assume for simplicity that the spin quantum number of the nuclei under consideration is I = 1/2.

Further to the arguments of Section 19, we can write for some given time, for example t = 0

$$M_z = \frac{1}{2}\gamma N_0 \hbar \left( < |a_1|^2 > - < |a_2|^2 > \right)$$

where < > denotes averaging over the spin assembly. We introduce the following quantities:

$$N_+ = N_0 < |a_1|^2 >$$

$$N_- = N_0 < |a_2|^2 >.$$

These numbers can be interpreted as the occupancy of the eigenstates of operator $I_z$ with eigenvalues m = + 1/2 and m = - 1/2. We can, in turn, express $M_z$ as a function of the difference in occupancy of the two states

$$M_z = \frac{1}{2}\gamma \hbar\, n \tag{23.1}$$

where

$$n = N_+ - N_- . \tag{23.2}$$

Because of Boltzmann's law (see Section 16), at thermodynamic equilibrium we have:

$$N_+/N_- = \exp \lambda \tag{23.3}$$

where $\lambda = \gamma \hbar\ B_0/kT$. Since $|\lambda| << 1$ (see Section 16), we can replace $\exp \lambda$ by $1 + \lambda$.

Let $w_{+-}$ be the probability of transition of a spin from state + 1/2 to state - 1/2 per spin per second. The probability of transition in the other direction is $w_{-+}$ . The total number of transitions from state + 1/2 to state - 1/2 in the sample per second is $w_{+-} N_+$, and transitions in the opposite direction $w_{-+} N_-$ . At equilibrium we have

$$w_{+-} N_+ = w_{-+} N_- .$$

The above relationship and equation (23.3) give

$$\frac{w_{-+}}{w_{+-}} = 1 + \lambda.$$

We see that the probabilities of transitions differ very little, and that the transition from the upper to the lower state is slightly more likely. The above equation is equivalent to $\lambda = (w_{-+} - w_{+-})/w_{+-}$ . It is experimentally impossible to carry out the measurement of the probabilities with sufficient accuracy to calculate $\lambda$ from their difference. The value of $\lambda$ can, however, be measured directly by measuring $M_\infty$ . The reader should be aware that the quantities $\lambda$ and $w_0 \approx w_{+-} \approx w_{-+}$ can, in practice, be considered to be independent. In Chapter 9 we demonstrate that $w_0$ is determined by the interactions of the spin with the environment. This is why $w_0$ is sometimes referred to as the probability of induced transitions. On the other hand, $\lambda$ does not depend on interactions with the environment and is known as the probability of spontaneous transitions. Einstein (1917) was the first to distinguish between the two probabilities, thereby laying the foundations of the theory of the interaction of radiation with matter.

Assume for simplicity that $w_0 = \frac{1}{2}(w_{+-} + w_{-+})$. We have

$$w_{+-} = w_0 (1 - \lambda/2)$$
$$w_{-+} = w_0 (1 + \lambda/2) \,. \qquad (23.4)$$

Since the transition of a single spin changes n by 2, we have the relationship

$$\frac{dn}{dt} = 2N_- w_{-+} - 2N_+ w_{+-}$$

which, upon substitution of equations (23.4), and using the definition $n_\infty = N_0 \lambda/2$, becomes

$$\frac{dn}{dt} = -2w_0 (n - n_\infty) \,. \qquad (23.5)$$

The physical sense of $n_\infty$ becomes clear when we apply (23.5) to the state of equilibrium at which $dn/dt = 0$, as then $n = n_\infty$.

Multiplying both sides of (23.5) by $\gamma \hbar /2$ we have, from (23.1),

$$\frac{dM_z}{dt} = -2w_0 (M_z - M_\infty) \qquad (23.6)$$

which is the same as the relaxation equation (22.1) after substitution

$$\frac{1}{T_1} = 2w_0 \,. \qquad (23.7)$$

We conclude that the approach to equilibrium is described by the constant $w_0$, and that the final value of $n = n_\infty$ depends on $\lambda$.

A general solution of the differential equation (23.6) is

$$M_z(t) = [M_z(0) - M_\infty] \exp(-t/T_1) + M_\infty \,. \qquad (23.8)$$

The process of *transverse* relaxation may be also viewed as the result of quantum transitions. To demonstrate this, we will use the rotating reference frame, in which the projection of the magnetization on the XY plane is static. The operator $I_{x'}$ has two eigenfunctions with eigenvalues + 1/2 and - 1/2. The states described by these functions do not differ in energy (unless the energy of interaction of spins is very large, see Redfield 1955) and thus correspond to $\lambda = 0$. Substituting zero in (23.3), and proceeding as in the derivation of (23.6), we find

$$\frac{dM_{x'}}{dt} = -2W_{ox}{}' M_{x'}$$

where $W_{ox}{}'$ is the probability of transition between the states of operator $I_x'$. Similarly, considering the states of operator $I_y'$ we have

$$\frac{dM_{y'}}{dt} = -2W_{oy}{}' M_{y'} .$$

In view of the symmetry $W_{oy}{}' = W_{ox}{}' = W_{o\perp}$, this leads to the conclusion that

$$\frac{d\,|M_\perp|}{dt} = -2W_{o\perp}\,|M_\perp| \tag{23.9}$$

where $|M_\perp| = \sqrt{M_x'^2 + M_y'^2}$. Defining $T_2$ as

$$\frac{1}{T_2} = 2W_{o\perp}$$

and substituting in (23.9), we obtain the equation of transverse relaxation (22.2).

## 24. Spin Temperature

Consider an assembly of identical spin systems and suppose that a system consists of single I = 1/2 nuclei immersed in the magnetic field $\mathbf{B}_0$. The spins distribute themselves between two energy levels $E = -m\gamma\hbar B_0$, where $m = \pm 1/2$ and $\gamma$ is the gyromagnetic ratio. Boltzmann's law gives the ratio of the populations, $N_-$ and $N_+$, of the states with m = - 1/2 and m = + 1/2, respectively, at thermodynamic equilibrium

$$\frac{N_-}{N_+} = \exp\left(\frac{E_+ - E_-}{kT}\right) \tag{24.1}$$

where k is the Boltzmann constant, and T the absolute temperature.

Thermodynamic equilibrium is reached when the sample is allowed to remain in the magnetic field for a sufficiently long time (on the scale of $T_1$), for example $5T_1$, where $T_1$ is the spin-lattice relaxation time. If the sample is not at thermodynamic equilibrium, the population ratio can be different, but there is always a quantity, Θ, with the dimension of temperature, known as *spin temperature*, such that

$$\frac{N_-}{N_+} = \exp\left(\frac{E_+ - E_-}{k\Theta}\right). \tag{24.2}$$

Unlike absolute temperature, spin temperature can be positive or negative. For the proton $\gamma > 0$ and $E_+ < E_-$. It follows that for positive spin temperatures $N_- < N_+$. Since the magnetization of the sample is proportional to the population difference, spin temperature may be positive or negative depending on whether the magnetization vector and the magnetic field are parallel or antiparallel. Very close to $N_+ = N_-$ (zero magnetization) spin temperature approaches $+\infty$ or $-\infty$ and is indeterminate at $N_+ = N_-$. Figure 24.1 and equation (24.2) show that "warmer" systems (those with a higher energy content) have negative spin temperatures. Zero spin temperature is equivalent to only one energy level being populated, the other state being empty (see Figure 24.1). This amounts to a perfect polarization of nuclear spins.

To distinguish it from spin temperature, the sample temperature T (which can be measured with a thermometer) is referred to as lattice temperature. This is because, both in solids and in liquids, T is related to the thermal energy of the sample as determined by the vibration of molecules. We can thus treat the lattice as a reservoir of thermal energy.

The definition of spin temperature becomes more complicated when either $I > 1/2$ or the system consists of more than one spin 1/2, and thus there are more than two spin energy levels. In this case, Boltzmann's law takes the form of a set of equations

$$N_m = c \exp\left(\frac{-E_m}{k\Theta}\right) \tag{24.3}$$

where m assumes all integer values between + I and - I, and c is a constant (see Section 16). Figure 24.2(a) shows the energy levels of a spin 3/2 system as bars, the length of which is proportional to their population at thermodynamic equilibrium. In accordance with (24.3), the ends of the bars can be connected by an exponential curve, with parameter T equal to the temperature of the lattice. In this case, the spin system is at thermodynamic equilibrium with the lattice.

| | | |
|---|---|---|
| ——————— $N_-$ <br> •—•—•—•—• $N_+$ | $\dfrac{N_-}{N_+} = 0$ | $\Theta = 0$ |
| •—•—• <br> $\Delta E$ <br> •—•—• | $1 > \dfrac{N_-}{N_+} > 0$ | $\Theta > 0$ |
| •—•—• <br> •—•—• | $\dfrac{N_-}{N_+} = 1$ | $\Theta = \pm\infty$ |
| •—•—•—• <br> •—•—• | $\dfrac{N_-}{N_+} > 1$ | $\Theta < 0$ |
| •—•—•—•—• <br> ——————— | $\dfrac{N_-}{N_+} = \infty$ | $\Theta = 0$ |

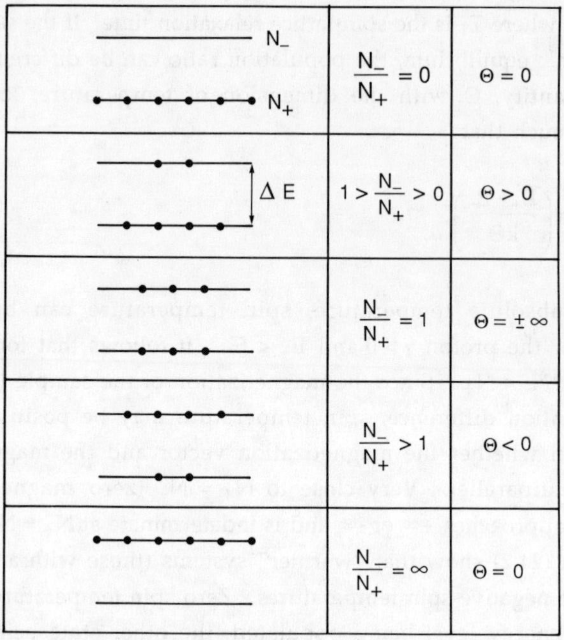

**Figure 24.1.** Positive and negative spin temperatures $\Theta$ for the case of two energy levels. The populations $N_+$ and $N_-$ are represented by the numbers of dots at the two levels.

Two further possibilities may arise. In one of them, spin populations can still be described by an exponential curve

$$N_m = c \exp\left(\frac{-E_m}{k\Theta}\right) \tag{24.4}$$

but with $\Theta \neq T$. In this case, the spins are at equilibrium with one another, but not with the lattice. Spin temperature is then different from the sample temperature, as seen in Figure 24.2(b).

In the two cases considered so far, the populations of spin states can be described by a single parameter, T or $\Theta$. However, when there are more than two energy levels, it may happen that spin populations do not obey *any* exponential law. This means that the ends of the bars representing the populations of the various spin states cannot be connected by *any* exponential curve and these populations cannot be described by a single parameter. In this case, illustrated in Figure 24.2(c), the spins are not at internal equilibrium and spin temperature cannot be defined.

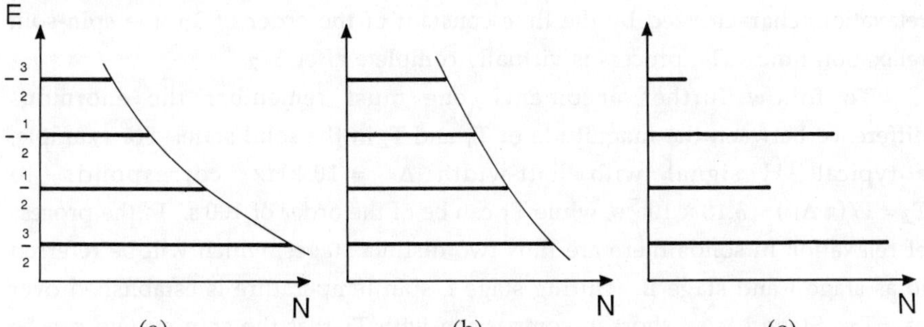


**Figure 24.2.** Populations of levels for I = 3/2. (a) At thermodynamic equilibrium, i.e. with Θ = T; (b) for Θ > T; (c) a case for which spin temperature cannot be defined.

In practice we never encounter a total polarization of nuclear spins, and we may exclude this unrealistic situation from our considerations. We can therefore assume that $E_m << k\Theta$, so that

$$\exp\left(\frac{-E_m}{k\Theta}\right) \approx 1 - \frac{E_m}{k\Theta}.$$

Equation (24.4) then becomes

$$\frac{N_m}{N_{m+1}} = 1 + \left(\frac{E_{m+1} - E_m}{k\Theta}\right). \quad (24.5)$$

Equations (24.4) and (24.5) state that the condition for the existence of spin temperature is that the population ratios of equidistant energy levels be constant.

How does a spin system in a state which cannot be described by a spin temperature evolve towards a state which can be so described? Spin-spin relaxation is caused by interactions, for example between proton (1) and proton (2), the Hamiltonian of which contains the term $I_+^{(1)} I_-^{(2)}$ (see Chapter 8). This term causes "flip-flop" transitions in which spin (1) flips "up" and spin (2) "down" with $\Delta m = \pm 1$. These transitions do not affect the total energy of the spin system and cannot therefore constitute the mechanism by which it exchanges energy with the lattice. They can, however, reduce the irregularity of the very improbable distribution of populations and result in a situation where the populations follow the exponential law (24.5). Flip-flop processes will always tend to bring the spin system to a situation in which spin temperature exists, because this situation is thermodynamically the most probable. To summarize, spin temperature is established through the process of spin-spin relaxation, characterized by the time constant of the order of $T_2$, the spin-spin relaxation time. The process is virtually complete after $5T_2$.

To follow further arguments, one must remember the enormous difference between the magnitude of $T_1$ and $T_2$ in the solid state. For example, a typical $^1H$ signal with half-width $\Delta\nu = 10$ kHz corresponds to $T_2 = 1/(\pi\,\Delta\nu) = 3.18 \times 10^{-5}$ s, while $T_1$ can be of the order of 100 s. In the process of relaxation in solids there are thus two distinct stages, which will be referred to as stage I and stage II. During stage I, spin temperature is established over ca. $5T_2$. Stage I is so short in comparison with $T_1$ that the spin system can be considered to be completely isolated from the lattice. When stage I is complete, the system has a spin temperature. During stage II, spin temperature $\Theta$ approaches lattice temperature T. The process proceeds via spin-lattice relaxation with a time constant $T_1$ according to

$$\frac{d}{dt}\frac{1}{\Theta} = \left(\frac{1}{T} - \frac{1}{\Theta}\right)\exp\left(-\frac{t}{T_1}\right). \tag{24.6}$$

In solids stage II is, of course, much longer than stage I, and can be considered complete after time $5T_1$. As a result of stage II the sample is at thermodynamic equilibrium.

From the moment of completion of stage I, we can calculate the value of magnetization from the Langevin-Curie formula using spin temperature instead of lattice temperature:

$$M = \frac{\gamma^2 \hbar^2 N_0 B_0}{3k\Theta} I(I+1) = C\frac{B_0}{\Theta} \tag{24.7}$$

where $N_0$ is the number of spins in 1 $m^3$ of the sample.

During stage II the vector of sample magnetization is always parallel to the external magnetic field $B_0$ (which we assume to point in the Z direction), because during stage I any non-Z components have disappeared through spin-spin relaxation. Inserting equation (24.6) into equation (24.7) we obtain the Bloch law of longitudinal relaxation (22.1)

$$\frac{dM_z}{dt} = -\frac{M_z - M_\infty}{T_1} \tag{24.8}$$

where $M_\infty$, the magnetization at thermodynamic equilibrium, is given by equation (24.7) with $\Theta = T$.

## 25. Bloch's Equations

In Section 20 we derived the equation

$$\frac{d\mathbf{M}}{dt} = \gamma \mathbf{M} \times \mathbf{B}_{eff} \tag{25.1}$$

describing the motion of the vector of magnetization under the influence of the sum of two magnetic fields: $\mathbf{B}_0$ and the much weaker field $\mathbf{B}_1$ which rotates in a plane perpendicular to $\mathbf{B}_0$ with angular velocity $\omega_e$. The field $\mathbf{B}_{eff}$ is given by

$$\mathbf{B}_{eff} = \left(B_0 + \frac{\omega_e}{\gamma}\right)\mathbf{k} + B_1\,\mathbf{i}$$

where $\mathbf{k}$ and $\mathbf{i}$ are unit vectors coinciding respectively with the Z and the X' axes of the rotating frame. However, (25.1) was derived without taking relaxation into account.

The problem of the evolution of magnetization under the influence of the sum of a constant and a rotating magnetic field with simultaneous relaxation was first solved by Bloch (1946). His theory is based on two hypotheses: (i) that the motion of magnetization is a superposition of precessive motion in field $\mathbf{B}_{eff}$ and of relaxative motion; and (ii) that the velocity of the relaxative motion is described by equations (22.1) and (22.2). Our further considerations will be conducted exclusively in the rotating frame in which the components of vector $\mathbf{M}$ are denoted by $(u, v, M_z)$. Calculate first the components of the velocity of the motion. From (25.1) we get the coordinates of the tip of vector $\mathbf{M}$ during precessive motion

$$\left[v\left(\gamma B_0 + \omega_e\right),\; M_z \gamma B_1 - u\left(\gamma B_0 + \omega_e\right),\; -v \gamma B_1\right]$$

and from (22.1) and (22.2) the coordinates of velocity in the relaxative motion

$$-u/T_2,\; -v/T_2,\; -\left(M_z - M_\infty\right)/T_1 .$$

Summing the above two velocities we obtain, according to Bloch's hypothesis, the total velocity of the vector **M**

$$\frac{d}{dt}u = -u/T_2 + v\,\Delta\omega$$

$$\frac{d}{dt}v = -u\,\Delta\omega - v/T_2 + \gamma B_1 M_z \qquad (25.2)$$

$$\frac{d}{dt}M_z = -v\gamma B_1 - (M_z - M_\infty)/T_1$$

where $\Delta\omega = \omega_e + \gamma B_0 = \omega_e - \omega_0$. Equations (25.2) are known as the Bloch equations. Their correctness has been experimentally confirmed many times, especially for liquid samples. In solids, particularly crystalline, their applicability is less general, but sufficient for a satisfactory description of the evolution of magnetization.

General solutions of a set of linear differential equations, such as Bloch's equations, can be found in Lösche (1957). We will limit ourselves to solving Bloch's equations in the so-called stationary state - when the rotating field of constant angular velocity acts on the sample for a sufficiently long period. An equilibrium is then established between precessive and relaxative motion, with the result that the magnetization vector is static in the rotating frame. This last conclusion is often given without justification, although it may not appear obvious. To prove it rigorously, one has to provide a general solution to the set of Bloch's equations, which is precisely what we would wish to avoid. We shall therefore describe physical arguments which support its correctness.

Assume that the contrary is true, i.e. that in the stationary state the vector **M** moves in the rotating frame. This motion cannot be aperiodic, because this would lead to $M = 0$ or $M = \infty$. The remaining possibility is a periodic motion, but this would induce in the receiver coil a variable voltage of different frequency from the frequency of the field with which the sample is being irradiated. This, however, is not physically acceptable.

We must therefore assume that in a stationary state

$$\frac{du}{dt} = \frac{dv}{dt} = \frac{dM_z}{dt} = 0\,. \qquad (25.3)$$

With this assumption Bloch's equations become a set of three linear equations with three unknowns. The solutions are

$$u = \frac{\Delta\omega\, \gamma\, B_1\, T_2^2}{1 + (\Delta\omega\, T_2)^2 + \gamma^2 B_1^2\, T_1\, T_2} M_\infty \tag{25.4a}$$

$$v = \frac{\gamma\, B_1\, T_2}{1 + (\Delta\omega\, T_2)^2 + \gamma^2 B_1^2\, T_1\, T_2} M_\infty \tag{25.4b}$$

$$M_z = \frac{1 + (\Delta\omega\, T_2)^2}{1 + (\Delta\omega\, T_2)^2 + \gamma^2 B_1^2\, T_1\, T_2} M_\infty\, . \tag{25.4c}$$

Note that, far from resonance, i.e. for large values of $\Delta\omega$, we have $u = v = 0$ and $M_z = M_\infty$. Non-zero values of u and v appear only in a small interval around $\Delta\omega = 0$. This means that nuclear magnetic resonance occurs.

The transverse component of the magnetization vector, i.e. the component perpendicular to Z, which, as we know, is static in the rotating frame, can be written as a complex number

$$M_\perp = u + i\, v\, .$$

Assume that at $t = 0$ the laboratory and the rotating frames exactly coincide. In the laboratory frame $M_\perp$ is then

$$M_\perp = (u + i\, v) \exp\left(i\, \omega_e\, t\right)\, . \tag{25.5}$$

Similarly, the intensity of the oscillating field inside the coil, $B_x/\mu_0 = H_x = 2H_1 \cos\left(\omega_e\, t\right)$ can be expressed in the complex notation as

$$H_x = 2H_1 \exp\left(i\, \omega_e\, t\right)\, . \tag{25.6}$$

Considering that transverse magnetization $M_\perp$ is caused by the oscillating field $H_x$, we may expect that the relationship between $M_\perp$ and $H_x$ can be reduced to form (18.3). Indeed, substituting (25.6) into (25.5) we obtain

$$M_\perp = \left(\chi' + i\, \chi''\right) H_x$$

where $\chi' = u/2H_1$ and $\chi'' = v/2H_1$.

The physical meaning of $\chi'$ and $\chi''$ has been discussed in Section 18. We know that $\chi'$, known as the dispersion coefficient, determines the self-induction of the coil filled with the sample, while $\chi''$ determines the absorption of energy from field $B_x$ by the sample, and is known as the absorption coefficient. In view of their proportionality to $\chi'$ and $\chi''$, we shall continue to refer to components u and v as dispersion and absorption.

## 26. The NMR Signal

We shall now consider the external manifestation of nuclear magnetic resonance: the electromotive force induced by the precessing magnetization which appears in the coil surrounding the sample.

According to (17.3), the precessing transverse component of magnetization $M_\perp$ causes precessing additional magnetic induction in the bulk of the sample

$$B_\perp = \mu_0 M_\perp .$$

On the other hand, $M_\perp$ appears as a result of nuclear magnetic resonance or, in other words, as a result of the spins being subjected to the action of the rotating vector of magnetic intensity

$$H_1 \exp\left(i\, \omega_e\, t\right)$$

where $\omega_e$ is equal to, or very close to, the Larmor angular frequency $-\gamma B_0$. We can therefore relate the two quantities using a time-independent complex factor $\chi$ (known as magnetic susceptibility) as follows:

$$M_\perp = \chi\, 2H_1 \exp\left(i\, \omega_e\, t\right) .$$

Assume that the coil surrounding the sample is parallel to the X axis. The X component of $B_\perp = \mu_0 M_\perp$ (i.e. $\mathrm{Re}\, B_\perp = \mu_0\, \mathrm{Re}\, M_\perp$) penetrates the coil at right angles to its cross-section, thereby inducing the electromotive force (10.3)

$$E = -S\, n\, \zeta \frac{d}{dt} \mathrm{Re}\, B_\perp = -S\, n\, \zeta\, \chi\, \mu_0\, 2H_1\, \omega_e \cos\left(\omega_e\, t + \pi/2\right) \tag{26.1}$$

where $\zeta$ is the so-called "filling factor" and the meaning of S and n is the same as in (10.3).

The coil is normally connected to a capacitor and a resistance, to form an RLC circuit tuned to electrical resonance of frequency $\nu = |\omega_e| / 2\pi$. As shown by the theory of resonant circuits, the amplitude of the alternating voltage $U_{x\,res}$ measured at the terminals of the coil is increased by the so-called "quality factor"

$$Q = \frac{\omega_e L}{R}$$

(where L is the self-inductance of the coil and R the resistance of the circuit), and the phase of the voltage is shifted forward by $\pi/2$. As a result, the phase shift in (26.1) is increased to $\pi$. Since $\cos(\alpha + \pi) = -\cos\alpha$, the voltage across the coil is

$$U_{x\,res} = Q\,S\,n\,\zeta\,\omega_e\,\chi\,\mu_0\,2H_1 \cos(\omega_e t) = Q\,\zeta\,\omega_e\,n\,S\,\chi\,B_x\,. \tag{26.2}$$

The filling factor $\zeta$ accounts for:

1. The fact that the cross-section of the coil is normally only partly filled by the sample.
2. Finite dimensions of the sample, which mean that some lines of field generated by the magnetization "escape" through the sides of the coil and miss some of the turns.
3. Finite dimensions of the coil, which mean that the oscillating field $\mathbf{B}_1$ is inhomogeneous, and thus different for different parts of the sample.

# Chapter 5. Continuous-Wave NMR

## 27. Separate Observation of Absorption and Dispersion

The voltage $U_{x\ res}$ measured at the coil near the resonance condition is very small, in comparison with the voltage $U_x$ connected to the coil from the outside to generate the oscillating field $B_x$

$$U_x = -\, n\, S \frac{d}{dt} B_x = -\, i\, \omega\, n\, S\, B_x\,. \tag{27.1}$$

One of the ways of measuring $U_{x\ res}$ consists of compensating the voltage $U_x$ (normally only partially) with another voltage, which is equal in amplitude but of the opposite phase. This is done using a high-frequency bridge.

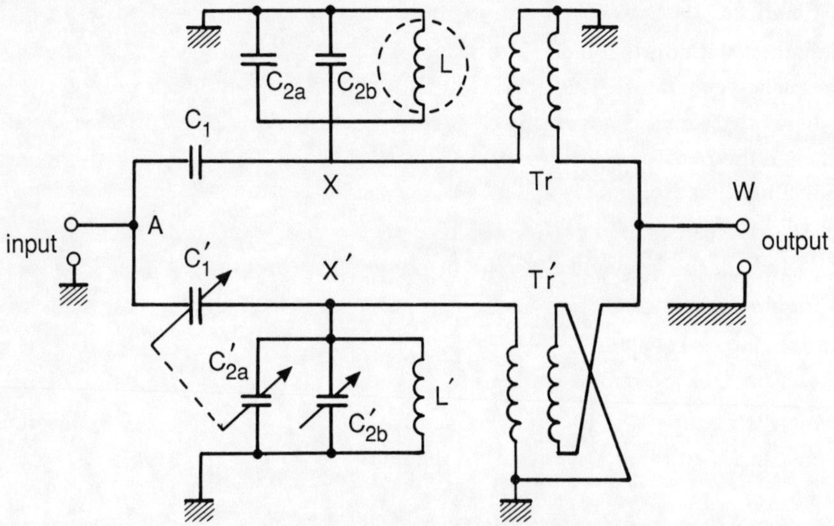


**Figure 27.1.** Pake's high-frequency bridge. The coil (circled) contains the sample and is placed in the magnetic field $B_0$.

The bridge shown in Figure 27.1 illustrates the general principle of the method. Voltage from a high-frequency generator is brought to the input. At point A, the high-frequency current flowing to earth is divided into two branches. In the upper branch, part of the current flows through a coil with a self-induction coefficient L. The coil (circled) with the sample inside, is placed in the magnetic field in a plane perpendicular to $\mathbf{B_0}$. The lower branch is identical to the upper one, but the coil L' is not placed in a magnetic field and does not contain a sample. When far from the resonance condition, the voltage at point X is $U_X$, with respect to the ground. This voltage passes through transformer Tr to point W, where it appears with a changed phase and amplitude as voltage $z\,U_X$ (z is the appropriate complex number). On the other hand, the voltage $U_{X'}$ at point X' corresponds to voltage $-z\,U_{X'}$ at point W. The change of sign of z is caused by the opposite (in comparison with the upper branch) connection of the secondary winding of the transformer Tr' to point W. Thus the voltage at W is $U_W = z\left(U_X - U_{X'}\right)$. Additional equipment, not shown for clarity, amplifies and detects this voltage.

The idea behind the compensating apparatus is to be able to change the amplitude and phase of $U_W$ with respect to $U_X$. In the circuit shown in Figure 27.1, this is done by changing the capacitances $C_1' + C_{2a}'$ and $C_{2b}'$. The impedance of the individual elements of the branches is so large that the output impedance of the power supply connected to point A (usually ca. 75 Ω) can be neglected, and the capacitance $C_1'$ can be considered as connected in parallel with $C_2' = C_{2a}' + C_{2b}'$. The value of the sum $C_1' + C_2'$ is chosen so as to form, together with inductance L', a tuned circuit for frequency $\nu$ of the high-frequency generator. This applies to both branches. The theory of LRC circuits tells us that small changes of capacitance, in the vicinity of electrical resonance, change the phases of currents and voltages in the circuit very strongly, without affecting their amplitudes. Thus, by changing $C_{2b}'$, one only changes the phase of $U_{X'}$. We can change the amplitude of voltage $U_{X'}$ by changing the capacitance $C_1'$. In order to prevent a change of phase while adjusting the amplitude, the variable capacitors $C_1'$ and $C_{2a}'$ are mounted in such a way that their total capacitance is constant.

Consider a complex number α, such that $|\alpha| = |U_X - U_{X'}|$, the phase of which is equal to the phase of voltage $U_X$, and let $-\varphi$ be the phase difference between $U_X$ and $U_X - U_{X'}$. We have therefore

$$U_X - U_{X'} = \alpha \exp\left(-i\,\varphi\right).$$

Because of the way the bridge is designed, α and φ can be changed at will. When $|U_X - U_{X'}| << |U_X|$ we can consider three cases, depending on the way the bridge is set.

**Case 1.** $\varphi = 0$ (see Figure 27.2a). Voltages $U_x$ and $U_{x'}$ have the same phase, but different amplitudes.

**Case 2.** $\varphi = 90°$ (see Figure 27.2b). Voltages $U_x$ and $U_{x'}$ have the same amplitude, but their phases slightly differ.

**Case 3.** Voltages $U_x$ and $U_{x'}$ differ in phase and in amplitude (Figure 27.2c).

We neglect the case in which phases and amplitudes of $U_x$ and $U_{x'}$ are precisely equal, as this is not experimentally achievable.

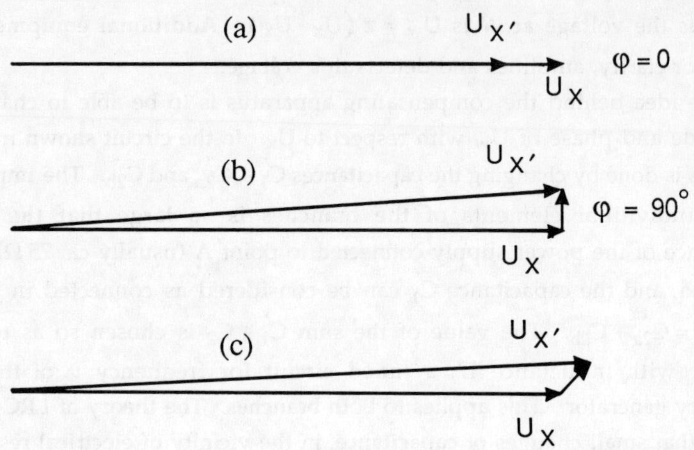


**Figure 27.2.** The three states of the bridge, close to compensation, which can be achieved by the appropriate setting.

When the condition of nuclear magnetic resonance is satisfied, voltage $U_{x\,res}$ appears at point X and voltage $z\,U_{x\,res}$ at point W. Substituting (27.1) into (26.2) we find

$$U_{x\,res} = -\,i\,\beta\,(\chi' + i\,\chi")$$

where $\beta$ is a complex number with the same phase as $U_x$, namely

$$\beta = -\,Q\,\xi\,U_x\,.$$

Therefore, at resonance, the voltage at point W is

$$U_W = z\,(U_x - U_{x'} + U_{x\,res}) = z\left[\alpha \exp(-\,i\,\varphi) - i\,\beta\,\chi' + \beta\,\chi"\right].$$

A detector monitors the amplitude of voltage $U_W$.

In the calculation of $|U_W|$ we use the following approximation. Consider two vectors **A** and **B** on a plane with $\mathbf{A} \perp \mathbf{B}$ and $|\mathbf{B}| << |\mathbf{A}|$. We then have

$$|\mathbf{A} + \mathbf{B}| = \sqrt{|\mathbf{A}|^2 + |\mathbf{B}|^2} \approx |\mathbf{A}| \tag{27.2}$$

which means that the addition of a small perpendicular vector does not alter the magnitude.

The quantity $U_{x\,res}$ is normally so small that the bridge can be easily adjusted in such a way that, apart from

$$|U_x - U_{x'}| << |U_x|$$

we also have

$$|U_{x\,res}| << |U_x - U_{x'}|, \quad \text{so that } |\beta| << |\alpha|.$$

Bearing in mind that the complex quantities α and β have the same phase, and using the approximate equation (27.2), we obtain the following results:

For Case 1, i.e. for $\varphi = 0$

$$|U_W| = |z|\,|\alpha - i\,\beta\,\chi' + \beta\,''| \approx |z|\,|\alpha + \beta\,\chi''|.$$

For Case 2, i.e. for $\varphi = -90^o$

$$|U_W| = |z|\,|-i\alpha - i\,\beta\,\chi' + \beta\,\chi''| \approx |z|\,|\alpha + \beta\,\chi'|.$$

We see therefore that, depending upon the way the bridge is set, we can separately measure the coefficients of absorption χ" and dispersion χ', while in Case 3 we measure a mixture of these coefficients.

A change of generator frequency $\nu$ would detune the bridge. Therefore, to sweep through the region of resonance, the external magnetic field $\mathbf{B}_0$ has to be changed at constant $\nu$. Through such a sweep, we obtain χ' and χ" as functions of $\mathbf{B}_0$. If needed, χ' and χ" may be expressed as functions of ω using the relation $\omega = -\gamma B_0$.

Another device for a separate measurement of χ' and χ" is known as the autodyne. Here the coil surrounding the sample forms part of the resonance circuit of a frequency generator oscillating at $\omega$, close to $\gamma B_0$ and $B_0$, or $\omega$ is swept through the region of resonance. The basic principle governing the operation of such equipment becomes clear considering the arguments of Section 18: $\chi'$ is measured by monitoring the change of the oscillation frequency caused by nuclear resonance, and $\chi''$ by observing the change in amplitude.

## 28. The Lorentzian, the Gaussian and Other Lineshapes

We shall now discuss the properties of several functions which are important in NMR. The function described by the equation

$$L(x) = \frac{A}{1 + \Gamma^2 (x - x_0)^2} \tag{28.1}$$

where A and $\Gamma$ are constants and $x_0$ is the *offset*, is known as the Lorentzian. The Lorentzian, shown in Figure 28.1, has many applications in physics. For example, it describes the oscillation amplitude of the damped harmonic oscillator as a function of the driving frequency. The slope of the curve depends on the "steepness parameter" $\Gamma$. The Lorentzian has a maximum at $x = x_0$, and reaches half of its maximum height at $x_0 \pm 1/\Gamma$, so that its width measured at half-height is

$$\Delta L = 2/\Gamma\,. \tag{28.2}$$

Multiplying L (x) by an appropriate constant we obtain the so-called *normalized* Lorentzian $\ell(x)$, which satisfies the condition

$$\int_{-\infty}^{+\infty} \ell(x)\, dx = 1\,.$$

It is easily shown that

$$\ell(x) = \frac{\Gamma}{\pi A} L(x)\,. \tag{28.3}$$

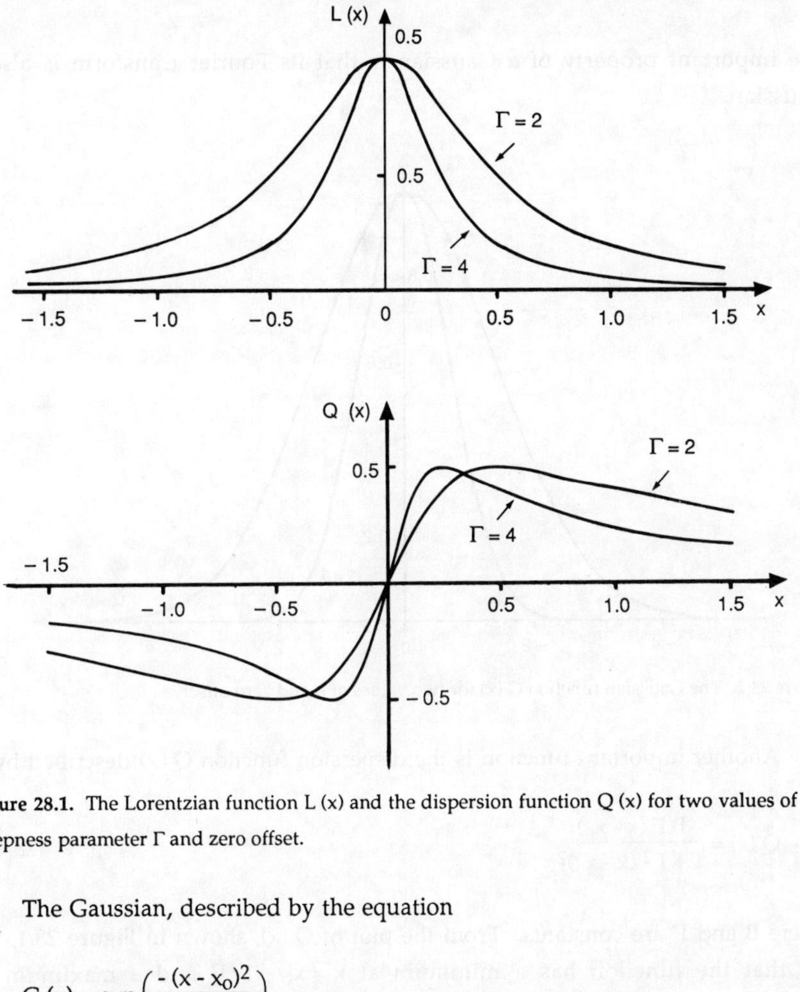


**Figure 28.1.** The Lorentzian function L (x) and the dispersion function Q (x) for two values of the steepness parameter Γ and zero offset.

The Gaussian, described by the equation

$$G(x) = \exp\left(\frac{-(x - x_0)^2}{\sigma^2}\right)$$

where σ is a constant, is shown in Figure 28.2. The normalized Gaussian is defined just as the normalized Lorentzian

$$g(x) = \frac{1}{\sqrt{\pi\,\sigma^2}}\exp\left(\frac{-(x - x_0)^2}{\sigma^2}\right)$$

and is often encountered in NMR. Its maximum is also at $x = x_0$. The half-width ΔG of the Gaussian is

$$\Delta G = 2\sigma \sqrt{\ln 2} = 1.66511\,\sigma\,.$$

The important property of a Gaussian is that its Fourier transform is also a Gaussian.

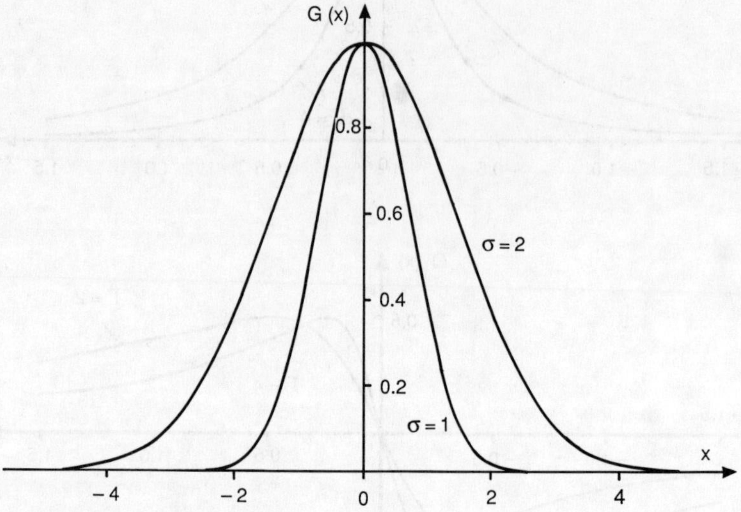


**Figure 28.2.** The Gaussian function G (x) for two values of σ and zero offset.

Another important function is the dispersion function Q (x) described by

$$Q\,(x) = \frac{B\,\Gamma\,(x - x_0)}{1 + \Gamma^2\,(x - x_0)^2} \tag{28.4}$$

where B and Γ are constants. From the plot of Q (x), shown in Figure 28.1, we see that the function has a minimum at $x = x_0 - 1/\Gamma$ and a maximum at $x = x_0 + 1/\Gamma$. The value of the function at the extrema is

$$Q_{extr} = \pm B/2\,. \tag{28.5}$$

## 29. Stationary Solution of Bloch's Equations

The "continuous-wave" (CW) method of observing nuclear magnetic resonance consists of scanning either the frequency while keeping the magnetic field constant, or the magnetic field at constant frequency. Thus, generally speaking, the parameter $\Delta\omega = \omega_e + \gamma\,B_0$ is continuously varied in the vicinity of the value $\Delta\omega = 0$, while the functions u $(\Delta\omega)$ and v $(\Delta\omega)$ are recorded. These functions are known as dispersion and absorption.

A passage slow enough for equations (25.3), describing the equilibrium between the action of the radiofrequency field and the action of relaxation, to be satisfied is known as a "slow passage". If, in addition, Bloch's equations apply, the lines of absorption and dispersion are given by equations (25.4).

Because of net spin interactions, the shape of nuclear magnetic resonance signals from crystals is generally quite different, and the application of Bloch's equations to the description of the behaviour of magnetization during the passage through the line is a rough approximation - even then, a qualitatively correct description of the event is given. Line structures in liquids are characteristic of a given nucleus and a given compound. However, this structure can be observed only in highly homogeneous magnetic fields. If the magnetic field over the sample varies by more than ca. $10^{-6}$ T, the natural structure of the lines from liquids becomes invisible. In that case Bloch's equations apply very well.

For the time being, we assume the applicability of Bloch's equations and, relying on (25.4), limit ourselves to slow-passage experiments. The equations indicate that the sign of the gyromagnetic ratio $\gamma$ influences only the sign of absorption and dispersion, and since we are now interested only in their amplitude and shape, we assume that $\gamma > 0$.

Equations (25.4) can be rewritten in a clearer form by introducing the quantity $Z_0$, known as the saturation coefficient, and defined as

$$Z_0 = \frac{1}{1 + \gamma^2 B_1^2 T_1 T_2}. \tag{29.1}$$

We shall consider these equations in turn.

**A. Absorption**

Multiplying the numerator and the denominator of the right-hand side of (25.4b) by $Z_0$ we find

$$v\,(\Delta\omega) = \frac{M_\infty \gamma B_1 T_2 Z_0}{1 + (\Delta\omega\, T_2)^2 Z_0} \tag{29.2}$$

which tells us that the shape of absorption is Lorentzian (28.1), with steepness parameter $\Gamma = Z_0^{1/2} T_2$.

The value of the function v $(\Delta\omega)$ falls by 50% at the following points

$$\Delta\omega_d = \pm \frac{1}{T_2 \sqrt{Z_0}}.$$

It follows that the transverse relaxation time also determines the half-width of the absorption line. This is particularly clear where $Z_0 = 1$, when the half-width of the line of absorption is $2/T_2$. This line width can be caused either by the process of spin-spin relaxation, or by the inhomogeneity of the magnetic field. As was shown in Section 22, in the latter case $T_2$ should be replaced by $T_2^*$.

**B. Dispersion**

Multiplying the numerator and the denominator of the right-hand-side of equation (25.4a) by $Z_0$, we obtain a function of the Q (x) type

$$u\,(\Delta\omega) = \frac{\gamma B_1 T_2^2 Z_0 \Delta\omega}{1 + (\Delta\omega\, T_2)^2 Z_0} M_\infty$$

with extrema at points

$$\Delta\omega = \pm \frac{1}{T_2 \sqrt{Z_0}}.$$

The value of the function at the extrema is

$$u_{max} = - u_{min} = \frac{1}{2} M_\infty B_1 T_2 \sqrt{Z_0}.$$

Redfield (1955) has shown that in some cases the behaviour of dispersion in strong oscillating fields may be different.

**C. The longitudinal component**

The longitudinal component is not observed in the continuous-wave experiment. Nevertheless, it is interesting to consider its dependence on $H_1$. The formula (25.4c) can be transformed into a more convenient form

$$M_z = \frac{\left[1 + (\Delta\omega\, T_2)^2\right] Z_0}{1 + (\Delta\omega\, T_2)^2 Z_0} M_\infty$$

showing that $M_Z$ decreases when $Z_o \rightarrow 0$ through increasing $B_1$. The dependence is strongest for $\Delta\omega = 0$. The decrease in $M_Z$ means that saturation occurs. Since $M_Z$ is proportional to the difference of occupancy of the states, we conclude that the essence of saturation is the equalization of occupancy of the lower and upper spin states.

## 30. The Adiabatic Theorem

The arguments of this section are based on the following theorem about the adiabatic change of the magnetic field: *If the change of direction of the magnetic field is sufficiently slow, the axis of the precession cone of the magnetization vector follows the direction of the field, and the angle of the cone does not change.*

The theorem requires some clarification. By a "sufficiently slow" change of the direction of **B** we understand a change in which the angular velocity of vector **B** is much smaller than the angular velocity $-\gamma\mathbf{B}$ of the precession of the spin. The angle of the cone of precession is the angle formed by the vectors **M** and **B**. As we know, this angle determines the energy of interaction of magnetization with field **B**. This is why the change of direction of the field, which takes place while the angle of the cone is unchanged, is known as the adiabatic passage.

The adiabatic change theorem applies not only to the real magnetic field in the laboratory frame, but also to the effective field in the rotating frame. Its proof is as follows (Abragam 1983, p. 34). Consider the momentary rate of change of **B** written in the general form

$$\frac{d}{dt}\mathbf{B} = \Omega \times \mathbf{B} + \Omega_1 \mathbf{B}$$

in which the rate of change of **B** is represented as the sum of two components, perpendicular and parallel to **B**. The quantities $\Omega$ and $\Omega_1$ with dimensions of $s^{-1}$ can be interpreted as follows: $\Omega$ determines the angular velocity with which vector **B** changes its direction, and $\Omega_1$ determines the speed of change of the length of **B**. Consider a coordinate system X'Y'Z' in which the axis Z' follows the vector **B** and maintains its direction. From (19.10), the motion of the magnetization in this rotating frame of reference can be written as

$$\frac{d}{dt}\mathbf{M} = \gamma\mathbf{M} \times \left(\mathbf{B} + \frac{\Omega}{\gamma}\right)$$

since vector $\Omega$ is also the vector of angular velocity of this frame. Let us write the above equation in the X'Y'Z' reference frame and use our assumption that $|\Omega| << \gamma\ |\mathbf{B}|$ by omitting the terms containing the coordinates of the vector $\Omega$ with respect to terms containing the coordinates of vector $\gamma\,\mathbf{B}$. We find

$$\frac{d}{dt} M_{X'} = M_{Y'}\,\gamma\,B$$

$$\frac{d}{dt} M_{Y'} = -\,M_{X'}\,\gamma\,B$$

$$\frac{d}{dt} M_{Z'} = M_{X'}\,\Omega_{Y'} - M_{Y'}\,\Omega_{X'}\,.$$

The above equations show that $M_{X'}$ and $M_{Y'}$ are sinusoidal functions of time with frequency $\nu = |\gamma| B/2\pi$.

After a long time interval t the change of $M_{Z'}$ is

$$\Delta M_{Z'} = M_{Z'}(t) - M_{Z'}(0) = \int_0^t \left[M_{X'}(t')\,\Omega_{Y'}(t') - M_{Y'}(t')\,\Omega_{X'}(t')\right] dt\,. \qquad (30.1)$$

It is easy to show that

$$\int_0^t A \sin\left(2\,\pi\,\nu\,t\right) dt \le \frac{A}{\pi\nu} \qquad (30.2)$$

since the integral between the limits, which are multiples of $1/\nu$, vanishes.

If the values of $\Omega_{Y'}(t)$ and $\Omega_{X'}(t)$ are changing with time so slowly that they can be approximately assumed to be constant with respect to $\sin\left(2\pi\,\nu\,t\right)$ and can be taken before the sign of the integral, then the inequality (30.2) allows us to estimate the magnitude of the right-hand side of (30.1). We obtain the inequality

$$\Delta M_{Z'} \le 4M\frac{\Omega}{\gamma B} << M\,.$$

The change of $M_Z$ can thus be neglected in comparison with M and, since during precession M = const, from the constancy of $M_Z$ and M it follows that the angle between **M** and the axis Z' parallel to **B** is also constant. This is the proof we were seeking.

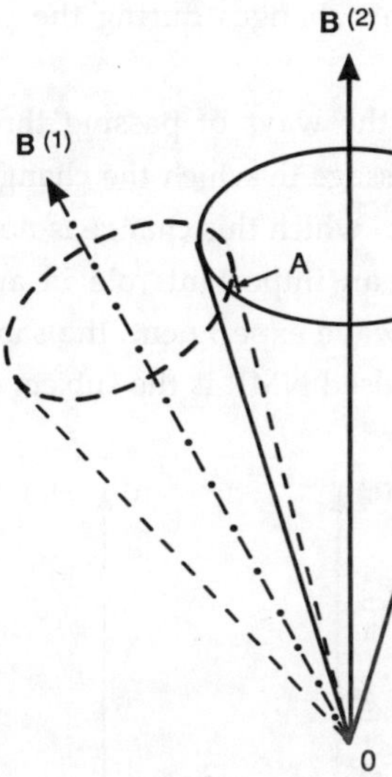


**Figure 30.1.** The change of the precession angle during a non-adiabatic change of direction of the magnetic field.

The opposite of adiabatic change is non-adiabatic change, during which the angular velocity of vector **B** is much larger than the velocity of precession in field **B**, i.e. $|\Omega| >> |\gamma| B$. Since the only possible way of changing the direction of magnetization is via precession, during non-adiabatic changes magnetization is unable to "catch up" with the change of the direction of the magnetic field.

An extreme example of the behaviour of magnetization during non-adiabatic change of the direction of the field is given in Figure 30.1. Assume that the original direction of **B** was $\mathbf{B}^{(1)}$. Precession of the magnetization took place around this direction over the surface of the cone marked with broken lines. A fast change of the direction of the field to position $\mathbf{B}^{(2)}$ occurs when magnetization is in position OA, after which the vector **B** is again static. We neglect the small change of the position of the magnetization during the change of the direction of **B**. After the change the magnetization precesses, beginning from the position OA around the new direction of **B**, i.e. $\mathbf{B}^{(2)}$, on the surface of the cone drawn with solid lines. The angle of the cone of precession is now $AOB^{(2)}$.

Consider now the situation in which nuclear magnetic resonance occurs. We know from Section 19 that when vector $\mathbf{B}_1$ rotates in plane XY, which is perpendicular to the direction of the static field $\mathbf{B}_0$, the effective field vector is the sum of two mutually perpendicular vectors, of which one is parallel to Z and the other parallel to XY. The angle formed by the effective field with Z depends on $\Delta\omega = \omega_e + \gamma \mathbf{B}_0$ and changes during the passage through the line (Figure 30.2).

We can therefore divide the ways of passing through an NMR line into two categories: (i) adiabatic passage in which the change of the direction of $\mathbf{B}_{eff}$ is adiabatic; (ii) rapid passage in which this change is non-adiabatic.

The rapid passage plays an important role in another NMR method in which, unlike the continuous-wave experiment, the sample is irradiated with a short radiofrequency pulse. Pulsed NMR is the subject of Chapter 6.

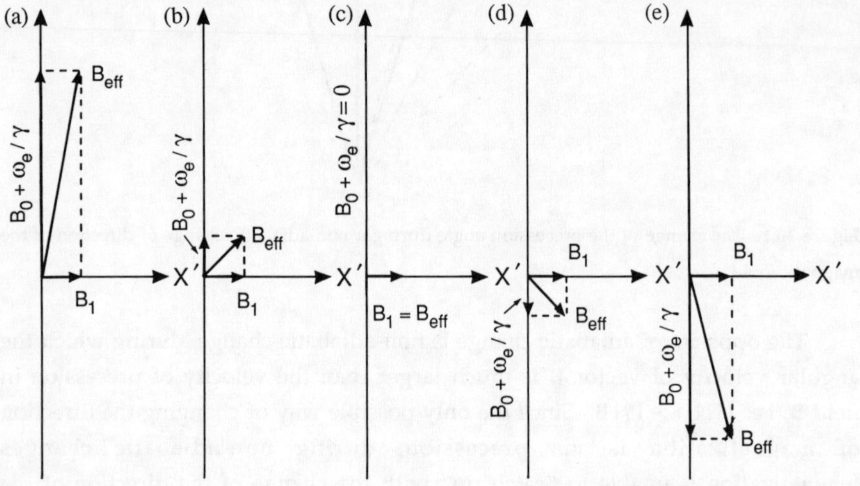


**Figure 30.2.** Several successive arbitrarily chosen values of the vector of effective field $\mathbf{B}_{eff}$ during passage through a line of magnetic resonance. (c) represents the situation in which the resonance condition is satisfied.

# Chapter 6. Pulsed NMR

## 31. Free Induction Signal

Soon after the discovery of NMR in condensed matter, Torrey (1949) and Hahn (1950a) showed that the phenomenon of nuclear magnetic resonance can also be brought about by subjecting the sample to one or more resonant radiofrequency pulses. When the pulses end, the sample induces in the receiver coil an oscillating voltage of the resonance frequency. Depending on the experimental conditions, this voltage can be observed as the free induction decay (FID) or the spin echo.

As before, a sample containing nuclei with spin quantum number I and gyromagnetic ratio $\gamma$, is placed in a strong magnetic field $\mathbf{B}_0$. It is then irradiated with a short pulse of oscillating magnetic field generated by a coil surrounding the sample and perpendicular to $\mathbf{B}_0$. During the pulse an alternating electric current of frequency $\nu_e$, known as the carrier frequency (the subscript "e" refers to "electric", so that there is no confusion with other frequencies which may be present), is passed through the windings of the coil. The carrier frequency is usually chosen so as to be equal or nearly equal to the Larmor frequency $\nu_0 = |\gamma| B_0/2\pi$. As soon as the pulse is over, voltage induced by the magnetization in the coil is observed. The duration and amplitude of the pulses can be varied at will. The phase difference between consecutive pulses is constant (the pulses are "coherent"), and can be varied using an electronic device known as the phase shifter.

We will use (a) the laboratory reference frame XYZ in which the Z axis is parallel to $\mathbf{B}_0$ and (b) the rotating reference frame X'Y'Z in which the Z axis coincides with the Z axis of the laboratory frame, but which rotates around this axis at the rate $|\omega_e| = 2\pi\,\nu_e$ and the sign is the same as that of $\omega_0 = -\gamma B_0$. In other words, we assume that the reference system rotates in the same sense as that of the Larmor precession, but not necessarily at precisely the same velocity. In the special case of $\omega_e = \omega_0$ we call the rotating frame "resonant".

As in Section 20, we decompose the field of amplitude $2B_1$ generated by the coil into two circularly polarized vectors, each of length $B_1$, of which one is static in the rotating frame and the other can be ignored. The static vector determines the so-called "axis of the pulse" in the rotating frame The phase of the rotation of the frame may be chosen in such a way that the pulse axis coincides with the X' axis.

Assume that before the pulse is applied the sample is at thermodynamic equilibrium, i.e. that $M = M_\infty$ and $\mathbf{M} \,||\, \mathbf{Z}$, and consider the behaviour of the magnetization in the rotating frame during the pulse. We know from Section 19 that when $\omega_e = -\gamma B_0$, the external magnetic field $\mathbf{B_0}$ has no effect on the magnetization in the rotating reference frame. We can therefore assume that the sample is subjected only to the field $\mathbf{B_1}$ parallel to the pulse axis (the X' axis). As soon as the pulse begins (we assume that its onset is rapid in the sense of Section 30), the magnetization starts to precess around $\mathbf{B_1}$ at the rate $-\gamma\, \mathbf{B_1}$ without leaving the ZY plane. The angle traversed by the magnetization during the duration of the pulse $\tau$ is

$$\alpha = -\gamma B_1 \tau\,. \tag{31.1}$$

Consider pulses for which, by the appropriate setting of $\mathbf{B_1}$ and $\tau$, the pulse angle $\alpha$ is made equal to $\pi/2$ or to $\pi$. The $\pi/2$ pulse will be denoted by P, and if its axis coincides with X', -X', Y' or -Y' axes, we will write $P_x$, $P_{-x}$, $P_y$ and $P_{-y}$, respectively. Figure 41.1(a) later shows that the $P_x$ pulse moves the magnetization from its equilibrium position along the Z axis to the position coincident with Y'. Upon the termination of the pulse, the magnetization seen from the laboratory frame precesses in the external field $\mathbf{B_0}$ and its transverse component $M_\perp$ (i.e. the projection onto the XY plane) induces in the coil an oscillating voltage of resonance frequency known as the "free induction signal" or, because it decays as a result of transverse relaxation, "free induction decay" (FID).

## 32. Rotation Operators and the Action of Pulses

Consider two vectors, **A** and **B**, related by an operator G

$$G\,\mathbf{A} = \mathbf{B} \tag{32.1}$$

and another operator, R, which transforms vectors **A** and **B** as follows

$$\begin{aligned} R\,\mathbf{A} &= \mathbf{A'} \\ R\,\mathbf{B} &= \mathbf{B'}\,. \end{aligned} \tag{32.2}$$

We wish to find the operator G' which relates **A'** and **B'** in a manner similar to (32.1), so that

$$G'\,\mathbf{A}' = \mathbf{B}'\,.$$

We will show that operator G' exists provided that the operator R is reversible, i.e. that there is an operator $R^-$ such that

$$R^- R = 1\,. \tag{32.3}$$

Acting with R on both sides of (32.1) we have

$$R\,G\,\mathbf{A} = R\,\mathbf{B}\,.$$

Using (32.3) we may rewrite the above as

$$R\,G\,R^-\,R\,\mathbf{A} = R\,\mathbf{B}$$

or

$$R\,G\,R^-\,\mathbf{A}' = \mathbf{B}'\,.$$

We see therefore that **A'** and **B'** are related via the operator

$$G' = R\,G\,R^- \tag{32.4}$$

known as the rotation operator. This result finds useful applications in relating representations in different coordinate systems. Suppose that the coordinates of vector **A** are $(a_x, a_y, a_z)$ in the XYZ coordinate system, and $(a'_x, a'_y, a'_z)$ in the X'Y'Z' coordinate system. In physics, a vector is a real quantity independent of the choice of the coordinate system. The two sets of three numbers are simply different representations of the same vector, and are related by a $3 \times 3$ matrix $\{R\}$ as follows

$$\{R\}\begin{bmatrix} a_x \\ a_y \\ a_z \end{bmatrix} = \begin{bmatrix} a'_x \\ a'_y \\ a'_z \end{bmatrix}.$$

The matrix elements of $\{R\}$ depend only on the two coordinate systems, but not on the vector **A**. In other words, $\{R\}$ is common to all possible vectors.

It is convenient to use the following approach. We treat the set of numbers $(a'_x, a'_y, a'_z)$ as coordinates of the vector **A'** in the XYZ coordinate system. In this sense we may speak of two different vectors, **A** and **A'**, which, although their coordinates are different, both represent the same physically real vector **A**. In other words, for any vector **A**, the change of a coordinate system results in a new vector **A'**. This defines the operator R

$$R\,\mathbf{A} = \mathbf{A}' .$$

The operator R is common for all possible vectors **A** and depends only on the two coordinate systems. We say that R describes the change of the coordinate system, and we call the matrix $\{R\}$ a representation of the operator R in the coordinate system XYZ.

We now return to (32.2). If we interpret the action of the operator R as an effect of changing the coordinate system on vectors, then (32.4) shows how this change affects the operators. In other words, the form of the operator G depends on the coordinate system in which the vectors are expressed.

From now on we shall confine ourselves to operators R which are *rotations* around specific axes. The change of the coordinate system by rotating it by angle $\alpha$ around a specific axis is represented by the operator $R(\alpha)$. Rotation $R(-\alpha)$ of the system by the angle $-\alpha$ is equivalent to rotation of a vector by angle $+\alpha$ without changing the coordinate system. It is clearly the same whether we rotate the system by the angle $-\alpha$ or the vector by the angle $+\alpha$ around the same axis. We consider the angle $\alpha$ to be positive if it forms a right-handed screw with the direction of the rotation axis, and negative otherwise. In other words, $\alpha > 0$ if, when looking at the vector undergoing rotation in the direction of the axis of rotation, the rotation is clockwise. A Cartesian coordinate system is called "right-handed" if rotation by the angle $+\pi/2$ about the Z axis aligns the X axis with the original Y axis. In what follows, we shall be concerned only with right-handed coordinate systems.

Consider now the rotation of the spin vector **I** by the angle $\alpha$ around the Z axis of a Cartesian coordinate system. Assume that the vector lies in the XY plane. After the rotation the coordinates of **I** are

$$I'_x = I_x \cos\alpha - I_y \sin\alpha$$

$$I'_y = I_x \sin\alpha + I_y \cos\alpha . \qquad (32.5)$$

These results follow from the well known trigonometric relationships

$$\cos(\alpha + \beta) = \cos\alpha\cos\beta - \sin\alpha\sin\beta$$

$$\sin(\alpha + \beta) = \sin\alpha\cos\beta + \cos\alpha\sin\beta \,.$$

Treating the transverse part of the vector **I** as a complex number $I_+ = I_x + i\,I_y$ equation (32.5) can be written as

$$I'_x + i\,I'_y = (I_x + i\,I_y)\exp(i\,\alpha) \,.$$

We know, however, that quantum mechanics treats spin coordinates as operators. There must therefore exist an operator of rotation around the Z axis, the action of which is equivalent to multiplication by the complex number $\exp(i\,\alpha)$. In view of (32.4), this operator, which we denote by $R_z(\alpha)$, must satisfy the relation

$$R_z(\alpha)\, I_+\, R_z^-(\alpha) = \exp(i\,\alpha)\, I_+ \,. \tag{32.6}$$

We will see that $R_z(\alpha) = \exp(i\,\alpha\, I_z)$ where (see Chapter 1)

$$\exp(i\,\alpha\, I_z) = 1 + \sum_{n=1}^{\infty} \frac{(i\,\alpha\, I_z)^n}{n!}$$

and $R_z^-(\alpha) = \exp(-i\,\alpha\, I_z)$. In order to prove this, we must show that the result of the action of operators

$$\exp(i\,\alpha\, I_z)\, I_+ \exp(-i\,\alpha\, I_z) \qquad \text{and} \qquad I_+ \exp(i\,\alpha)$$

on an arbitrary wavefunction is the same. Since any function can be represented as a linear combination of eigenfunctions of the energy operator (the Hamiltonian), it is sufficient to confine the argument to the energy eigenfunctions $\varphi_m$. We have

$$\exp(i\alpha I_z)\, I_+ \exp(-i\alpha I_z)\, \varphi_m = \exp(i\alpha I_z)\, I_+ \varphi_m \exp(-i\alpha m)$$

$$= \exp(i\alpha I_z)\, k_+ \varphi_{m+1} \exp(-i\alpha m)$$

$$= k_+ \exp[i\alpha(m+1)]\, \varphi_{m+1} \exp(-i\alpha m)$$

$$= \exp(i\alpha)\, k_+ \varphi_{m+1}$$

and

$$\exp(i\alpha)\, I_+ \varphi_m = \exp(i\alpha)\, k_+ \varphi_{m+1}$$

where $k_+ = \sqrt{(I - m)(I + m + 1)}$. In the above calculations we have used the rules (4.17) of the operation of $I_+$ and the equality

$$I_z^n \varphi_m = m^n \varphi_m$$

so that $\exp(i\alpha I_z)\, \varphi_m = \exp(i\alpha m)\, \varphi_m$.

In a completely analogous manner we can show that

$$\exp(i\alpha I_z)\, I_- \exp(-i\alpha I_z) = \exp(-i\alpha)\, I_- \qquad (32.7)$$

where $I_-$ is the "lowering" operator. By adding the (32.6) and (32.7) side by side we see that the rotation operator acts on the coordinate $I_x = (I_+ + I_-)/2$ as follows

$$\exp(i\alpha I_z)\, I_x \exp(-i\alpha I_z) = I_x \cos\alpha - I_y \sin\alpha\,. \qquad (32.8)$$

Equation (32.8) makes it possible to derive expressions for the rotation of *any* spin coordinate around *any* axis, because it is immaterial which labels and signs of the axes of a Cartesian system we take, provided that the right-handedness of the axes is preserved. Thus we introduce in turn the following labelling of the axes:

| | | |
|---|---|---|
| X | Y | Z |
| X | Z | - Y |
| Y | - X | Z |
| Y | Z | X |
| Z | Y | - X |
| Z | X | Y |

and insert the labels into (32.8) to obtain the following important results:

$$\exp\left(i\,\alpha\,I_z\right) I_x \exp\left(-\,i\,\alpha\,I_z\right) = I_x \cos\alpha - I_y \sin\alpha$$

$$\exp\left(i\,\alpha\,I_y\right) I_x \exp\left(-\,i\,\alpha\,I_y\right) = I_x \cos\alpha + I_z \sin\alpha$$

$$\exp\left(i\,\alpha\,I_z\right) I_y \exp\left(-\,i\,\alpha\,I_z\right) = I_y \cos\alpha + I_x \sin\alpha$$

$$\exp\left(i\,\alpha\,I_x\right) I_y \exp\left(-\,i\,\alpha\,I_x\right) = I_y \cos\alpha - I_z \sin\alpha \tag{32.9}$$

$$\exp\left(i\,\alpha\,I_x\right) I_z \exp\left(-\,i\,\alpha\,I_x\right) = I_z \cos\alpha + I_y \sin\alpha$$

$$\exp\left(i\,\alpha\,I_y\right) I_z \exp\left(-\,i\,\alpha\,I_y\right) = I_z \cos\alpha - I_x \sin\alpha\,.$$

To summarize, the operator $\exp\left(i\,\alpha\,I_k\right)$ where $k = x, y, z$ corresponds to a rotation around the axis K by an angle $\alpha$, provided that for $\alpha > 0$ the rotation forms a right-handed screw with the direction of the axis. Note that the formulae (32.9) can be expressed in the general form

$$\exp\left(i\,\alpha\,I_j\right) I_k \exp\left(-\,i\,\alpha\,I_j\right) = I_k \cos\alpha - I_\ell \sin\left(\alpha\, e_{jk\ell}\right)$$

where $e_{jk\ell}$ is the Levi-Civita symbol, which is 0 if any of j, k or $\ell$ are identical, unity if j, k and $\ell$ are in cyclic order (for example z, x, y) and -1 if j, k and $\ell$ are in anticyclic order (for example x, z, y).

We shall illustrate the above considerations by calculating the action of the $\pi/2$ pulse. Assume that at the beginning of the experiment the spin system is at equilibrium with the external magnetic field $\mathbf{B_0}$ directed along the Z axis. According to (7.12) the effective density operator has the form

$$\sigma_\infty = \frac{-\,\mathcal{H}_Z}{k\,T\,L} = \frac{\gamma\,\hbar\,B_0}{k\,T\,L} I_z \tag{32.10}$$

and the coordinates of the magnetization vector are

$$M_x = 0 \qquad M_y = 0 \qquad M_z = M_\infty$$

where $\mathcal{H}_Z = -\,\gamma\,\hbar\,B_0\,I_z$ is the Zeeman interaction with $\mathbf{B_0}$ and L is the dimension of the appropriate Hilbert space (see Section 15).

We now apply the $P_x$ pulse. Since in the resonant rotating frame the Zeeman interaction with $\mathbf{B_0}$ is eliminated, we only need to consider the interaction with the stationary field component $\mathbf{B_1}$ coincident with the X' axis

$$\mathcal{H}'_{Z1} = -\gamma \hbar B_1 I'_x . \tag{32.11}$$

We neglect other interactions, such as dipolar or quadrupolar, by assuming that they are much weaker than $\mathcal{H}'_{Z1}$.

The density operator must also be transformed to the rotating coordinate system. However, since it is proportional to $I_z$ it remains unchanged, so that $\sigma'_\infty = \sigma_\infty$.

According to (7.6), the time dependence of $\sigma'$ has the form

$$\sigma'(t) = \exp\left(-i\,\hbar^{-1} \mathcal{H}'_{Z1}\, t\right) \sigma_\infty \exp\left(i\,\hbar^{-1} \mathcal{H}'_{Z1}\, t\right)$$

Substituting (32.10) and (32.11) and using (32.9) we obtain

$$\sigma'(t) = \frac{\gamma \hbar B_0}{k T L} \exp\left(i \gamma B_1 t I'_x\right) I_z \exp\left(-i \gamma B_1 t I'_x\right)$$

$$= \frac{\gamma \hbar B_0}{k T L} \left[ I_z \cos\left(\gamma B_1 t\right) + I'_y \sin\left(\gamma B_1 t\right) \right].$$

At the end of the pulse ($t = \tau$) the angle of precession around $\mathbf{B_1}$ is $\gamma B_1 t = \pi/2$ for $\gamma > 0$ (as is the case for the proton), and we obtain for the density operator

$$\sigma'(\tau) = \frac{\gamma \hbar B_0}{k T L} I'_y .$$

The effects of $P_{-x}$, $P_y$ and $P_{-y}$ pulses on the various spin coordinates, calculated in a similar manner, are listed in Table 32.1.

As a result of the above calculations we have derived rules showing how a $\pi/2$ pulse acts on the density operator expressed in terms of the spin coordinates. We shall now demonstrate that the same rules are valid if P pulses act on the magnetization $\mathbf{M}$. As an example we calculate the coordinates of $\mathbf{M}$ after the $P_x$ pulse.

$$M'_k = \langle\langle \mathcal{M}' \rangle\rangle = \mathrm{Tr}\left[\sigma'(\tau)\, \mathcal{M}'_k\right] = \frac{\gamma^2 \hbar^2 B_0 N_0}{k T L} \mathrm{Tr}\left\{ I'_y I'_k \right\}$$

where $\mathcal{M}'_k = N_0 \gamma \hbar I'_k$ is the operator of $M'_k$ and $N_0$ is the number of spins per unit of volume. For k = x and y we have $\mathrm{Tr}\{I'_y I'_k\} = 0$, hence $M'_x = 0$ and $M_z = 0$. For k = y we have $\mathrm{Tr}\, I'^2_y = \frac{1}{3} I(I+1) L$, so that $M'_y = M_\infty$. We conclude that, as shown later in Figure 41.1(a), the $P_x$ pulse transfers the magnetization from the Z axis to the Y' axis. This is the case for nuclei with $\gamma > 0$, such as $^1H$. For nuclei with $\gamma < 0$, such as $^{17}O$ or $^{29}Si$, a $P_x$ pulse aligns it with the - Y' axis.

**Table 32.1.** The action of $\pi/2$ pulses on spin coordinates for $\gamma > 0$.

| | Pulse applied | | | |
|---|---|---|---|---|
| Acting on | $P_x$ | $P_{-x}$ | $P_y$ | $P_{-y}$ |
| $I_x$ | $I_x$ | $I_x$ | $I_z$ | $-I_z$ |
| $I_y$ | $-I_z$ | $I_z$ | $I_y$ | $I_y$ |
| $I_z$ | $I_y$ | $-I_y$ | $-I_x$ | $I_x$ |

## 33. The Interaction Representation

In terms of quantum mechanics, the rotating coordinate system is only a special case of a more general theory. In order to show this, we first consider the form the Liouville-von Neumann equation derived in Section 7

$$\dot{\rho} = i\hbar^{-1}[\rho, \mathcal{H}] \tag{33.1}$$

takes as a result of a change of basis. The dot in $\dot{\rho}$ denotes differentiation with respect to time. Let R be the operator describing the change of basis (or, in other words, the coordinate frame in Hilbert space). We confine ourselves only to such changes R which are reversible, so that there exists $R^-$ such that $R^- R = R R^- = 1$. We know that the change of basis transforms wavefunction $\varphi$ into wavefunction $\varphi' = R\varphi$, and that every operator, including the density operator, is transformed according to

$$\rho' = R \rho R^- . \tag{33.2}$$

We also have the relationship

$$\rho = R^{-} \rho' R \tag{33.3}$$

which is derived by multiplying each side of (33.2) by $R^{-}$ from the left and by R from the right. If R is time-dependent, the new coordinate frame moves with respect to the old frame. For the time being, we treat R in a general manner, without assuming that it represents a rotation or a unitary transformation.

Differentiation of both sides of (33.3) gives

$$\dot{\rho} = \dot{R}^{-} \rho' R + R^{-} \dot{\rho}' R + R^{-} \rho' \dot{R} . \tag{33.4}$$

Substituting (33.3) and (33.4) in (33.1) and multiplying both sides of the resulting equation by R from the left and by $R^{-}$ from the right, we obtain

$$\dot{\rho}' = i \hbar^{-1} [ \rho', R \mathcal{H} R^{-} ] - \rho' \dot{R} R^{-} - R \dot{R}^{-} \rho' .$$

Note that by differentiating $R R^{-} = 1$ we have

$$\dot{R} R^{-} = - R \dot{R}^{-} .$$

We use this to derive the required form of the Liouville-von Neumann equation in the new reference system

$$\dot{\rho}' = i \hbar^{-1} \Big[ \rho', ( R \mathcal{H} R^{-} - i \hbar R \dot{R}^{-} ) \Big] . \tag{33.5}$$

The form of (33.5) is very similar to that of (33.1), which becomes clear when we put

$$\mathcal{H}' = R \mathcal{H} R^{-} - i \hbar R \dot{R}^{-} \tag{33.6}$$

because then

$$\dot{\rho}' = i \hbar^{-1} [ \rho', \mathcal{H}' ] . \tag{33.7}$$

We can therefore consider (33.6) to be the form of the Hamiltonian in the new reference frame. Note that when the frame is static, $\dot{R}^{-} = 0$ and the Hamiltonian transforms in the usual way according to (32.4).

The transition to a mobile reference frame turns out to be a particularly useful method of solving equations of motion, provided that the Hamiltonian can be divided into a time-independent part $\mathcal{H}_0$ and a time-dependent part $\mathcal{H}_1$

$$\mathcal{H} = \mathcal{H}_0 + \mathcal{H}_1 .$$

It is then convenient to go over to a mobile reference frame using the operator

$$R = \exp\left(i\,\hbar^{-1}\,\mathcal{H}_0\, t\right) .$$

This reference frame is known as the interaction frame, and the representations of wavefunctions and operators in this frame are known as interaction representations. The transition to the interaction representation is a unitary operation, because matrix elements of the operator R calculated in any basis satisfy the condition (6.12), which can be proved using (1.8).

Considering that $R^{-} = \exp\left(-\,i\,\hbar^{-1}\,\mathcal{H}_0\, t\right)$ and that $\dot{R}^{-} = -\,i\,\hbar^{-1}\,\mathcal{H}_0\, R^{-}$ (because $\mathcal{H}_0$ is time-independent), we can transform (33.6) as follows

$$\mathcal{H}' = R\,\mathcal{H}\,R^{-} - i\,\hbar\; R\left(-\,i\,\hbar^{-1}\,\mathcal{H}_0\,R^{-}\right)$$

$$= R\,\mathcal{H}_0\,R^{-} + R\,\mathcal{H}_1\,R^{-} - R\,\mathcal{H}_0\,R^{-} = R\,\mathcal{H}_1\,R^{-} .$$

We see that, by virtue of the transition to the interaction representation, we are free of $\mathcal{H}_0$ and that in this representation the Liouville-von Neumann equation takes on the simple form

$$\dot{\rho}' = i\,\hbar^{-1}\left[\,\rho', R\,\mathcal{H}_1\,R^{-}\,\right] \qquad (33.8)$$

in which $\mathcal{H}_0$ does not appear. The advantage is that (33.8) is often much easier to solve than (33.1). Having calculated $\rho'$ we can, if required, obtain $\rho$ from

$$\rho = R^{-}\,\rho'\,R$$

but often the knowledge of $\rho'$ alone leads to a satisfactory clarification of the problem in hand.

By writing (33.1) as a sum $\dot{\rho} = i\hbar^{-1}\left[\rho, \mathcal{H}_o\right] + i\hbar^{-1}\left[\rho, \mathcal{H}_1\right]$ we can see that the rate of change of the density operator consists of two contributions: one induced by $\mathcal{H}_o$ and the other by $\mathcal{H}_1$. By contrast, the interaction frame moves in such a way that motion induced by $\mathcal{H}_o$ is absent.

When $\mathcal{H}_o$ is taken to be the Zeeman interaction with the external magnetic field $\mathbf{B}_o \,||\, Z$, i.e. when

$$\mathcal{H}_o = \omega_0 I_z$$

where $\omega_0 = -\gamma B_o$, then the operator of transition to the interaction system is the operator of rotation about the Z axis (see Section 32)

$$R = \exp\left(i\,\omega_0\, t\, I_z\right). \tag{33.9}$$

We see therefore that transition to the rotating frame of reference is a special case of the interaction representation.

Transition to the interaction representation changes the time dependence of $\mathcal{H}_1$. Often this enables one to establish which components of $R\mathcal{H}R^-$ may be discarded, thereby simplifying calculations. Take as an example the interaction of a spin with an oscillating radiofrequency field generated by a coil aligned along the X axis through which there passes a current of frequency $\nu_e$ and consider this interaction as $\mathcal{H}_1$

$$\mathcal{H}_1 = 2\omega_1 \hbar\, I_x \cos\left(\omega_e t\right)$$

where $\omega_1 = -\gamma B_1$ and $2B_1$ is the amplitude of the oscillating field and $|\omega_e| = 2\pi\,\nu_e$. We go over to the interaction representation using the operator (33.9) and applying the well known trigonometric relationships

$$\cos\alpha \cos\beta = \frac{1}{2}\left[\cos\left(\alpha+\beta\right) + \cos\left(\alpha-\beta\right)\right]$$

$$\sin\alpha \cos\beta = \frac{1}{2}\left[\sin\left(\alpha+\beta\right) + \sin\left(\alpha-\beta\right)\right]$$

we find

$$R\mathcal{H}_1 R^- = \omega_1 \hbar\, I_x \left[\cos\left(\omega_0 + \omega_e\right) t + \cos\left(\omega_0 - \omega_e\right) t\right]$$

$$- \omega_1 \hbar\, I_y \left[\sin\left(\omega_0 + \omega_e\right) t + \sin\left(\omega_0 - \omega_e\right) t\right]. \qquad (33.10)$$

If we assume that the frequency is on resonance, i.e. that $\omega_0 + |\omega_e| = 0$ and $\omega_0 - |\omega_e| = 2\omega_0$ for $\gamma > 0$ and $\omega_0 + |\omega_e| = 2\omega_0$ and $\omega_0 - |\omega_e| = 0$ for $\gamma < 0$, equation (33.10) takes the form

$$R\mathcal{H}_1 R^- = \omega_1 \hbar \left[I_x + I_x \cos\left(2\omega_0 t\right) - I_y \sin\left(2\omega_0 t\right)\right] \qquad (33.11)$$

in which the sum of the last two terms in the square brackets is the projection of a vector rotating around the Z axis in the sense opposite to that of the precession of the spins. These terms (known as "non-secular terms") can be discarded, because they oscillate at a very high frequency about zero and thus have a vanishingly small influence on the solution of the differential equation (33.8).

Discarding the non-secular terms and substituting (33.11) in (33.8) we obtain

$$\dot{\rho}' = i\, \omega_1 \left[\rho', I_x\right]$$

with the solution

$$\rho'(t) = \exp\left(-i\, \omega_1 I_x t\right) \rho'(0) \exp\left(i\, \omega_1 I_x t\right).$$

We know from Section 32 that for $\gamma > 0$ such time dependence of the density operator in the rotating coordinate frame results in precession of the magnetization about the X' axis in the direction which forms a left-handed screw with this axis.

## 34. The Fourier Transformation

The starting point of Fourier transform NMR (often abbreviated as FT NMR) is the theorem discovered by Jean Baptiste Joseph Fourier in 1807 and published in 1822. We will not give the proof of Fourier's theorem itself, but we will dwell on its implications in some detail. More information can be found in various textbooks (e.g. Bracewell 1965).

Consider a real or complex function f (t) which has a finite number of discontinuities in any finite interval, and is integrable and integrable in quadrature, so that the integrals

$$\int_{-\infty}^{+\infty} f(t)\,dt \quad \text{and} \quad \int_{-\infty}^{+\infty} |f(t)|^2\,dt$$

exist. The Fourier transform of f (t) is another function F (ω), such that

$$F(\omega) = \frac{1}{2\pi} \int_{-\infty}^{+\infty} f(t) \exp\left(-i\,\omega\,t\right) dt\,. \tag{34.1}$$

The above formula can be written in a shorter form using the Fourier transform operator $\mathfrak{F}$

$$F(\omega) = \mathfrak{F}\, f(t)\,.$$

Fourier's theorem states that f (t) can be expressed in terms of its Fourier transform as follows

$$f(t) = \int_{-\infty}^{+\infty} F(\omega) \exp\left(i\,\omega\,t\right) d\omega \tag{34.2}$$

which is written in a shorter form using the operator $\mathfrak{F}^-$

$$f(t) = \mathfrak{F}^-\, F(\omega)\,.$$

The inverse transformation $\mathfrak{F}^-$ has the property that $\mathfrak{F}^- \mathfrak{F}\, f(t) = f(t)$.

The Fourier transformation is composed of the cosine Fourier transform

$$F_{\cos}(\omega) = \frac{1}{2\pi} \int_{-\infty}^{+\infty} f(t) \cos\left(\omega\,t\right) dt$$

and the sine Fourier transform

$$F_{\sin}(\omega) = \frac{1}{2\pi} \int_{-\infty}^{+\infty} f(t) \sin(-\omega t)\, dt .$$

This is because (34.1) can be written as

$$F(\omega) = \int_{-\infty}^{+\infty} f(t) \left[\cos(-\omega t) + i \sin(-\omega t)\right] dt = F_{\cos}(\omega) + i\, F_{\sin}(\omega) .$$

Fourier's theorem finds many applications in various areas of physics, in which the precise meaning of the variable t and of the functions f (t) and F (ω) may differ. In NMR the variable t signifies time, and f (t) is the time-dependent physical quantity which is being measured. To be more precise, f (t) is derived from two simultaneous measurements, one of which determines its real part, $\mathrm{Re}\left[f(t)\right]$, and the other its imaginary part, $\mathrm{Im}\left[f(t)\right]$. Only when we know that one of the measurements must yield zero for all t, the function f (t) is purely real or purely imaginary, and a single measurement is sufficient to determine its value for a given value of t.

Our further arguments require that certain terminology be established first. Thus by a "circular function" we shall understand the function $\exp\left[i(\omega t + \varphi)\right]$. It can be interpreted as a vector of unit length on the Argand diagram (Appendix 1), which rotates with the angular velocity ω, and with projections on the X and Y axes of $\cos(\omega t + \varphi)$ and $\sin(\omega t + \varphi)$, respectively. The angular velocity ω can be positive or negative, depending on whether the direction of rotation forms with the Z axis a right or a left screw, respectively. In accordance with the accepted custom we shall refer to ω as *angular frequency*. We have therefore $|\omega| = 2\pi\nu$, because the frequency $\nu$ (number of revolutions per second) cannot be negative. Adding the constant φ, known as the "phase shift", is equivalent to shifting the time scale $t' = t + \varphi/\omega$ or to multiplying by the phase factor $z = \exp(i\varphi)$.

Multiplication of the circular function by a real periodic function, as for example in the product $\cos(\omega_m t) \exp\left[i(\omega t + \varphi)\right]$, is known as "amplitude modulation". When the circular function is multiplied by a complex periodic function, as for example in the product $\exp(i\omega_m t) \exp\left[i(\omega t + \varphi)\right]$, we have "phase modulation".

We shall begin by calculating the Fourier transform of a damped circular function with a phase shift $\varphi = 0$

$$f(t) = \exp\left(\frac{-|t|}{T_2}\right)\exp(i\,\omega_0\,t)$$

where $T_2 > 0$. From (34.1) we obtain

$$F(\omega) = \frac{1}{2\pi}\int_{-\infty}^{+\infty}\exp\left(\frac{-|t|}{T_2}\right)\exp\left[i(\omega_0 - \omega)\,t\right]dt$$

$$= \frac{1}{2\pi}\int_{-\infty}^{+\infty}\exp\left(\frac{-|t|}{T_2}\right)\cos\left[(\omega_0 - \omega)\,t\right]dt + \frac{i}{2\pi}\int_{-\infty}^{+\infty}\exp\left(\frac{-|t|}{T_2}\right)\sin\left[(\omega_0 - \omega)\,t\right]dt\,.$$

The second integral (the sine Fourier transformation) vanishes because $\sin(-\alpha) = -\sin(\alpha)$, while to the first integral we apply the equality true for $a > 0$

$$\int_{0}^{+\infty}\exp(-a\,x)\cos(m\,x)\,dx = \frac{a}{a^2 + m^2}$$

to obtain the absorption curve discussed in Section 28

$$F(\omega) = \frac{1}{\pi}\,\frac{T_2}{1 + T_2^2(\omega_0 - \omega)^2}$$

with a maximum at $\omega = \omega_0$. The area under this curve can be calculated from

$$\int_{0}^{+\infty}\frac{a}{a^2 + m^2}\,dm = \frac{\pi}{2}$$

giving

$$\int_{-\infty}^{+\infty}F(\omega)\,d\omega = 1\,.$$

This means that the area is independent of $T_2$. However, the *steepness* of the curve does depend on $T_2$. When $T_2$ tends to infinity, we have

$$F(\omega) \rightarrow \delta(\omega_0 - \omega)$$

according to the definition of Dirac's δ function (Appendix 4). Also

$$\exp\left(-t/T_2\right) \rightarrow 1$$

so that we can write for the limiting case

$$\frac{1}{2\pi} \int_{-\infty}^{+\infty} \exp\left[i(\omega_0 - \omega)t\right] dt = \delta(\omega_0 - \omega)$$

and also

$$\frac{1}{2\pi} \int_{-\infty}^{+\infty} \exp\left(i\,\omega\, t\right) dt = \delta(\omega)\,.$$

Two circular functions

$$f_1(t) = \frac{1}{\sqrt{2\pi}} \exp\left(i\,\omega_1 t\right) \qquad \text{and} \qquad f_2(t) = \frac{1}{\sqrt{2\pi}} \exp\left(i\,\omega_2 t\right)$$

are mutually orthonormal, since

$$\int_{-\infty}^{+\infty} f_1^*(t)\, f_2(t)\, dt = \frac{1}{2\pi} \int_{-\infty}^{+\infty} \exp\left[i(\omega_2 - \omega_1)t\right] dt = \delta(\omega_2 - \omega_1)\,.$$

As another example, we calculate the Fourier transform of a linear combination of two circular functions $g(t) = a_1 f_1(t) + a_2 f_2(t)$, where $a_1$ and $a_2$ are complex constants. Thus

$$F(\omega) = \frac{1}{2\pi} \int_{-\infty}^{+\infty} g(t) \exp\left(-i\,\omega\,t\right) dt = \frac{1}{2\pi} \int_{-\infty}^{+\infty} \left[a_1 f_1(t) + a_2 f_2(t)\right] \exp\left(-i\,\omega\,t\right) dt$$

$$= a_1\, \delta(\omega_1 - \omega) + a_2\, \delta(\omega_2 - \omega)\,.$$

We see that Fourier transformation enables us to expand a given function in terms of circular functions, by finding their angular velocities and coefficients of expansion. We can therefore treat the Fourier transformation as a sort of mathematical analysis, and apply it to a given function in order to discover which frequencies appear in it, and with what amplitudes and phases.

In the above example we were dealing with discrete values of $\omega$. However, this is a special case. In general, we deal with a continuum of values of $\omega$, and the function $F(\omega)$ is continuous. In this case, in order to expand function $f(t)$ into a series of circular functions, we must first divide the entire domain of the variable $\omega$ into very small intervals and assume that the interval from $\omega$ to $\omega + d\omega$ gives rise to the term $F(\omega) \exp\left(-i\,\omega\,t\right) d\omega$. Summing over all intervals and using the limit $d\omega \to 0$ we obtain the integral

$$f(t) = \int_{-\infty}^{+\infty} F(\omega) \exp\left(i\,\omega\,t\right) d\omega\,.$$

Such is the meaning of equation (34.2).

In further sections we shall deal with functions $f(t)$ which represent a signal[1] induced by a spin system. Normally this signal begins at a specific time which we take to correspond to $t = 0$. Thus $f(t) \equiv 0$ for $t < 0$, and integration (34.1) *can begin from zero* instead of minus infinity. Consider the case when for $t > 0$ the function $f(t)$ is the damped circular function with $\varphi = 0$, so that $f(t) = \exp\left(-t/T_2\right) \exp\left(i\,\omega_0\,t\right)$. We have

$$\mathcal{F}\left\{\exp\left(-t/T_2\right) \exp\left(i\,\omega_0\,t\right)\right\} = a + i\,b$$

[1] By "signal" we understand a voltage which carries information about the spectrum.

where

$$a = \frac{1}{2\pi} \int_0^{+\infty} \exp\left(-t/T_2\right) \cos\left[\left(\omega_0 - \omega\right) t\right] dt$$

$$= \frac{T_2}{2\pi} \frac{1}{1 + T_2^2 \left(\omega_0 - \omega\right)^2} = \frac{T_2}{2\pi} \operatorname{abs}\left(\omega_0 \mid \omega\right) \qquad (34.3a)$$

$$b = \frac{1}{2\pi} \int_0^{+\infty} \exp\left(-t/T_2\right) \sin\left[\left(\omega_0 - \omega\right) t\right] dt$$

$$= \frac{T_2}{2\pi} \frac{T_2\left(\omega_0 - \omega\right)}{1 + T_2^2 \left(\omega_0 - \omega\right)^2} = \frac{T_2}{2\pi} \operatorname{dsp}\left(\omega_0 \mid \omega\right). \qquad (34.3b)$$

Integral (34.3b) was calculated using the well known formula valid for $a > 0$

$$\int_0^{+\infty} \exp(-ax) \sin(mx)\, dx = \frac{m}{a^2 + m^2}.$$

We finally obtain

$$\mathcal{F}\left\{\exp\left(-t/T_2\right) \exp\left(i\, \omega_0\, t\right)\right\} = \frac{T_2}{2\pi}\left[\operatorname{abs}\left(\omega_0 \mid \omega\right) + i \operatorname{dsp}\left(\omega_0 \mid \omega\right)\right]. \qquad (34.3c)$$

On the other hand, when $\varphi \neq 0$ both the real and the imaginary parts of the Fourier transform are linear combinations of absorption and dispersion

$$\mathcal{F}\left\{\exp\left(-t/T_2\right) \exp\left(i\, \omega_0\, t + \varphi\right)\right\} = \frac{T_2}{2\pi}\left[\operatorname{abs}\left(\omega_0 \mid \omega\right) \cos\varphi - \operatorname{dsp}\left(\omega_0 \mid \omega\right) \sin\varphi\right]$$

$$+\, i\, \frac{T_2}{2\pi}\left[\operatorname{abs}\left(\omega_0 \mid \omega\right) \sin\varphi + \operatorname{dsp}\left(\omega_0 \mid \omega\right) \cos\varphi\right].$$

These results are of considerable importance to NMR spectroscopy.

Note that according to the definition of the functions $\operatorname{abs}(\omega_0 \mid \omega)$ and $\operatorname{dsp}(\omega_0 \mid \omega)$, $\omega_0$ is the value of the variable $\omega$ for which $\operatorname{abs}(\omega_0 \mid \omega)$ is at a maximum and the value of $\operatorname{dsp}(\omega_0 \mid \omega)$ is zero. These functions are the Lorentzian absorption curve L (x) and the dispersion curve Q (x), both known from Section 28. Indeed, with the substitution $\Gamma = T_2$, $x_0 = -\omega_0$ and $x = -\omega$ we have

$$A^{-1} L(x) = \text{abs}(\omega_0 \mid \omega)$$

$$B^{-1} Q(x) = \text{dsp}(\omega_0 \mid \omega) .$$

In two-dimensional NMR spectroscopy the result of a measurement is a complex function of two time variables, $f(t_1, t_2)$. This function is subjected to the so-called two-dimensional Fourier transformation

$$\mathfrak{F}_2 f(t_1, t_2) = \frac{1}{(2\pi)^2} \int_{-\infty}^{+\infty} dt_1 \int_{-\infty}^{+\infty} dt_2 \, f(t_1, t_2) \exp\left(-i\,\omega_1 t_1\right) \exp\left(-i\,\omega_2 t_2\right) .$$

In this case the Fourier transformation is a function of two angular frequency variables $\omega_1$ and $\omega_2$

$$\mathfrak{F}_2 f(t_1, t_2) = F(\omega_1, \omega_2) .$$

In NMR we often come across functions of two variables which can be represented as a product of two functions, each of a single variable: $f(t_1, t_2) = f_1(t_1)\, f_2(t_2)$. In the case at hand, we can treat the two-dimensional Fourier transformation as a product of two one-dimensional transformations

$$F(\omega_1, \omega_2) = \frac{1}{2\pi} \int_{-\infty}^{+\infty} f_1(t_1) \exp\left(-i\,\omega_1 t_1\right) dt_1 \; \frac{1}{2\pi} \int_{-\infty}^{+\infty} f_2(t_2) \exp\left(-i\,\omega_2 t_2\right) dt_2 .$$

This leads to a considerable simplification of theoretical calculations. Unfortunately, the computer which calculates the spectrum cannot take advantage of this simplification, because measurements yield the values of the product $f_1(t_1)\, f_2(t_2)$, rather than of $f_1(t_1)$ and $f_2(t_2)$ separately. As discussed in Section 40, this leads to difficulties in obtaining suitable lineshapes in two-dimensional spectra.

## 35. Spectrum of a Pulse

It may seem paradoxical, but a pulse of a single strictly defined frequency, $\omega_e$, contains a continuous spectrum of many frequencies. This is because a truncated cosine curve is no longer a cosine, but a completely different function defined as follows

$$f(t) = 0 \qquad \text{for } t < -\tau/2$$

$$f(t) = 0 \qquad \text{for } t > \tau/2$$

$$f(t) = A\cos(\omega_e t + \varphi) = \frac{A}{2}\left\{\exp\left[i(\omega_e t + \varphi)\right] + \exp\left[-i(\omega_e t + \varphi)\right]\right\}$$

$$\text{for } -\tau/2 \le t \le \tau/2 .$$

The Fourier transform of f (t) is

$$\frac{A}{2\pi}\int_{-\infty}^{+\infty} f(t)\exp(-i\omega t)\,dt = \exp(i\varphi)\,a_1(\omega) + \exp(-i\varphi)\,a_2(\omega)$$

where

$$a_1(\omega) = \frac{A}{4\pi}\int_{-\tau/2}^{\tau/2}\exp\left[i(\omega_e - \omega)t\right]dt = \frac{A}{4\pi}\int_{-\tau/2}^{\tau/2}\left[\cos(\omega_e - \omega)t + i\sin(\omega_e - \omega)t\right]dt .$$

The imaginary part of the transform is antisymmetric, which means that its integral is zero. We have therefore

$$a_1(\omega) = \frac{A}{4\pi}\left[\frac{\left[\sin(\omega_e - \omega)t\right]}{\omega_e - \omega}\right]_{-\tau/2}^{\tau/2} = \frac{A\tau}{4\pi}\,\frac{\sin\left[(\omega_e - \omega)\tau/2\right]}{(\omega_e - \omega)\tau/2} . \qquad (35.1)$$

In an analogous manner we find that

$$a_2(\omega) = \frac{A\tau}{4\pi}\,\frac{\sin\left[(-\omega_e - \omega)\tau/2\right]}{(-\omega_e - \omega)\tau/2} . \qquad (35.2)$$

The expressions (35.1) and (35.2) involve the so-called sinc function

$$\operatorname{sinc} x = \frac{\sin x}{x}$$

which has the absolute maximum at x = 0, since $\lim \left[(\sin x)/x\right] = 1$ for $x \to 0$. The plot of sinc x is given in Figure 35.1.

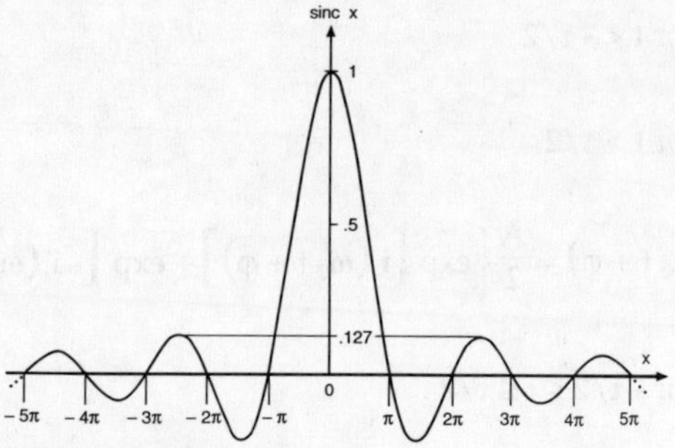


**Figure 35.1.** The plot of the function sinc x versus x.

The plots of the functions $a_1(\omega)$ and $a_2(\omega)$ are identical, but are centred at $\omega = \omega_e$ and $\omega = -\omega_e$, respectively. Neglecting the smaller side peaks we can approximately say that frequencies contained in the pulse are grouped in two separate compartments

$$\omega_e \pm 2\pi/\tau \qquad \text{and} \qquad -\omega_e \pm 2\pi/\tau\,.$$

The latter compartment lies far from the resonance and can be ignored. It is also clear that the pulse has a discrete spectrum in the limit of $\tau \to \infty$. In this case, the cosine curve is not truncated, so that the integrations in $a_1$ and $a_2$ extend from $-\infty$ to $+\infty$.

In Section 31 we considered the action of a radiofrequency pulse which satisfies the condition $\omega_e = -\gamma B_o$. In this case the effective field in the rotating frame coincides exactly with the axis of the pulse and has the amplitude $B_1$. However, the resonance condition cannot normally be satisfied exactly for all spins we wish to observe in the sample, because as a result of chemical shifts, spin-spin interactions and inhomogeneity of $\mathbf{B}_0$ their Larmor frequencies differ. The effective field around which spins precess in the rotating frame is shown in Figure 30.2(c) which corresponds to the resonance condition being satisfied. We see that the rotation of all observed spins in the sample by the same angle is possible only approximately. The smaller the resonance offset $|\omega_e - \omega_0|$ in comparison with the value of $\gamma B_1$, the smaller the inaccuracy. Therefore, if the condition

$$|\omega_e - \omega|_{max} << |\gamma B_1| \quad (35.3)$$

is satisfied, the pulse will rotate all spins by approximately the same angle. The pulse which satisfies (35.3) is known as a "hard" (or "non-selective") pulse.

Because of cost and technical difficulties, the manufacturers of NMR equipment resort to a compromise when it comes to satisfying the condition that the strongest possible field $B_1$ be used. We must bear in mind that the appearance of the effective field must be rapid, i.e. non-adiabatic in the sense of Section 30 (the pulse must have a short "rise time"). This requires the use of high power radiofrequency transmitters. Otherwise, magnetization of the sample will follow the slowly rising *effective* field and will not precess around the axis of the pulse. Also the termination of the pulse must be sudden. A discussion of these problems can be found in Clark (1964).

Consider now the relationship between the width of the NMR spectrum under study and the width of the spectrum of a hard pulse. Consider, for example, the $\pi$ pulse. Substituting $|\alpha| = \pi$ in (31.1) we obtain

$$2\pi/\tau = 2\,|\gamma B_1|\,.$$

Since a hard pulse satisfies (35.3), we can write

$$2\pi/\tau >> |\omega_e - \omega|\,.$$

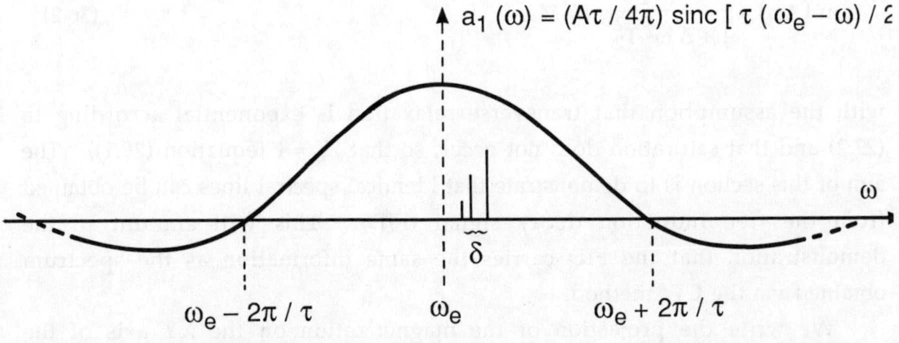


**Figure 35.2.** The measured spectrum of width $\delta$ and the spectrum of a hard pulse of duration $\tau$. Here the carrier frequency $\omega_e$ is placed outside the spectrum and, as a consequence, a half of the pulse spectrum is completely unused. Note that shifting $\omega_e$ to a point within the measured spectrum, especially close to the centre of interval $\delta$, will allow us to apply a pulse with much longer $\tau$.

This means that the measured spectrum is not only entirely contained under the main maximum of the function $a_1(\omega)$, but lies in its small region near the centre (see Figure 35.2). In this region the function $a_1(\omega)$ is weakly dependent on $\omega$. We therefore conclude that a hard impulse irradiates the sample with a continuous spectrum of frequency of approximately constant amplitude.

By (31.1), short $\tau$ implies large field $B_1$ and vice versa. It is thus convenient to reduce the value of $|\omega_e - \omega|_{max}$ by fixing $\omega_e$ in the vicinity of the centre of the spectrum which we desire to measure. However, this requires that we use equipment which can distinguish which frequencies in the spectrum are higher and which are lower than $\omega_e$. This device, known as the quadrature detector, is described in the next section.

## 36. Derivation of a Spectrum from a Free Induction Signal

We know from Section 29 that the shape of the absorption spectrum obtained in a slow passage through resonance (the CW method) is Lorentzian

$$v(\Delta\omega) = \frac{T_2}{1 + \Delta\omega^2 T_2^2} \gamma B_1 M_\infty \tag{36.1}$$

while the dispersion spectrum has the shape of the Q curve (Section 28)

$$u(\Delta\omega) = \frac{\Delta\omega T_2^2}{1 + \Delta\omega^2 T_2^2} \gamma B_1 M_\infty \tag{36.2}$$

with the assumption that transverse relaxation is exponential according to (22.2) and that saturation does not occur, so that $Z_0 = 1$ (equation (29.1)). The aim of this section is to demonstrate that identical spectral lines can be obtained from the free induction decay signal (FID). This will amount to the demonstration that the FID carries the same information as the spectrum obtained via the CW method.

We write the projection of the magnetization on the XY axis of the laboratory frame as the complex number $M_\perp = M_x + i M_y$ and as $M_{\perp'} = M_{x'} + i M_{y'}$ in the frame rotating around the Z axis with angular frequency $\omega_e$. We assume that $\omega_e$ is not very different from the Larmor frequency $-\gamma B_0$. The absolute value of $\omega_e$ is determined by the carrier frequency $|\omega_e| = 2\pi\nu_e$ generated by the spectrometer. The relationship between the so-defined quantities is

$$M_\perp = M_{\perp'} \exp\left[ i (\omega_e t + \varphi)\right]$$

where $\varphi$ is the angle between the coordinate systems at t = 0.

In the rotating frame, the action of the $P_x$ pulse consists of rotating the vector $M_\infty$ from the position parallel to the Z axis to the position along the +Y axis. This means that just after the end of the pulse

$$M_\perp' = i\, M_\infty$$

because then $M_x' = 0$ and $M_y' = M_\infty$. Very close to that moment, before the magnetization has the time to leave the +Y' axis, the spectrometer begins to measure the time. The value of the angle $\varphi$ depends on which moment the spectrometer chooses as the origin of the time axis. It follows that in the laboratory frame we have at time t = 0

$$M_\perp = i\, M_\infty \exp\left(i\,\varphi\right).$$

Precession of the magnetization in the external magnetic field at the Larmor angular frequency and in the presence of transverse relaxation described by $\exp\left(-t/T_2\right)$ begins at that same moment. As a result, the motion of the magnetization in the laboratory and the rotating frames is described by

$$M_\perp(t) = i\, M_\infty \exp\left(-t/T_2\right) \exp\left[i\left(\omega_i\, t + \varphi\right)\right] \qquad (36.3a)$$

$$M_\perp'(t) = i\, M_\infty \exp\left(-t/T_2\right) \exp\left[i\left(\omega_i - \omega_e\right) t\right]. \qquad (36.3b)$$

Nuclei of the same kind in the sample may have slightly different Larmor frequencies $-\gamma B_0$ as a result of the chemical shift. The Larmor frequency of the ith nucleus under consideration will be denoted by $\omega_i$.

According to (17.3) with the substitution H = 0 (because we assume that no current flows through the coil), magnetization $M_\perp(t)$ rotating in the laboratory frame generates magnetic induction $\mu_0 M_\perp(t)$. In practice the coil is part of an RLC resonant circuit, but the current flowing through it is so small that its influence on the magnetization can be neglected.

Assume that the axis of the coil is collinear with the X axis of the laboratory frame. Then the component $\left(B_\perp\right)_x = \mathrm{Re}\, B_\perp$ penetrates the coil and induces in it an electromotive force. From Faraday's law (10.3) the voltage $U_{FID}$ generated in the coil is

$$U_{FID} = - S\,n\,\zeta \frac{d}{dt}(B_\perp)_x$$

$$= S\,n\,\zeta\,\mu_0\,M_\infty \left[ T_2^{-1} \exp\left(-t/T_2\right) \cos\left(\omega_i t + \varphi + \pi/2\right)\right.$$

$$\left. + \,\omega_i \exp\left(-t/T_2\right) \sin\left(\omega_i t + \varphi + \pi/2\right)\right]$$

where S is the cross-sectional area of the coil, n is the number of turns and $\zeta$ is the filling factor. In general $T_2^{-1} << \omega_i$, so that the first term can be neglected in comparison with the second and we obtain

$$U_{FID} = A \exp\left(-t/T_2\right) \cos\left(\omega_i t + \varphi\right) \tag{36.4}$$

where $A = S\,n\,\zeta\,\mu_0\,M_\infty\,\omega_i$. Equation (36.4) describes the time evolution of the FID. As the coil is part of an RLC circuit, there is a phase shift between the electromotive force and the measured voltage, which affects the value of $\varphi$. The value of the amplitude A is also changed.

A similar calculation of the voltage induced by precessing magnetization continuously subjected to the oscillating field ("CW") was given in Section 26.

After amplification the signal enters a device known as the quadrature detector (Figure 36.1). One of its functions is the reduction of the frequency of the signal. The quadrature detector is composed of two channels, A and B, in which the signal is respectively multiplied by voltages $\cos(\omega_e t)$ and $-\sin(\omega_e t)$ (known as reference voltages) coming from the generator of the carrier frequency $\omega_e$. The reference voltages must have the same amplitude, and differ in phase by precisely $\pi/2$, which is achieved using a phase shifter. The principle of the voltage multiplying circuit is shown in Figure 36.2.

In each channel the result of the multiplication is then integrated using the integrating circuit shown in Figure 36.3. Integration is carried out continuously over a time period $\delta t$ beginning at an arbitrary moment. It is not necessary to know $\delta t$ exactly, but it is essential that the following two conditions are met

$$\frac{2\pi}{|\omega + \omega_e|} << \delta t << \frac{2\pi}{|\omega - \omega_e|}$$

$$\delta t << T_2 .$$

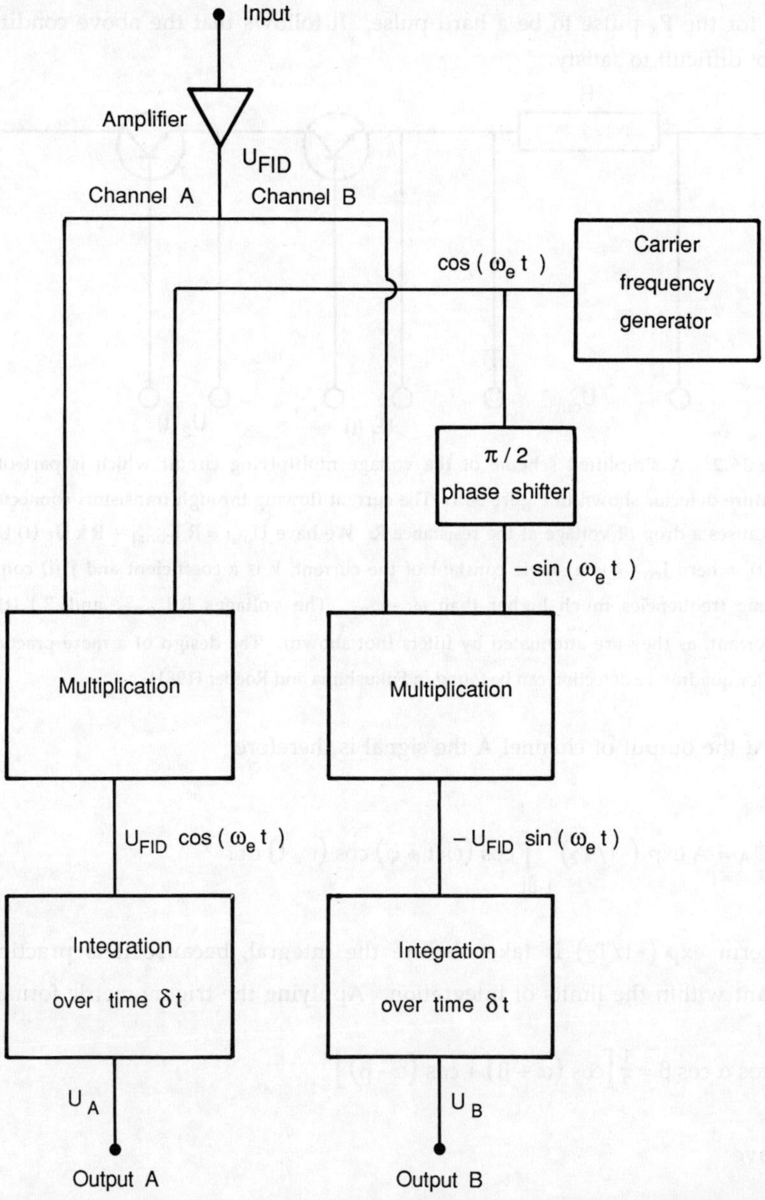


**Figure 36.1.** The quadrature detector has two identical channels known as phase-sensitive detectors. In each, the amplified FID signal is multiplied by the so-called reference signal, and then integrated. Both reference signals come from the generator of the carrier frequency, but are shifted in phase by $\pi/2$ with respect to each other. Principles of operation of multiplying and integrating circuits are given in Figures 36.2 and 36.3, respectively.

We know from Section 35 that the difference $|\omega - \omega_e|$ must be sufficiently small for the $P_x$ pulse to be a hard pulse. It follows that the above conditions are not difficult to satisfy.

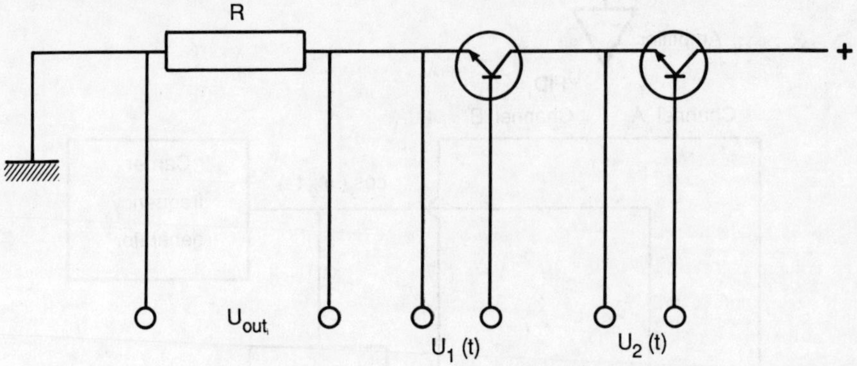


**Figure 36.2.** A simplified scheme of the voltage multiplying circuit which is part of the quadrature detector shown in Figure 36.1. The current flowing through transistors connected in series causes a drop of voltage at the resistance R. We have $U_{out} = R\,J_{const} + R\,k\,U_1(t)\,U_2(t) + R\,J'(t)$, where $J_{const}$ is a stable constant of the current, k is a coefficient and J' (t) contains harmonic frequencies much higher than $\omega_i - \omega_e$. The voltages $R\,J_{const}$ and $R\,J'(t)$ are unimportant, as they are attenuated by filters (not shown). The design of a more practicable device for quadrature detection can be found in Fukushima and Roeder (1981).

At the output of channel A the signal is therefore

$$U_A = A \exp\left(-t/T_2\right) \int_{t-\delta t}^{t} \cos\left(\omega_i t + \varphi\right) \cos\left(\omega_e t\right) dt .$$

The term $\exp\left(-t/T_2\right)$ is taken before the integral, because it is practically constant within the limits of integration. Applying the trigonometric formula

$$\cos\alpha\cos\beta = \frac{1}{2}\left[\cos\left(\alpha+\beta\right) + \cos\left(\alpha-\beta\right)\right]$$

we have

$$U_A = \frac{1}{2} A \exp\left(-t/T_2\right) \int_{t-\delta t}^{t} \cos\left[\left(\omega_i + \omega_e\right) t + \varphi\right] dt$$

$$+ \frac{1}{2} A \exp\left(-t/T_2\right) \int_{t-\delta t}^{t} \cos\left[\left(\omega_i - \omega_e\right) t + \varphi\right] dt .$$

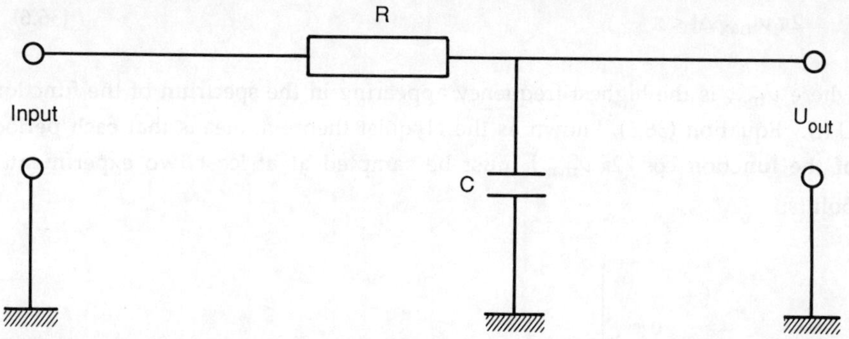


**Figure 36.3.** The integrating circuit which is part of the quadrature detector shown in Figure 36.1. The voltage U (t) applied to the input causes a flow of electric charges through resistor R and their accumulation in the capacitor C. Simultaneously, the capacitor discharges through R at a rate proportional to exp (- t/RC). We assume that the resistance of the source of the voltage is close to zero. At any given moment t, the voltage at the capacitor (i.e. at the output) is approximately equal to the integral $\int_{t-\delta t}^{t} U(t')\,dt'$ (where $\delta t = RC$), and depends very little on U (t') for $t' << t - \delta t$.

The first term can be neglected because $\omega_i + \omega_e$ is very large and the integral of every complete period vanishes. On the other hand, in the second term the integrand is practically constant in the entire interval $\delta t$ and can be taken before the sign of the integral. We have therefore

$$U_A = A \exp\left(-t/T_2\right) \cos\left(\Omega_i t + \varphi\right) \tag{36.5a}$$

where $\Omega_i = \omega_i - \omega_e$, and the coefficient $\delta t/2$ is now incorporated in the constant A. In a completely analogous manner we show that at the output of channel B

$$U_B = -A \exp\left(-t/T_2\right) \sin\left(\Omega_i t + \varphi\right). \tag{36.5b}$$

Signals $U_A$ (t) and $U_B$ (t), which appear during the course of the experiment, that is "in real time", are sampled at evenly spaced time intervals as shown in Figure 36.4. The results, in the form of pairs of numbers, are sent into the memory of a computer. In this way, the computer receives information about a continuous function $U_A$ (t) as an array of discrete values $U_A(t_1), U_A(t_2), U_A(t_3), \ldots, U_A(t_N)$. The same applies to the function $U_B$ (t). According to the sampling theory (Bracewell 1965), the above array contains complete information about the function U (t) provided that the time interval between the successive measurements $\Delta t = t_{i+1} - t_i$ (often referred to as "dwell time") satisfies the condition

$$2\pi\,\nu_{max}\,\Delta t < \pi \tag{36.6}$$

where $\nu_{max}$ is the highest frequency appearing in the spectrum of the function U (t). Equation (36.6), known as the Nyquist theorem, means that each period of the function $\cos\left(2\pi\,\nu_{max}\right)$ must be sampled at at least two experimental points.

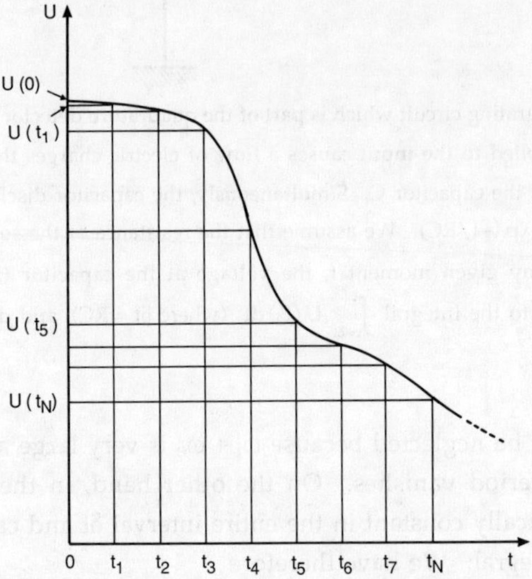


**Figure 36.4.** The sampling of signals. A time-dependent quantity U (t) (here the voltage) is measured at equal time intervals $t_{n+1} - t_n = \Delta t$. We assume that time taken for a single measurement is negligibly short. The series of results U (0), U ($t_1$), ... , U ($t_N$) is equivalent to a continuous function U (t) provided that the Nyquist condition (36.6) is satisfied.

When condition (36.6) is satisfied, we can describe the role of the computer as if it were dealing with continuous functions, although in reality it handles discrete values. Readers interested in the ways in which the Fourier transformation is performed by computers may wish to consult Cooley and Tukey (1965) and Brigham (1974).

The computer treats real functions $U_A$ (t) and $U_B$ (t) as parts of a complex function Z (t)

$$Z(t) = U_A(t) - i\,U_B(t)\,. \tag{36.7}$$

According to (36.5)

$$Z(t) = A\exp\left(-t/T_2\right)\exp\left(i\,\Omega_i\,t\right)\exp\left(i\,\varphi\right) \tag{36.8}$$

where A is a real constant. The computer first multiplies Z (t) by the phase factor $\exp(i\alpha)$ (the so-called "phase correction"), where the number $\alpha$ can be chosen arbitrarily, and then Fourier transforms the product. In the special case of $\alpha + \varphi = 0$ we have

$$\mathcal{F} Z(t) = \frac{1}{2\pi} \int_{-\infty}^{+\infty} Z(t) \exp(-i\,\omega\, t)\, dt .$$

However, for $t < 0$ and $t > N\,\Delta t$ we have $Z(t) = 0$, because the signal begins at time $t = 0$ and because after time $N\,\Delta t$ the signal is no longer being observed. Assume for simplicity that relaxation reduces the signal to nearly zero even before sampling is completed, so that $N\,\Delta t >> T_2$. Integration can then be carried out to infinity, which enables us to use (34.3c)

$$\mathcal{F} Z(t) = \frac{A}{2\pi} \int_{0}^{\infty} \exp(-t/T_2) \exp\left[i\,(\Omega_i - \omega)\, t\right] dt$$

$$= \frac{A\,T_2}{2\pi} \left[\mathrm{abs}\,(\Omega_i \,|\, \omega) + i\,\mathrm{dsp}\,(\Omega_i \,|\, \omega)\right]. \qquad (36.9)$$

This result appears on the computer screen as a function of $\omega$ in the form of the separate plots of the real and the imaginary parts. It is clear that the real part is an absorption curve (36.1) and the imaginary part a dispersion curve (36.2). If sampling were to be completed after a time shorter than or comparable with $T_2$, the resulting curves would be broadened. This is because, as we know from Section 34, truncation of a cosine wave results in the broadening of its spectrum.

We conclude that the FID contains information about the spectrum, which is obtained by subjecting it to the Fourier transformation. This means that the CW method described in Chapter 5 and the pulse method (known as Fourier transform NMR) described in the present section are exactly equivalent.

We have demonstrated this equivalence for the case in which transverse relaxation is exponential. The spectrum then consists of a single Lorentzian line. In fact the equivalence of the two methods of measurement is much more general and applies also to the case when the spectrum is composed of many lines. For example, when the sample contains several kinds of nuclei of the same species such as $^1H$, which do not interact with one another and have different resonance frequencies as a result of different chemical shifts, the complex signal Z (t) is given by the sum

$$Z(t) = U_A(t) - i\,U_B(t) = \sum_i A_i \exp\left(-t/T_{2(i)}\right) \exp\left[i\left(\Omega_i t + \varphi\right)\right] \qquad (36.10)$$

the Fourier transform of which is a spectrum composed of separate lines. The equivalence of the two methods also applies when the shape of the spectrum is determined by the dipolar interaction. This will be demonstrated in Section 45 for a pair of interacting protons in a solid sample. A general proof can be found in Chapter 4 of Abragam (1983).

When $\varphi + \alpha \neq 0$ or $2\pi$, the real and imaginary parts of the function $\mathfrak{F}\,Z(t)$ are linear combinations of absorption and dispersion lines. A spectroscopist is interested in the value of $\Omega_i = \omega_i - \omega_e$, or in other words the position of the line on the frequency axis. Experience shows that the most convenient way of determining the value of $\omega_i - \omega_e$ is from the position of the maximum of the absorption line. It can also be determined from the dispersion line, but a linear combination of absorption and dispersion is very poorly suited for the purpose. In particular, it is important that the wings of the absorption curve decrease proportionately to $\omega^{-2}$, while the wings of the dispersion curve decrease as $\omega^{-1}$. As a result of this, in a spectrum composed of many lines, giving them the absorption shape leads to the minimum possible overlap of neighbouring lines and leads to the best possible resolution. This is why it is very important to fix the angle $\alpha = -\varphi$ precisely. This can be done by trial and error by repeating the Fourier transformation until the result is symmetric (absorption) or antisymmetric (dispersion). In modern NMR spectrometers this procedure is followed automatically by the computer.

When the spectrum is composed of separate lines, they can all be simultaneously given the same shape (for example absorption) only when the following two conditions are met:

1. The $\pi/2$ pulse must rotate all the spins simultaneously, independently of their resonance frequency $\omega_i$, so that at a certain moment all magnetization is aligned along the +Y' axis.
2. The computer chooses that moment as time origin $t = 0$ of the FID.

The use of a hard pulse ensures that condition 1 above is satisfied. If condition 2 is not satisfied, then on the wrong time scale $t' = t - \delta t$ (where $\delta t$ is the error) the complex signal has the form

$$Z(t') = \sum_i A_i \exp\left(\frac{-(t' + \delta t)}{T_2}\right) \exp\left\{i\left[\left(\omega_i - \omega_e\right) t' + \beta_i\right]\right\}$$

where $\beta_i = (\omega_i - \omega_e)\,\delta t + \varphi$. This shows that the phase shift depends on the frequency, and cannot be compensated for all spectral lines at the same time. In this situation we need to determine the error $\delta t$ and ask the computer to correct the time scale by this amount. We see from the above definition of $\beta_i$ that $\delta t$ can be found from the relationship

$$\delta t = \frac{\beta_i - \beta_j}{\omega_i - \omega_j}$$

where the subscripts refer to two different spectral lines. The determination of $\delta t$ is the most accurate when the two lines lie on either extremum of the spectrum.

Consider further some interesting aspects of pulsed NMR. As a consequence of (36.3b) and (36.7) the relationship between $M_{\perp'}(t)$ and $Z(t)$ is

$$-i \exp(i\varphi)\, M_{\perp'}(t) = b\, Z(t)$$

where b is real. It follows that the function $Z(t)$ determines the position of the magnetization in a rotating frame with a certain constant phase shift. The quadrature detector generating the signal $Z(t)$ is therefore an electronic equivalent of the transition from the laboratory frame, in which the signal is induced, to the rotating frame. Because of this transition we avoid the need to sample the very high-frequency signal (36.4) of frequency $\omega_i \approx -\gamma B_0$ and sample at a much lower "audiofrequency" of the order of $\omega_i - \omega_e$. Although this method limits us to the determination of the difference $\omega_i - \omega_e$, we can still gain information about $\omega_i$, since $\omega_e$ can be measured separately to a very high accuracy. The inconvenient aspect of the transition from the laboratory frame to the rotating frame is the appearance of the phase shift $\varphi$. Its magnitude depends on the design of the equipment and does not change in successive experiments, but is at the same time very difficult to calculate from the known parameters of the spectrometer. It must therefore be determined by trial and error on the basis of the observed lineshapes.

The word "quadrature" in the name of the device shown in Figure 36.1 refers to the $\pi/2$ phase difference between the reference signals at the input of the channels A and B. As we have seen, this is important for the formation of the complex function $Z(t) = U_A(t) - i\,U_B(t)$. Some spectrometers use single-channel detectors providing the spectroscopist with only one real function $U_A(t)$, which does not contain the complete information about the direction of magnetization in the rotating frame. We can demonstrate this by considering only those spins which precess with the same angular frequency $\omega_i$ and assume for simplicity that $\varphi = 0$. Then the Fourier transformation of the function $U_A(t)$ given by equation (36.5a) will give us two absorption signals, one at $(\omega_i - \omega_e)$ and the other at $-(\omega_i - \omega_e)$. This follows from Euler's equation

$$\cos \alpha = \frac{1}{2}\left[\exp\left(i\,\alpha\right) + \exp\left(-\,i\,\alpha\right)\right].$$

Given the function $U_A(t)$ alone we cannot therefore decide whether on the frequency scale $\omega_i$ is on the right or on the left of $\omega_e$. The computer takes into account both these possibilities, and the resulting spectrum is composed of two lines instead of one: the true signal and its reflection with respect to point $\omega_e$. This leads to serious complications in the interpretation of the spectra containing many lines, in which real lines cannot readily be distinguished from "aliased" (or "folded-over") lines.

There are two ways of dealing with this difficulty. If we choose the carrier frequency to lie outside the range of the spectrum to be measured, we will obtain two separate, non-overlapping spectra. Since one of them is the reflection of the other with respect to $\omega_e$, the directions of the $\omega$ axes in these spectra are opposite. In certain cases, for example when the structure of the sample substance is not completely unknown, we can simply guess the correct direction of the axes. The drawback of this method, however, is that the spectrum of noise is so wide that it is impossible to place $\omega_e$ outside it. As a result, the folded-over noise increases the amplitude of spectral noise by the factor of $\sqrt{2}$. Additionally, the choice of the carrier frequency beyond the range of resonance requires that the NMR pulse be sufficiently powerful for its spectrum to contain the entire experimental spectrum. Only a part of the spectrum of the pulse is then used for the excitation of the spin system (Figure 35.2 earlier). The second way of working with a single-channel detector consists of doing the measurement twice: once with a $P_x$ pulse and once with a $P_y$ pulse. The output of the detector in the first experiment is $U_A(t)$ and in the second experiment $U_B(t)$, so that one can form a complex function $Z(t)$. Also this method, known as "artificial quadrature detection", increases the noise by the factor of $\sqrt{2}$.

All NMR experiments consist of exciting the spins by a radiofrequency and observing the response to the excitation. The difference is that in the CW method the spins are excited by monochromatic radiation, the frequency of which is monotonically swept throughout the spectral range, while in the pulse method the entire spectrum is excited simultaneously. Because of this, the time needed for a measurement in the pulse method is much shorter, typically by a factor of 100. Ernst and Anderson (1966) realized the great practical importance of this. The "random-walk theorem" tells us that by summing the results of n identical experiments the signal increases by the factor of n, but the noise increases only by a factor of $\sqrt{n}$, so that the signal-to-noise (S/N) ratio also increases as $\sqrt{n}$. In practice this means that if a single NMR spectrum takes 100 minutes to measure, a four-fold increase in S/N requires 1600 minutes or 26.7 hours. When, however, the same spectrum can be measured in 1 minute (as is often the case in FT NMR), the same degree of improvement in S/N requires only 16 minutes. Thus the faster the method, the more accurate the result which can be obtained within a fixed time period. The discovery of Ernst and Anderson enlarged the scope of the applications of NMR in chemistry to nuclei of low value of $\gamma$ and of low abundance. For example, it is only the pulse method which made possible the enormous development of $^{13}C$ NMR, so important to organic chemistry.

For all its undoubted advantages, pulsed NMR does have certain drawbacks. The most important concerns the so-called "dead time" of the spectrometer: the time which elapses between the end of the $\pi/2$ pulse to the moment when the instrument is able to register the FID. To understand this effect we must consider that the voltage in the NMR coil during the pulse is generally of the order of 1 kV, while the induced signal is at most several hundred $\mu$V. Together with the receiver and the transmitter, the NMR coil is an RLC (resistance, induction and capacitance) circuit, the oscillation of which does not stop suddenly, but follows the law $\exp(-t/RC)$. The product, RC, of the resistance and capacitance, is known as the damping constant. For the voltage in the coil to fall to, say, 10 $\mu$V, when the measurement of the FID begins to be possible, we must wait for the time $t = 18RC$ known as the dead time. An additional factor which increases the dead time is the saturation recovery of the receiver.

The early part of the FID carries information about the highest frequencies, so that its loss during the dead time may lead to a distortion of the extremes of the spectrum. This drawback of pulse NMR is particularly serious for solid samples, the spectra of which are almost invariably much wider than those of liquids. There is considerable literature concerning dead times (Clark 1964). A typical dead time in a modern solid-state spectrometer is 4 $\mu$s, which permits the measurement of spectra up to 100 kHz wide. The CW method does not suffer from this particular limitation.

Finally, we return to the situation when the spectrum contains a number of lines as a result of different chemical shifts (i.e. different chemical environments) of the nucleus under observation. In this case the signal has the form of the sum (36.9). It is of great interest to the chemist to know whether the spectrum allows him or her to determine the fraction of the total number of nuclei which are responsible for a given line.

Consider the ith spectral line. If prior to the measurement the sample was at thermodynamic equilibrium, the amplitude $A_i$ is proportional to the magnetization of the ith kind of nucleus. However, after Fourier transformation the absorption line coming from these nuclei has the form (36.9)

$$\frac{A\, T_{2(i)}}{2\pi}\ \mathrm{abs}\,(\Omega_i \mid \omega)\,.$$

Since the maximum of abs $(\Omega_i \mid \omega)$ is 1, the height of the line is $A\, T_{2(i)}/2\pi$. We see therefore that the height of the line is not a good measure of the number of nuclei which contribute to it, because the value of $T_{2(i)}$ may be different for different lines. On the other hand, the area under the absorption line *is* proportional to the number of nuclei which contribute to it. This is because the area of the absorption line does not depend on the value of $T_2$ (see Section 34).

## 37. Comparison of CW and FT NMR Using a Mechanical Analogy

It is useful to make an analogy between the spin system and a damped harmonic oscillator. Imagine that we have a weight of mass m suspended on a spring. We fix one end of the spring firmly to the ceiling, place the weight in a viscous liquid, pull the weight downwards so as to stretch the spring away from its equilibrium position, and let go of the weight. The system will perform an oscillation damped by the friction of the weight in the liquid. We measure the number of oscillations as a function of time. This is known as the "transient" approach. According to Newton's second law, the time-independent force F, acting on the mass and dampened by frictional resistance proportional to the velocity of the moving mass, varies with distance x, measured from some arbitrary origin, as

$$F = m\frac{d^2x}{dt^2} = -\,k\,x - f\frac{dx}{dt} \tag{37.1}$$

where k is a constant and f is the coefficient of friction. To find the displacement at any given time, we need to solve the differential equation

$$m\frac{d^2x}{dt^2} + k\,x + f\frac{dx}{dt} = 0\,. \tag{37.2}$$

with an initial condition $x = x_0$, where $x_0$ is the displacement of the weight. The solution is

$$x = x_0 \exp\left(-t/\Gamma\right) \cos\left(W\ t\right) \tag{37.3}$$

where $\Gamma = 2m/f$ and $W = \sqrt{\omega_0^2 - (1/\Gamma)^2}$, and $\omega_0 = \sqrt{k/m}$ is the "natural" angular frequency of the mass (in the absence of damping). If damping is weak, $(1/\Gamma) << \omega_0$ and (37.3) simplifies to

$$x = x_0 \exp\left(-t/\Gamma\right) \cos\left(\omega_0\, t\right). \tag{37.4}$$

The mass displaced by $x_0$ at $t = 0$ will therefore oscillate at approximately its "natural" frequency $\omega_0$ with an amplitude which decreases exponentially with a time constant $\Gamma$, as shown in Figure 37.1.

It turns out that there is an alternative, but entirely equivalent, way of discovering what this natural frequency is. Thus in the "steady-state" approach, we attach the upper end of the spring to a motor, which will vibrate the system with a varying frequency: when the driving frequency is equal to the natural frequency, the weight will oscillate with a maximum amplitude. This experiment is equivalent to the CW method in NMR.

If the mass is subjected to a continuous driving force $F_0 \cos\left(\omega\, t\right)$, it will eventually settle into a steady oscillation at the driving frequency $\omega$. Note that according to (37.4) in the transient experiment the undriven mass will vibrate at the *natural* frequency $\omega_0$. However, the displacement of the driven spring will lag behind the driver as shown in Figure 37.1(c). It is convenient to decompose the steady-state displacement, x, into a sum of two components, x' (dispersion) and x'' (absorption), each oscillating at the driver frequency, which are in phase and $\pi/2$ out of phase with the driver, respectively (Figure 37.1(d)).

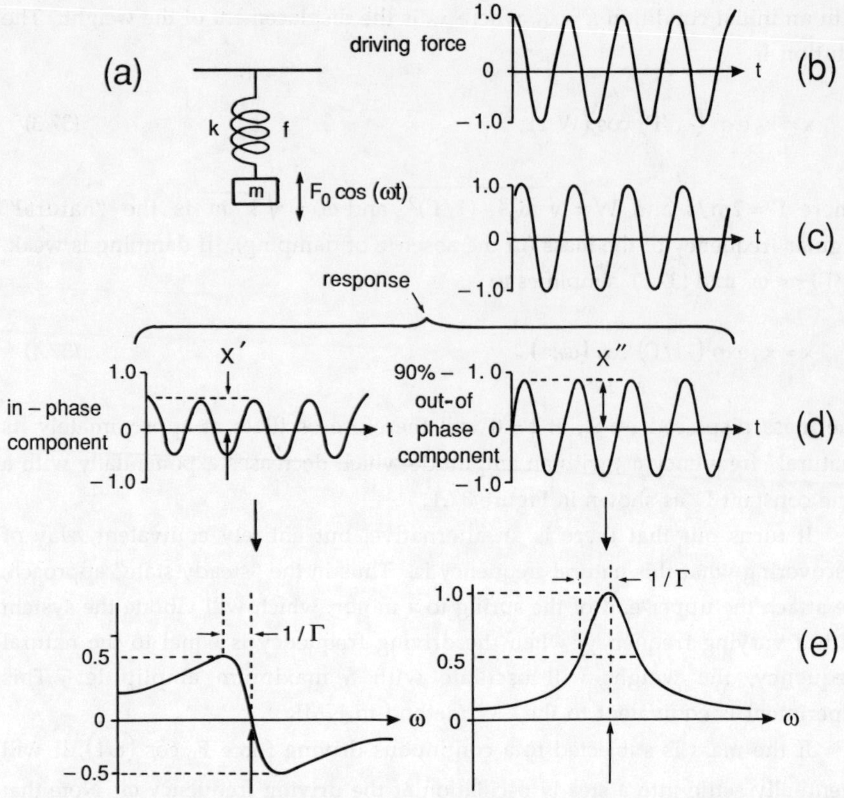


**Figure 37.1.** Oscillation of a driven mass on a spring. (a) Mass m suspended on a spring is driven by a force $F_0 \cos(\omega t)$; (b) the driving force as a function of time; (c) steady-state displacement of the mass as a function of time; (d) displacement in terms of components which are in phase and $\pi/2$ out of phase with the driver; (e) amplitudes of the components in (d) for various values of the driving frequency $\omega$. (After Marshall 1982).

The equation of motion for a driven mass is

$$m \frac{d^2x}{dt^2} + k\,x + f\,\frac{dx}{dt} - F_0 \cos(\omega\, t) = 0 \qquad (37.5)$$

with the steady-state solution

$$x = x' \cos(\omega\, t) + x'' \sin(\omega\, t) \qquad (37.6)$$

in which

$$x' = F_0 \left( \frac{m\,(\omega_0^2 - \omega^2)}{m^2\,(\omega_0^2 - \omega^2)^2 + f^2\,\omega^2} \right) \tag{37.7a}$$

$$x'' = F_0 \left( \frac{f\,\omega}{m^2\,(\omega_0^2 - \omega^2)^2 + f^2\,\omega^2} \right). \tag{37.7b}$$

Equations (37.7) simplify when, as is usual, the driving frequency $\omega$ is very close to the natural frequency $\omega_0$, so that

$$|\,\omega_0 - \omega\,| << \omega_0 + \omega\,. \tag{37.8}$$

With (37.8) and the substitution $\Gamma = 2m/f$ (see above), equations (37.7) become

$$x' = \frac{F_0}{2m\,\omega_0} \left( \frac{(\omega_0 - \omega)\,\Gamma^2}{1 + (\omega_0 - \omega)^2\,\Gamma^2} \right) \tag{37.9a}$$

$$x'' = \frac{F_0}{2m\,\omega_0} \left( \frac{\Gamma}{1 + (\omega_0 - \omega)^2\,\Gamma^2} \right). \tag{37.9b}$$

The expressions in large parentheses in equations (37.9) are clearly the absorption and dispersion functions known from Section 29, while $\Gamma$ is a mechanical equivalent of the relaxation time $T_2$. In Section 29 we have shown that the full width at half maximum of the absorption spectrum, and the peak-to-peak separation of the dispersion spectrum, are both equal to $2/\Gamma$. Note also that the dispersion spectrum is not the same as the derivative of the absorption spectrum, even though they are superficially similar.

We said at the beginning of this section that the transient and the steady-state approaches to the mechanical problem in hand are essentially equivalent, and each experiment contains precisely the same information. Bearing in mind the considerations of Section 34, it is instantly clear from the comparison of (37.4) on the one hand and (37.9) on the other that the function of time measured by the transient experiment, and the function of frequency provided by the steady-state experiment, are linked via the Fourier transformation.

# Chapter 7. NMR in Liquids

## 38. The Chemical Shift

When nuclear magnetic resonance was first discovered, physicists saw it as the ideal method for measuring absolute properties of atomic nuclei. These expectations were frustrated when it was found that the precise frequency absorbed by a given nucleus in a sample depends on its chemical environment in the molecule. This effect, known as the "chemical shift", was discovered almost simultaneously by Dickinson (1950) and Proctor and Yu (1950). Dickinson observed that the resonance frequency of $^{19}F$ in solution depends to a certain, albeit small, degree on the type of chemical compound to which this nucleus belongs, while Proctor and Yu found that the $^{14}N$ nuclei in two distinct chemical environments in a solution of $NH_4NO_3$ give two NMR signals. Furthermore, Proctor and Yu found that the frequency difference between the two $^{14}N$ signals in the spectrum is proportional to the strength of the external magnetic field. Soon after, Hahn (1950b) showed the presence of chemical shift in a $^1H$ NMR spectrum. The discovery of the chemical shift turned out to have momentous consequences, and forms the basis of the application of NMR in chemistry. Indeed, if all the nuclei of the same kind (for instance all protons) in the sample resonated at the same (Larmor) frequency $\omega = -\gamma B_0$, NMR would be of little chemical interest. Even the fact that different nuclei resonate at very different frequencies could not be easily used for quantitative bulk chemical analysis because it is difficult to compare reliably the intensity of NMR signals in different parts of the radiofrequency spectrum.

A quantitative theory of the chemical shift was given by Ramsey (1950). According to this, the magnetic field at the site of a given nucleus in a molecule is not the same as the external magnetic field in which the sample is immersed

$$\mathbf{B} = \mathbf{B}_0 + \mathbf{B}' \tag{38.1}$$

where the extra field $\mathbf{B}'$ is caused by the field $\mathbf{B}_0$ inducing an electric current in the electron cloud surrounding the nucleus. When nuclei of the same kind, such as $^{14}N$ in the $NH_4^+$ cation and in the $NO_3^-$ anion in the experiment of Proctor and Yu, appear in chemically distinct environments, the electron clouds generate at nuclei in each environment additional fields of different magnitudes and directions. The effect depends on the density of the circulating electrons, which is often modified by the functional groups. This is why the resonance of a given nuclear species may give a spectrum composed of several lines and also why the spectrum of the same nucleus in different compounds may be different.

The result of chemical shift is that the actual resonance frequency differs slightly from the Larmor frequency, and must be written as

$$\omega = \gamma B_0 (1 - \sigma) \tag{38.2}$$

where $\sigma$ is a small dimensionless number known as the "shielding constant" and expressed in parts per million (1 ppm = $1 \times 10^{-6}$). The value of $\sigma$ depends on the location of the nucleus in the molecule. Further, since the disposition of electrons in a molecule is related to the orientation of chemical bonds and is therefore anisotropic, shielding depends on the orientation of the molecule with respect to the applied magnetic field. This effect is known as chemical shift anisotropy. It follows that the shielding constant should be expressed by a tensor.

In a solid in which molecules are generally immobile, the field **B'** depends on the direction of $\mathbf{B_0}$ in such a way that between the coordinates of the fields **B'** and $\mathbf{B_0}$ there is a linear relationship

$$B'_i = - \sum_j \sigma_{ij} B_{oj} \tag{38.3}$$

where i, j = x, y, z. It is customary to place the minus sign in front of the sum in (38.3), so that positive values of the proportionality coefficients $\sigma_{ij}$ correspond to a reduction of the effective field, so that the tensor $\tilde{\sigma}$ with components $\sigma_{ij}$ can properly be called "the shielding tensor".

The numerical values of the components $\sigma_{ij}$ depend on the coordinate system. In a system in which the Z axis coincides with $\mathbf{B_0}$, we have $B_{ox} = 0$, $B_{oy} = 0$ and $B_{oz} = B_0$. Introducing these values into (38.3) we find that the form of the Zeeman Hamiltonian modified by the chemical shift, $\mathcal{H}_{CS}$, is as follows

$$\mathcal{H}_{CS} = - \gamma \hbar (\mathbf{B_0} + \mathbf{B'}) \cdot \mathbf{I} = - \gamma \hbar B_0 \left[ - I_x \sigma_{xz} - I_y \sigma_{yz} + I_z (1 - \sigma_{zz}) \right]. \tag{38.4}$$

This Hamiltonian may be truncated (see Section 8) by discarding the terms containing $I_x$ and $I_y$.

The component $\sigma_{zz}$ depends on the orientation of the molecule with respect to the Z axis. In liquids, where the molecules undergo rapid isotropic reorientation we only need to consider the mean value

$$\bar{\sigma}_{zz} = \frac{1}{3} \mathrm{Tr} \{ \sigma_{ij} \} = \sigma$$

and the truncated Hamiltonian takes the form

$$\mathcal{H}_{CS} = \hbar\, \omega_0 (1 - \sigma)\, I_z = \hbar\, \omega_i\, I_z$$

where $\omega_0 = -\gamma B_0$ is the angular frequency of resonance in the absence of screening, and $\omega_i$ the angular frequency of resonance as a result of screening in the same external magnetic field $\mathbf{B_0}$. We shall call $\omega_i$ the ith resonance in the sample, because there may be many distinct values of $\omega_i$ for the same nucleus as a result of different screening associated with different chemical situations. We will see that the resonances manifest themselves as different lines in the NMR spectrum.

Unfortunately, the absolute value of a magnetic field is difficult to measure accurately, and the magnitudes of $\mathbf{B'}$ and $\mathbf{B_0}$ in (38.1) differ very little. Because of this, chemical shift is measured by comparing the resonance angular frequency $\omega_i$ with a specific resonance $\omega_{ref}$ in a reference compound. The usual reference for $^1H$, $^{13}C$ and $^{29}Si$ is $Si(CH_3)_4$ (tetramethylsilane, abbreviated as TMS), which gives a single narrow signal for each of the three nuclei. The additional advantage of TMS is that in each case the resonance lies just outside the normal range of the spectrum. The reference is either "internal" (mixed with the sample) or "external" (placed in the NMR coil in a sealed glass capillary in the sample tube). In both cases the resulting spectrum is a superposition of the spectra of the reference and of the sample. For the ith resonance the difference between

$$\omega_i = -\gamma B_0 (1 - \sigma_i) \quad \text{and} \quad \omega_{ref} = -\gamma B_0 (1 - \sigma_{ref})$$

is

$$\omega_i - \omega_{ref} = -\gamma B_0 (\sigma_{ref} - \sigma_i)\,. \tag{38.5}$$

It would be inconvenient to express the chemical shift in form (38.5), because the difference $\omega_i - \omega_{ref}$ depends on the magnetic field, i.e. on the experimental conditions. To eliminate $B_0$ from (38.5) we divide it through by $\omega_i$ with the result

$$\frac{\omega_i - \omega_{ref}}{\omega_i} = \frac{\sigma_{ref} - \sigma_i}{1 - \sigma_i}\,. \tag{38.6}$$

Since $\sigma_i << 1$, we make a negligible error when rewriting (38.6) as

$$\frac{\omega_i - \omega_{ref}}{\omega_i} = \sigma_{ref} - \sigma_i . \qquad (38.7)$$

Thus, instead of detecting small differences in the intensity of magnetic field, we actually measure a difference in frequency, one of the most accurately measurable physical quantities. The ratio of frequencies in (38.7) is dimensionless.

It is important to be aware of the size of chemical shifts. Table 38.1 gives the range of coefficients $\sigma_{ij}$ for three selected nuclei. We see that the higher the atomic number of the nucleus, the wider the range of possible chemical shifts. The reason is the larger number of electrons surrounding the nucleus. This is why $^1H$ has the narrowest range of chemical shift of any nuclear species. Because at the same time the protons produce the largest dipolar interactions (because of the highest value of $\gamma$), chemical shifts of protons in solids are completely overwhelmed by the effects of strong dipolar interactions. In other words, the $^1H$ spectrum of a solid is normally so wide as to make chemical shift unobservable. It is only in liquids, where dipolar interactions are averaged to zero, that the effects of chemical shift and the even weaker scalar interactions become apparent.

**Table 38.1.** Typical size of the various line-splitting interactions.

| Nucleus | Dipolar interaction (kHz) | Chemical shift (kHz) for B = 2 tesla | Scalar interaction to $^1H$ (Hz) |
|---|---|---|---|
| $^1H$ | 90 | 2 | 10 |
| $^{13}C$ | 20 | 10 | 100 |
| $^{31}P$ | 35 | 57 | 150 |

It is useful to consider the properties of the chemical shift tensor $\tilde{\sigma}$ in more detail. The Hamiltonian (38.4) can be written in a more compact form as

$$\mathcal{H}_{CS} = \hbar\, \mathbf{I} \cdot \tilde{\sigma} \cdot \mathbf{B}_0 . \qquad (38.8)$$

In large fields $\tilde{\sigma}$ is symmetric and a coordinate system can be found, known as the "principal coordinate system" and described by three principal diagonal components $\sigma_{ii}$ (i = 1, 2, 3) and three angles, which define its orientation with respect to the laboratory coordinate system. The non-diagonal components are zero, and $\sigma_{zz}$ can be written as

$$\sigma_{zz} = \sum_{i=1}^{3} \sigma_{ii} \cos^2 \theta_i \tag{38.9}$$

where the $\theta_i$ are the angles between the axes of the principal coordinate system and the direction of $\mathbf{B_0}$. Adding and subtracting $\frac{1}{3}\sum \sigma_{ii}$ in (38.9) we obtain

$$\sigma_{zz} = \sum \sigma_{ii} \cos^2 \theta_i + \frac{1}{3}\sum \sigma_{ii} - \frac{1}{3}\sum \sigma_{ii}$$

$$= \frac{1}{3} \mathrm{Tr}\, \tilde{\sigma} + \frac{1}{3}\sum \left(3 \cos^2 \theta_i - 1\right) \sigma_{ii} \tag{38.10}$$

where $\mathrm{Tr}\, \tilde{\sigma} = \sigma_{11} + \sigma_{22} + \sigma_{33}$ is the trace of the tensor. As we shall see, for spin 1/2 nuclei in solids the values of $\sigma_{11}$, $\sigma_{22}$ and $\sigma_{33}$ can be derived directly from the NMR spectrum of the static sample provided dipolar interactions are small.

We will now show that in the presence of a random thermal motion of molecules, the time-averaged value of the term $\langle 3\cos^2\theta - 1 \rangle$ in (38.10) is zero. This effect, found in liquids, is known as isotropic averaging. The calculation clearly reduces to finding the mean value of $\cos^2 \theta$, which is done as follows.

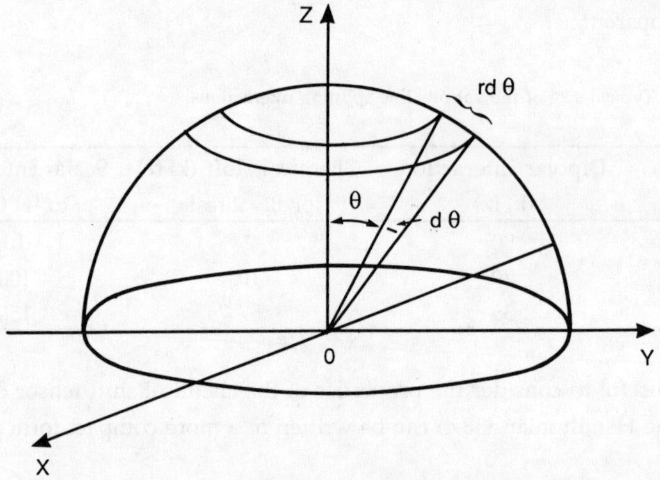


**Figure 38.1.** Isotropic averaging. One of the interacting nuclei is placed at the centre of a sphere of radius r. We calculate the fraction of internuclear vectors projecting into the annulus on the surface corresponding to angles from θ to θ + dθ. Note that an identical annulus, corresponding to the region -θ - dθ lies on the other hemisphere (not shown).

We place the observed spin at the centre of a sphere of radius r and consider the situation shown in Figure 38.1. The solid angle subtended by an annulus $d\theta$ is $2\pi\, r^2 \sin\theta\, d\theta$. Since the total solid angle over a sphere is $4\pi\, r^2$, the fraction of interactions at angle $\theta$ for a random distribution is

$$\frac{dn}{n} = \frac{2\pi\, r^2 \sin\theta\, d\theta}{4\pi\, r^2} = \frac{1}{2}\sin\theta\, d\theta\,.$$

The average value of any function $f(\theta)$ is

$$< f(\theta) > = \int_0^{\pi} F(\theta)\, f(\theta)\, d\theta$$

where the distribution function $F(\theta)$ is

$$F(\theta) = \frac{1}{n}\frac{dn}{d\theta} = \frac{1}{2}\sin\theta\,.$$

For $f(\theta) = \cos^2\theta$ we have

$$\int_0^{\pi} \frac{1}{2}\sin\theta\cos^2\theta\, d\theta = -\frac{1}{6}\left[\cos^3\theta\right]_0^{\pi} = \frac{1}{3}$$

and consequently

$$\left\langle 3\cos^2\theta - 1\right\rangle = 0. \qquad (38.11)$$

This is why in solution, where there is a rapid thermal motion of molecules, the chemical shielding tensor is reduced to the scalar quantity $\sigma$ which appears in (38.2):

$$\sigma = \frac{1}{3}\,\mathrm{Tr}\,\tilde{\sigma}\,. \qquad (38.12)$$

Other useful mean values, which are easily calculated by the same method, are

$$\left\langle \cos^4\theta\right\rangle = -\frac{1}{10}\left[\cos^5\theta\right]_0^{\pi} = \frac{1}{5}$$

$$\left\langle \left(3\cos^2\theta - 1\right)^2\right\rangle = \left[-\frac{1}{2}\cos\theta + \cos^3\theta - \frac{9}{10}\cos^5\theta\right]_0^{\pi} = \frac{4}{5}\,.$$

## 39. The High-Resolution Hamiltonian

The fine structure of NMR spectra in non-magnetic and non-metallic liquids is caused by the chemical shift and by the so-called scalar interaction. On the other hand, the dipolar interaction, which is normally much stronger (particularly for nuclei with large gyromagnetic ratios, such as $^1H$ and $^{19}F$), is of little or no importance in liquids, so that the dipolar Hamiltonian may be disregarded in the calculation of spectra. This is because in liquids all its terms (for example, see (38.8)) are averaged to zero by the fast thermal motion of molecules.

What remains is the influence of the dipolar interaction on the linewidth, via the reduction of the relaxation time $T_2$, because, as will be explained in Chapter 9, the probabilities of transition between states depend on the mean values of the squares of the dipolar terms, which are non-zero. However, in non-viscous liquids the effect of relaxation on linewidth is small. For example, for protons in water $T_2 = T_1 = 2.8$ s, and for protons in benzene $T_2 = T_1 = 18$ s, so that the resulting broadening of spectral lines is much smaller than the line broadening brought about by the unavoidable inhomogeneity of the magnetic field. It is only in very viscous liquids and in solutions of macromolecules that relaxation line broadening becomes observable.

Consider a system composed of two nuclei with spin 1/2 (such as two protons, or a proton and a fluorine nucleus), which we denote by I and S. Assume that they have different chemical shifts and interact by the scalar interaction with the coupling constant J. Since we are neglecting the dipolar interaction between the nuclei, the Hamiltonian of the system has the following form

$$\mathcal{H}_{HR} = \hbar\, \omega_I I_z + \hbar\, \omega_S S_z + 2\pi\, \hbar\, J\, \mathbf{I} \cdot \mathbf{S}\,. \qquad (39.1)$$

We will refer to $\mathcal{H}_{HR}$ as the "high-resolution Hamiltonian". The first two terms in (39.1) describe the Zeeman interaction, and if $\omega_I \neq \omega_S$ either the chemical shift is present or the gyromagnetic ratios of the nuclei differ. The third term is the so-called "scalar interaction" described by the coupling constant J. In line with this notation, this interaction is often referred to as "J-coupling". It is sometimes called "spin-spin interaction", although this appellation is more appropriate to the dipolar interaction and is thus confusing. J-coupling is not reduced by the reorientation of molecules, because a scalar product of vectors is invariant with respect to rotation.

We begin by calculating the NMR spectrum associated with the high-resolution Hamiltonian for $\omega_I = \omega_S$. In this case the eigenfunctions of $\mathcal{H}_{HR}$ are linear combinations of the eigenfunctions of the combined Zeeman

Hamiltonian $\mathcal{H}_Z = \hbar\,\omega\,(I_z + S_z)$. These functions and the corresponding eigenvalues are given in Table 39.1.

**Table 39.1.** Eigenfunctions and eigenvalues of the Zeeman and the high-resolution Hamiltonian (39.1) for $\omega_I = \omega_S = \omega$.

| Level | Eigenfunction | Eigenvalue of $\mathcal{H}_Z = \hbar\,\omega\,(I_z + S_z)$ | Eigenvalue of $\mathcal{H}_{HR}$ |
|---|---|---|---|
| 1 | $\lvert ++\rangle$ | $\hbar\,\omega$ | $\hbar\,\omega + \frac{1}{2}\pi J \hbar$ |
| 2 | $\frac{1}{\sqrt{2}}(\lvert +-\rangle + \lvert -+\rangle)$ | 0 | $\frac{1}{2}\pi J \hbar$ |
| 3 | $\frac{1}{\sqrt{2}}(\lvert +-\rangle - \lvert -+\rangle)$ | 0 | $-\frac{3}{2}\pi J \hbar$ |
| 4 | $\lvert --\rangle$ | $-\hbar\,\omega$ | $-\hbar\,\omega + \frac{1}{2}\pi J \hbar$ |

A comparison of the columns 3 and 4 in the table reveals that the inclusion of the scalar interaction does not change the spacing between levels 1, 2 and 4, which are all shifted by the same value of $\frac{1}{2}\pi J \hbar$. Only level 3 is shifted by a different amount but, as will be shown in Section 45, it plays no part in the resonance since the probabilities of transitions involving this level are all zero. It follows that scalar interactions between two equivalent nuclei (for example two protons in the methyl group) *do not cause a splitting of the spectral line.*

Consider now a diametrically different situation

$$\lvert \omega_I - \omega_S \rvert >> 2\pi\ \lvert J \rvert \tag{39.2}$$

known as weak scalar coupling. In this case it is convenient to represent $\mathcal{H}_{HR}$ as a matrix using as basis the other known eigenfunctions of the operator $(I_z + S_z)$, i.e. $\lvert 1\rangle = \lvert ++\rangle, \lvert 2\rangle = \lvert +-\rangle$, $\lvert 3\rangle = \lvert -+\rangle$ and $\lvert 4\rangle = \lvert --\rangle$. These eigenfunctions are given in Table 15.1. First of all, we use the formula

$$\mathbf{I}\cdot\mathbf{S} = \frac{1}{2}\left(I_+ S_- + I_- S_+ + 2\, I_z S_z\right)$$

to bring the high-resolution Hamiltonian to the form

$$\mathcal{H}_{HR} = \hbar\,\omega_I\, I_z + \hbar\,\omega_S\, S_z + \pi\,\hbar\, J\left(I_+ S_- + I_- S_+ + 2\, I_z S_z\right). \tag{39.3}$$

Applying the rules of action of the spin operators (see (4.17)) we calculate the matrix elements of $\mathcal{H}_{HR}$ as follows:

$$\frac{\hbar}{2}\begin{Bmatrix} (\omega_I + \omega_S) + \pi J & 0 & 0 & 0 \\ 0 & (\omega_I - \omega_S) - \pi J & 2\pi J & 0 \\ 0 & 2\pi J & -(\omega_I - \omega_S) - \pi J & 0 \\ 0 & 0 & 0 & -(\omega_I + \omega_S) + \pi J \end{Bmatrix}.$$

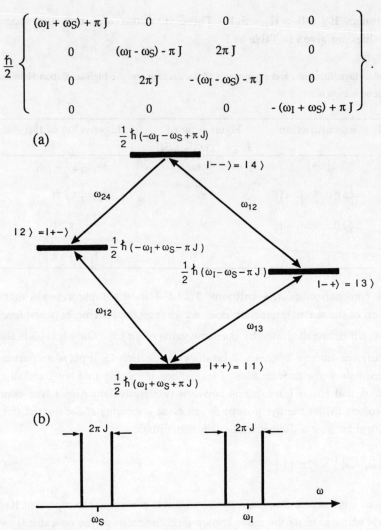

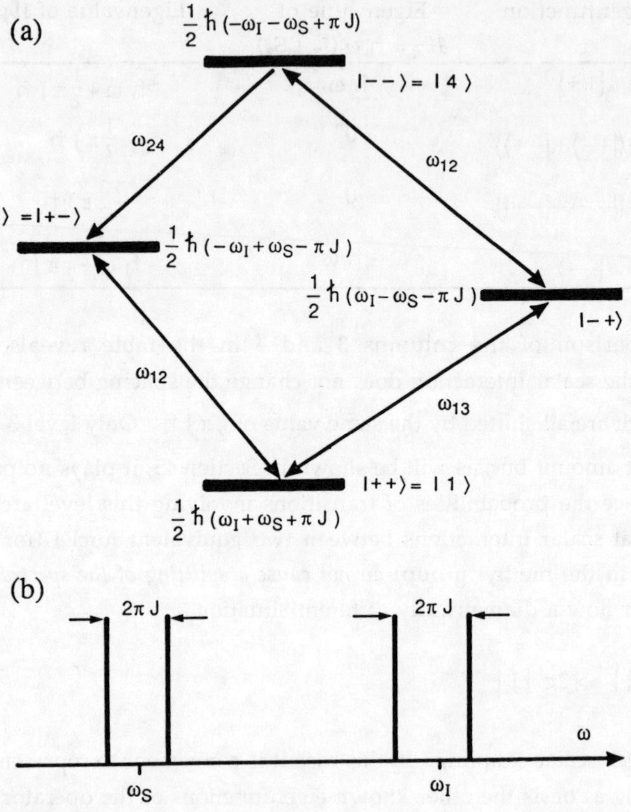


**Figure 39.1.** (a) Energy levels and eigenfunctions of a system of two weakly coupled spins 1/2. (b) The resulting NMR spectrum.

In view of (39.2), we can replace the two non-diagonal $2\pi J \hbar$ terms by zeros (for discussion of truncation see Section 8). The diagonal terms are then approximately equal to the eigenvalues. Figure 39.1 shows the energy levels and their eigenfunctions. The allowed transitions, i.e. those for which $\Delta m = \pm 1$, are represented by arrows. There are four such transitions, with angular frequencies $\omega_{24} = \omega_I - \pi J$, $\omega_{34} = \omega_S - \pi J$, $\omega_{12} = \omega_S + \pi J$ and $\omega_{13} = \omega_I + \pi J$. The resulting spectrum is composed of two doublets with a splitting $\Delta\nu = J$ (in frequency units). It will be shown in Section 45 that the probability of transitions with $\Delta m = \pm 1$ between states $|{+}{+}\rangle$, $|{+}{-}\rangle$, $|{-}{+}\rangle$ and $|{-}{-}\rangle$ is equal, so that the four spectral lines are of equal intensity.

Note that discarding non-diagonal terms in the full matrix of the Hamiltonian is equivalent to discarding terms $I_+ S_-$ and $I_- S_+$ in (39.3). This leads to the truncated high-resolution Hamiltonian

$$\mathcal{H}_{HR} = \hbar\, \omega_I I_z + \hbar\, \omega_S S_z + 2\pi \hbar J I_z S_z . \tag{39.4}$$

It is important to understand why we require that (39.2) be satisfied (which is only sometimes the case) before truncating the Hamiltonian (39.3), rather than the inequality $2\pi\, |J| << |\omega_I|, |\omega_S|$, which is always true in strong magnetic fields. The reason is that when the resolution of the spectrometer permits a very accurate determination of the difference $\omega_I - \omega_S$, then in order to resolve the two signals separately, we must require that the error involved in the truncation be smaller than the absolute value of the difference.

When $|\omega_I - \omega_S|$ is of the same order of magnitude as $2\pi\, |J|$, the matrix of the high-resolution Hamiltonian must be diagonalized without making any approximations. This amounts to diagonalizing the following $2 \times 2$ matrix obtained from the central part of the full matrix

$$\frac{\hbar}{2}\begin{Bmatrix} (\omega_I - \omega_S) - \pi J & 2\pi J \\ 2\pi J & -(\omega_I - \omega_S) - \pi J \end{Bmatrix}.$$

By solving the secular equation we obtain for the general case the eigenvalues

$$\lambda_1 = \frac{\hbar}{2}(\omega_I + \omega_S) + \frac{\hbar}{2}\pi J$$

$$\lambda_2 = \frac{\hbar}{2}\sqrt{(\omega_I - \omega_S)^2 + 4\pi^2 J^2} - \frac{\hbar}{2}\pi J$$

$$\lambda_3 = -\frac{\hbar}{2}\sqrt{(\omega_I - \omega_S)^2 + 4\pi^2 J^2} - \frac{\hbar}{2}\pi J$$

$$\lambda_4 = -\frac{\hbar}{2}(\omega_I + \omega_S) + \frac{\hbar}{2}\pi J .$$

Eigenvalue $\lambda_1$ appears with the eigenfunction $\chi^{(1)} = |{+}{+}\rangle$, and $\lambda_4$ with the eigenfunction $\chi^{(4)} = |{-}{-}\rangle$. Eigenvalues $\lambda_2$ and $\lambda_3$ appear with eigenfunctions $\chi^{(2)}$ and $\chi^{(3)}$, respectively

$$\chi^{(\ell)} = x_1^{(\ell)} \, |+-\rangle + x_2^{(\ell)} \, |-+\rangle \qquad \text{where } \ell = 2 \text{ and } 3.$$

The coefficients $x_1^{(\ell)}$ and $x_2^{(\ell)}$ are calculated according to the rules given in Section 6, i.e. by solving the set of linear homogeneous equations (6.17). Having calculated the eigenfunctions we calculate the squares of matrix elements

$$\left|\left\langle \chi^{(\ell)} \middle| I_x \middle| \chi^{(k)} \right\rangle\right|^2$$

to determine the intensities of the various lines. We will not perform these calculations here, as the method of calculating line intensities will be explained in Section 45. The result is that when $|\omega_I - \omega_S| \approx 2\pi J$, the intensities of the signals are unequal (Pople et al. 1959).

## 40. Correlated Spectroscopy (COSY)

When determining molecular structure from a high-resolution NMR spectrum, it is important to be able to establish which signals come from nuclei coupled via the scalar interaction. The scalar interaction allows us to infer the location of the nuclei in the molecule, because the coupling constant J depends on the number of chemical bonds separating these nuclei. It also depends on whether the bonds are single or double, and on the angles they form with other bonds.

The question arises of how to identify signals due to J-coupled nuclei. In relatively uncomplicated spectra of medium-sized molecules, we can spot multiplets with the same splitting J. Unfortunately, this simple method fails with spectra composed of a large number of signals, because many of them overlap. In such cases we resort to the technique known as correlated spectroscopy, abbreviated as COSY.

The basic idea of COSY is due to Jeener (1971) and its practical implementation to Aue et al. (1976). It gave rise to a new branch of NMR spectroscopy known as two-dimensional (2D) NMR (Ernst et al. Wokaun 1987), which opened a new era in structural determination. Although there are at present many 2D techniques, some of them highly sophisticated, COSY is still one of the most useful. Another reason why we describe COSY in some detail is to demonstrate the power of the density operator formalism in dealing with cases for which a simplified approach fails.

The principle of the COSY experiment is as follows. After thermodynamic equilibrium is established in the external magnetic field $\mathbf{B}_o$, the sample is irradiated with two $\pi/2$ radiofrequency pulses separated by a variable delay $t_1$ (Figure 40.1). The first pulse is the $P_x$ pulse, and the second a $P_\alpha$ pulse (known as the "mixing pulse"), where the phase $\alpha$ is x, y, -x and -y in successive experiments. We will refer to time $t_1$ between the pulses as the "evolution time", and to time $t_2$ which follows the second pulse as the "detection time". Both pulses are hard (non-selective), and affect all the observed nuclei equally, irrespective of their chemical shift. Each pulse is much shorter than either $t_1$ or $t_2$.

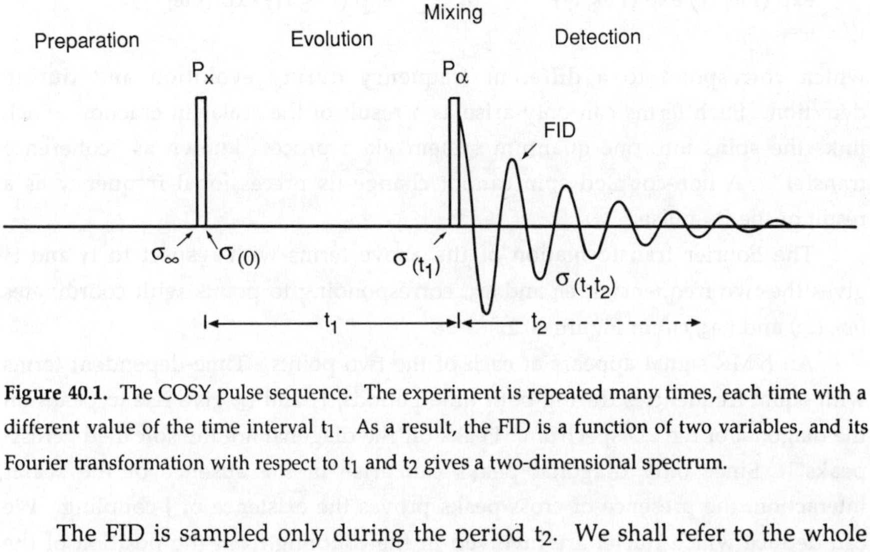


**Figure 40.1.** The COSY pulse sequence. The experiment is repeated many times, each time with a different value of the time interval $t_1$. As a result, the FID is a function of two variables, and its Fourier transformation with respect to $t_1$ and $t_2$ gives a two-dimensional spectrum.

The FID is sampled only during the period $t_2$. We shall refer to the whole basic process, from the moment that thermodynamic equilibrium is established to the moment in which the measurement is completed, as the "elementary experiment". The acquisition of a COSY spectrum requires a large number of elementary experiments with different values of the parameters $t_1$ and $\alpha$.

The FID which we measure is a function of $t_2$, but also depends on the stage of evolution of the spins at $t = t_1$ when the second pulse is applied. By repeating the elementary experiment for different values of $t_1$ we obtain the values of a function of two variables $Z_{FID} = Z(t_1, t_2)$. In other words, a single elementary experiment gives the dependence of $Z_{FID}$ on $t_2$ for a fixed value of $t_1$. The dependence of $Z_{FID}$ on $t_1$ is found by repeating the elementary experiment.

We shall describe only the homonuclear version of COSY, although heteronuclear equivalents are also possible. Take a system composed of two identical spins 1/2 (for example $^1H$), which we denote as I and S. Assume that the two spins have different chemical shifts, i.e. that $\omega_I \neq \omega_S$, and that they are weakly J-coupled, that is to say that $|\omega_I - \omega_S| >> 2\pi |J|$ (see (39.2)). This last assumption is not strictly necessary, but it leads to a considerable simplification of the calculations, bringing out the essential aspects of COSY more clearly.

The Hamiltonian of the system is thus the truncated high-resolution Hamiltonian (39.3). We shall see that, as a result of the evolution of the system between the pulses and after the second pulse, the density operator consists of sums of many terms, which are periodic in $t_1$ and $t_2$. Among them there are terms with time dependence of the form

$$\exp\left(i\,\omega_I\,t_1\right)\exp\left(i\,\omega_S\,t_2\right) \qquad \text{or} \qquad \exp\left(i\,\omega_S\,t_1\right)\exp\left(i\,\omega_I\,t_2\right)$$

which correspond to a different frequency during evolution and during detection. Such terms can only arise as a result of the scalar interaction which links the spins into one quantum system via a process known as "coherence transfer". A non-coupled spin cannot change its precessional frequency as a result of the $P_\alpha$ pulse.

The Fourier transformation of the above terms with respect to $t_1$ and $t_2$ gives the two frequencies, $\omega_I$ and $\omega_S$, corresponding to points with coordinates $(\omega_I, \omega_S)$ and $(\omega_S, \omega_I)$ in Figure 40.2.

An NMR signal appears at each of the two points. Time-dependent terms with equal frequencies during both time periods, $t_1$ and $t_2$, give rise to peaks on the diagonal of the 2D spectrum. Peaks off the diagonal are the so-called "cross-peaks". Since only diagonal peaks can arise in the absence of the scalar interaction, the presence of cross-peaks proves the existence of J-coupling. We can deduce which nuclei are involved in the coupling from the position of the cross-peaks.

After this introduction we can proceed with detailed calculations. The quantum system composed of weakly coupled spins I and S will be considered in a frame rotating at the carrier frequency $\omega_e$ set close to the resonance frequency $-\gamma B_0$. We will follow the evolution of the density operator $\rho'$ in the rotating frame over the successive stages of the COSY experiment, using the density operator to calculate the transverse components of the magnetization in the rotating frame

$$\left\langle\left\langle I_k' \right\rangle\right\rangle = \mathrm{Tr}\left[\rho'\,(t_1, t_2)\, I_k'\right] \tag{40.1}$$

$$\left\langle\left\langle S_k' \right\rangle\right\rangle = \mathrm{Tr}\left[\rho'\,(t_1, t_2)\, S_k'\right] \tag{40.2}$$

where k stands for x or y. The frequencies appearing in $\langle\langle I_k'\rangle\rangle$ and $\langle\langle S_k'\rangle\rangle$ give the desired two-dimensional spectrum.

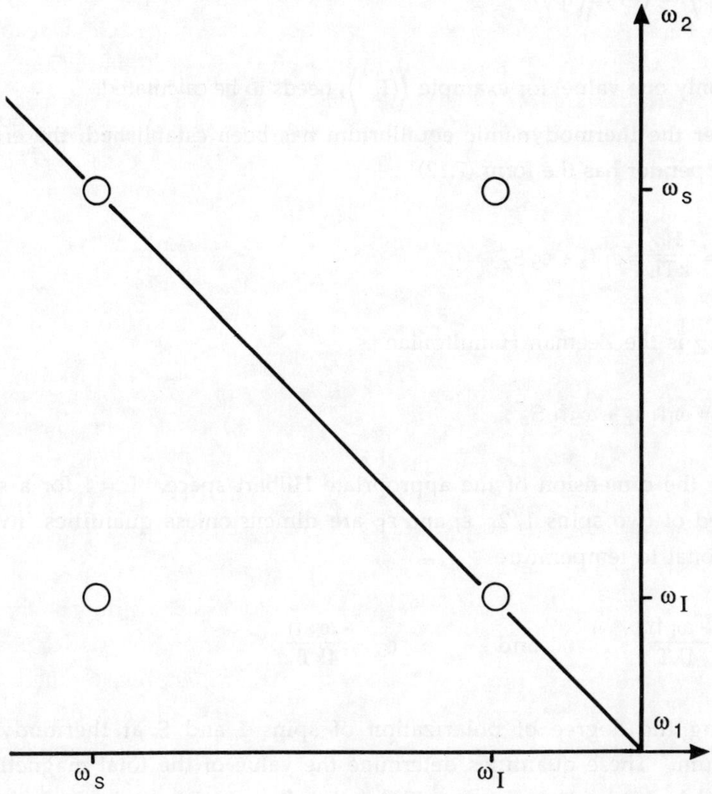


**Figure 40.2.** Simplified two-dimensional (2D) spectrum of two J-coupled protons with different chemical shifts.

The high-resolution Hamiltonian of the system under consideration in the rotating frame is

$$\mathcal{H}_{HR} = \hbar\ \Omega_I\, I_z + \hbar\ \Omega_S\, S_z + 2\pi J\hbar\ I_z\, S_z \tag{40.3}$$

(see Section 39), where $\Omega_I = \omega_I - \omega_e$ and $\Omega_S = \omega_S - \omega_e$.

In the sum of terms making up the density operator we omit the so-called "ineffective" terms, i.e. those which do not contribute to the traces (40.1) and (40.2). We denote the effective density operator by σ. An example of the procedure can be found in Section 7.

From the formal point of view, the spins I and S and the expressions for their frequencies $\Omega_I$ and $\Omega_S$ differ only by the symbol used (S or I). Introducing the operator $(\leftrightarrow)$ which interchanges S and I and vice versa, we can write

$$\left\langle\left\langle S_k' \right\rangle\right\rangle = (\leftrightarrow) \left\langle\left\langle I_k' \right\rangle\right\rangle$$

so that only one value, for example $\left\langle\left\langle I_k' \right\rangle\right\rangle$, needs to be calculated.

After the thermodynamic equilibrium has been established, the effective density operator has the form (7.12)

$$\sigma_\infty = \frac{-\mathcal{H}_Z}{kTL} = \varepsilon_I\, I_z + \varepsilon_S\, S_z$$

where $\mathcal{H}_Z$ is the Zeeman Hamiltonian

$$\mathcal{H}_Z = \omega_I \hbar\; I_z + \omega_S \hbar\; S_z$$

and L is the dimension of the appropriate Hilbert space. L = 4 for a system composed of two spins 1/2. $\varepsilon_I$ and $\varepsilon_S$ are dimensionless quantities inversely proportional to temperature

$$\varepsilon_I = \frac{-\omega_I\, \hbar}{4kT} \qquad \text{and} \qquad \varepsilon_S = \frac{-\omega_S\, \hbar}{4kT}$$

describing the degree of polarization of spins I and S at thermodynamic equilibrium. These quantities determine the value of the total magnetization generated by each kind of spin. This is because the Langevin-Curie formula (16.5) for spins of each kind can be written as

$$M_\infty^{(I)} = \varepsilon_I\, N^{(\rho)}\, \gamma\, \hbar\;\, \mathrm{Tr}\, I_z^2 = \varepsilon_I\, q \tag{40.4a}$$

$$M_\infty^{(S)} = \varepsilon_S\, N^{(\rho)}\, \gamma\, \hbar\;\, \mathrm{Tr}\, S_z^2 = \varepsilon_S\, q \tag{40.4b}$$

where $N^{(\rho)}$ is the number of I - S pairs per unit volume of the sample. Appendix 3 shows that for two spins 1/2 we have $\mathrm{Tr}\, I_z^2 = \mathrm{Tr}\, S_z^2 = 1$, so that $q = N^{(\rho)}\gamma\hbar$. The traces of $I_x^2$, $I_y^2$, $S_x^2$ and $S_y^2$ are also unity.

Note that $\sigma_\infty$ is invariant with respect to transition from the laboratory frame to the rotating frame. We know from Table 32.1 that in the rotating frame the $P_x$ pulse transforms $I_z$ and $S_z$ into $I_y'$ and $S_y'$, respectively. After the first pulse we have

$$\sigma'(0) = \varepsilon_I I_y' + \varepsilon_S S_y' = \left[1 + (\leftrightarrow)\right] \varepsilon_I I_y' .$$

In further arguments we shall omit the prime, while always bearing in mind that the calculations are carried out in the rotating reference frame.

From $t_1 = 0$, the moment when the $P_x$ pulse ends, the density operator evolves under the influence of $\mathcal{H}$ according to (7.6)

$$\sigma(t) = \exp\left(-i \mathcal{H}_{HR} t/\hbar\right) \sigma(0) \exp\left(i \mathcal{H}_{HR} t/\hbar\right) = \left[1 + (\leftrightarrow)\right] \varepsilon_I I_y(t) \quad (40.5)$$

where

$$I_y(t) = \exp\left(-i \mathcal{H}_{HR} t/\hbar\right) I_y \exp\left(i \mathcal{H}_{HR} t/\hbar\right) .$$

Note that $I_y(t)$ is part of the density operator which evolves from $I_y$ as the initial condition. Since all three terms in the expression (40.3) for $\mathcal{H}_{HR}$ commute, the order in which they are applied is unimportant, so that

$$I_y(t) = \exp\left(-i\, 2I_z S_z \pi J t\right) \left[\exp\left(-i\, \Omega_I I_z t\right) I_y \exp\left(i\, \Omega_I I_z t\right)\right] \exp\left(i\, 2I_z S_z \pi J t\right) .$$

Applying the rules of rotation (32.9) to the expression in the square brackets we find

$$I_y(t) = \left[\exp\left(-i\, 2I_z S_z \pi J t\right) I_y \exp\left(i\, 2I_z S_z \pi J t\right)\right] \cos\left(\Omega_I t\right)$$

$$- \left[\exp\left(-i\, 2I_z S_z \pi J t\right) I_x \exp\left(i\, 2I_z S_z \pi J t\right)\right] \sin\left(\Omega_I t\right) .$$

Applying the rules of rotation again to the above we obtain

$$I_y(t) = \left[I_y \cos\left(2S_z \pi J t_1\right) - I_x \sin\left(2S_z \pi J t_1\right)\right] \cos\left(\Omega_I t\right)$$

$$- \left[I_x \cos\left(2S_z \pi J t_1\right) + I_y \sin\left(2S_z \pi J t_1\right)\right] \sin\left(\Omega_I t\right) . \quad (40.6)$$

The operator $S_z$ in (40.6) appears in the argument of sine and cosine, which means that we are dealing with operators known from Appendix 5, where it is shown that $S_z$ can be taken before the sin and cos signs

$$\cos\left(2\pi J S_z t\right) = \{1\} \cos\left(\pi J t\right) \tag{40.7a}$$

$$\sin\left(2\pi J S_z t\right) = 2 S_z \sin\left(\pi J t\right). \tag{40.7b}$$

We transform (40.6) using these formulae. We next calculate

$$I_x(t) = \exp\left(-i \mathcal{H}_{HR} t/\hbar\right) I_x \exp\left(i \mathcal{H}_{HR} t/\hbar\right)$$

in an analogous manner. Finally, we use the change of symbol operator to find $S_x(t) = (\leftrightarrow) I_x(t)$ and $S_y(t) = (\leftrightarrow) I_y(t)$. The results are

$$I_y(t) = I_y a - 2I_y S_z b - I_x c - 2I_x S_z d \tag{40.8a}$$

$$I_x(t) = I_x a - 2I_x S_z b + I_y c + 2I_y S_z d \tag{40.8b}$$

$$S_y(t) = S_y \bar{a} - 2S_y I_z \bar{b} - S_x \bar{c} - 2S_x I_z \bar{d} \tag{40.8c}$$

$$S_x(t) = S_x \bar{a} - 2S_x I_z \bar{b} + S_y \bar{c} + 2S_y I_z \bar{d} \tag{40.8d}$$

where

$$\begin{aligned}
a &= \cos\left(\pi J t\right) \cos\left(\Omega_I t\right) & \bar{a} &= (\leftrightarrow)\, a = \cos\left(\pi J t\right) \cos\left(\Omega_S t\right) \\
b &= \sin\left(\pi J t\right) \sin\left(\Omega_I t\right) & \bar{b} &= (\leftrightarrow)\, b = \sin\left(\pi J t\right) \sin\left(\Omega_S t\right) \\
c &= \cos\left(\pi J t\right) \sin\left(\Omega_I t\right) & \bar{c} &= (\leftrightarrow)\, c = \cos\left(\pi J t\right) \sin\left(\Omega_S t\right) \\
d &= \sin\left(\pi J t\right) \cos\left(\Omega_I t\right) & \bar{d} &= (\leftrightarrow)\, d = \sin\left(\pi J t\right) \cos\left(\Omega_S t\right).
\end{aligned} \tag{40.9}$$

Equations (40.8) and (40.9) apply both during evolution time ($t = t_1$) and during detection time ($t = t_2$). For simplicity, we shall give a function of $t_1$ subscript "1" and a function of $t_2$ subscript "2". For example, we have

$$a_1 = \cos\left(\pi J t_1\right) \cos\left(\Omega_I t_1\right)$$

$$\bar{b}_2 = \sin\left(\pi J t_2\right) \sin\left(\Omega_S t_2\right) .$$

Using (40.8a) we write (40.5) as

$$\sigma(t_1) = \left[1 + (\leftrightarrow)\right] \varepsilon_I \left(I_y a_1 - 2I_y S_z b_1 - I_x c_1 - 2I_x S_z d_1\right) . \tag{40.10}$$

At time $t_1$ the mixing pulse $P_\alpha$ is applied, which transforms the density operator according to Table 32.1. We denote the new form of the operator immediately following the $P_\alpha$ pulse (i.e. at $t_2 = 0$) by $\sigma_\alpha(0)$. For the four values of $\alpha$ we have therefore

$$\sigma_x(0) = \left[1 + (\leftrightarrow)\right] \varepsilon_I \left[- I_z\left(a_1 - 2S_y b_1\right) - I_x\left(c_1 + 2S_y d_1\right)\right] \tag{40.11a}$$

$$\sigma_y(0) = \left[1 + (\leftrightarrow)\right] \varepsilon_I \left[I_y\left(a_1 + 2S_x b_1\right) - I_z\left(c_1 - 2S_x d_1\right)\right] \tag{40.11b}$$

$$\sigma_{-x}(0) = \left[1 + (\leftrightarrow)\right] \varepsilon_I \left[I_z\left(a_1 + 2S_y b_1\right) - I_x\left(c_1 - 2S_y d_1\right)\right] \tag{40.11c}$$

$$\sigma_{-y}(0) = \left[1 + (\leftrightarrow)\right] \varepsilon_I \left[I_y\left(a_1 - 2S_x b_1\right) + I_z\left(c_1 + 2S_x d_1\right)\right] . \tag{40.11d}$$

In order to gain a better insight into how the two-dimensional spectrum is generated, it is useful to consider two variants of the experiment, which we call COSY-I and COSY-II. In COSY-I the elementary experiment is repeated four times for each value of $t_1$, each time with a different phase of the $P_\alpha$ pulse: $P_x$, $P_y$, $P_{-x}$ and $P_{-y}$. The four complex FID signals are then summed as follows:

$$Z_\Sigma(t_1, t_2) = Z_x(t_1, t_2) - Z_y(t_1, t_2) + Z_{-x}(t_1, t_2) - Z_{-y}(t_1, t_2) . \tag{40.12}$$

The four pulses ($P_x$, $P_y$, $P_{-x}$ and $P_{-y}$) form a "cycle", thus named because the net rotation is zero. Procedures based on elementary experiments repeated in this way are known as "phase cycling" and are common in NMR. In COSY-I we perform 4n different elementary experiments involving 4nm samplings of the FID, where n is the number of chosen values of $t_1$ and m is the number of samplings within a single elementary experiment. In COSY-II the mixing pulse has a constant phase, and there are a total of nm samplings.

It is instructive to consider COSY-I in detail. Note that instead of summing signals according to (40.12) we can arrive at the same result by first forming a combination of operators

$$\sigma_\Sigma(0) = \sigma_x(0) - \sigma_y(0) + \sigma_{-x}(0) - \sigma_{-y}(0)$$

and then using it for the determination of the overall FID (40.12). This approach leads to a considerable simplification of the calculations. From (40.11) we have

$$\sigma_\Sigma(0) = \Big[1 + (\leftrightarrow)\Big]\,\varepsilon_I\,(-2I_y\,a_1 + 4I_z\,S_y\,b_1 - 2I_x\,c_1 - 4I_z\,S_x\,d_1)\,. \qquad (40.13)$$

We now need to calculate the evolution of $\sigma_\Sigma$ during $t_2$. Also this evolution proceeds under the Hamiltonian (40.3), so that for the terms in the round brackets in (40.13) we use expressions (40.8) with $t = t_2$. Take as an example the term $4I_z\,S_y\,b_1$ in (40.13). The operator $I_z$ does not evolve, because it commutes with the Hamiltonian, while the evolution of $S_y$ is described by (40.8c). Thus after time $t_2$ the term under consideration becomes

$$4I_z\,b_1\,S_y(t_2) = 4I_z\,S_y\,b_1\,\bar{a}_2 - 8I_z^2\,S_y\,b_1\,\bar{b}_2 - 4I_z\,S_x\,b_1\,\bar{c}_2 - 8I_z^2\,S_x\,b_1\,\bar{d}_2\,. \qquad (40.13a)$$

Proceeding in the same fashion with the other terms in (40.13) we obtain a total of 16 terms, and after applying the operator $\Big[1 + (\leftrightarrow)\Big]$ a total of 32 terms. Most of them are ineffective and may be discarded. In order for a term to be effective in the calculation of $\langle\langle I_x\rangle\rangle = \mathrm{Tr}\,\{\,\sigma_\Sigma(t_2)\,I_x\,\}$ or of $\langle\langle I_y\rangle\rangle = \mathrm{Tr}\,\{\,\sigma_\Sigma(t_2)\,I_y\,\}$, it must contain the coordinate to be calculated to the power 1, and the coordinate of spin S to the power of 0 or 2 (see Appendix 3). The effective terms are listed in Table 40.1, which also indicates from which terms of $\sigma_\Sigma(0)$ they derive by evolution. For example, the term $-2\,\varepsilon_I\,I_y\,a_1\,a_2$ is effective, because its contribution to $\mathrm{Tr}\,\sigma_\Sigma(t)\,I_y$ is $-2\,\varepsilon_I\,a_1\,a_2\,\mathrm{Tr}\,I_y^2$, and we know that $\mathrm{Tr}\,I_y^2 \neq 0$.

Summing the terms in Table 40.1 we obtain

$$\sigma_\Sigma(t_2) = 2I_x\Big[\varepsilon_I\Big(a_1\,c_2 - c_1\,a_2\Big) + 4\varepsilon_S\,S_z^2\Big(\bar{d}_1\,b_2 - \bar{b}_1\,d_2\Big)\Big]$$

$$- 2I_y\Big[\varepsilon_I\Big(a_1\,a_2 + c_1\,c_2\Big) + 4\varepsilon_S\,S_z^2\Big(\bar{b}_1\,b_2 + \bar{d}_1\,d_2\Big)\Big].$$

We must remember that the operator $\sigma_\Sigma(t_2)$ is also a function of $t_1$.

**Table 40.1.** Terms of the density operator $\sigma_\Sigma(t_1, t_2)$ which are effective in the calculation of the expectation values of $I_x$ and $I_y$. $\sigma_\Sigma(0)$ is given by (40.13).

| Source terms [terms in $\sigma_\Sigma(0)$] | Effective terms after evolution [terms in $\sigma_\Sigma(t_1, t_2)$] |
|---|---|
| $-2\,\varepsilon_I\, I_y\, a_1$ | $2\,\varepsilon_I\, I_x\, a_1\, c_2 - 2\,\varepsilon_I\, I_y\, a_1\, a_2$ |
| $4\,\varepsilon_I\, I_z\, S_y\, b_1$ | no effective terms |
| $-2\,\varepsilon_I\, I_x\, c_1$ | $-2\,\varepsilon_I\, I_x\, c_1\, a_2 - 2\,\varepsilon_I\, I_y\, c_1\, c_2$ |
| $-4\,\varepsilon_I\, I_z\, S_x\, d_1$ | no effective terms |
| $-2\,\varepsilon_S\, S_y\, \bar{a}_1$ | no effective terms |
| $4\,\varepsilon_S\, I_y\, S_z\, \bar{b}_1$ | $-8\,\varepsilon_S\, I_x\, S_z^2\, \bar{b}_1\, d_2 - 8\,\varepsilon_S\, I_y\, S_z^2\, \bar{b}_1\, b_2$ |
| $-2\,\varepsilon_S\, S_x\, \bar{c}_1$ | no effective terms |
| $-4\,\varepsilon_S\, I_x\, S_z\, \bar{d}_1$ | $8\,\varepsilon_S\, I_x\, S_z^2\, \bar{d}_1\, b_2 - 8\,\varepsilon_S\, I_y\, S_z^2\, \bar{d}_1\, d_2$ |

Using the density operator $\sigma_\Sigma(t_2)$ we calculate the overall transverse magnetization of spins I corresponding to the operator $\mathcal{M}_\perp^{(I)} = q\left(I_x + i\, I_y\right)$ to obtain

$$\left\langle\left\langle M_\perp^{(I)}\right\rangle\right\rangle = q\,\mathrm{Tr}\left[\left(I_x + i\, I_y\right)\sigma_\Sigma\right].$$

Using the traces calculated in a general way in Appendix 3 (which can also be obtained by calculating the diagonal elements in the basis of functions listed in Table 15.1) we have

$$\mathrm{Tr}\, I_x^2 = 1 \qquad \text{and} \qquad \mathrm{Tr}\left\{S_z^2 I_y^2\right\} = \frac{1}{4}\,. \tag{40.14}$$

We find that

$$\left\langle\left\langle M_\perp^{(I)}\right\rangle\right\rangle = 2\,\varepsilon_I\, q\left[\left(a_1\, c_2 - c_1\, a_2\right) - i\left(a_1\, a_2 + c_1\, c_2\right)\right]$$

$$+ 2\,\varepsilon_S\, q\left[\left(\bar{d}_1\, b_2 - \bar{b}_1\, d_2\right) - i\left(\bar{b}_1\, b_2 + \bar{d}_1\, d_2\right)\right].$$

The last expression can be written in a more convenient form

$$\left\langle\left\langle M_{\perp}^{(I)}\right\rangle\right\rangle = -2\,\varepsilon_I\, q\left[\left(c_1 + i\,a_1\right)\left(a_2 + i\,c_2\right)\right] - i\,2\,\varepsilon_S\, q\left[\left(\bar{d}_1 - i\,\bar{b}_1\right)\left(d_2 + i\,b_2\right)\right]. \quad (40.15)$$

In turn, we transform the expressions in the round brackets by substituting (40.9) and using the Euler equations

$$\cos\alpha = \frac{1}{2}\left[\exp\left(i\alpha\right) + \exp\left(-i\alpha\right)\right]$$
$$\sin\alpha = -\frac{i}{2}\left[\exp\left(i\alpha\right) - \exp\left(-i\alpha\right)\right] \quad (40.16)$$

to obtain

$$a_2 + i\,c_2 = \frac{1}{2}\exp\left[i\left(\Omega_I + \pi J\right)t_2\right] + \frac{1}{2}\exp\left[i\left(\Omega_I - \pi J\right)t_2\right]$$
$$c_1 + i\,a_1 = \frac{i}{2}\exp\left[i\left(-\Omega_I + \pi J\right)t_1\right] + \frac{i}{2}\exp\left[i\left(-\Omega_I - \pi J\right)t_1\right]$$
$$d_2 + i\,b_2 = -\frac{i}{2}\exp\left[i\left(\Omega_I + \pi J\right)t_2\right] + \frac{i}{2}\exp\left[i\left(\Omega_I - \pi J\right)t_2\right] \quad (40.17)$$
$$\bar{d}_1 - i\,\bar{b}_1 = -\frac{i}{2}\exp\left[i\left(-\Omega_S + \pi J\right)t_1\right] + \frac{i}{2}\exp\left[i\left(-\Omega_S - \pi J\right)t_1\right].$$

Using the above results we calculate the term in (40.15) which is proportional to $\varepsilon_I$:

$$\begin{aligned}
-2\,\varepsilon_I\, q\left[\left(c_1 + i\,a_1\right)\left(a_2 + i\,c_2\right)\right] &= -\frac{i}{2}\varepsilon_I\, q\Big\{\exp\left[i\left(-\Omega_I - \pi J\right)t_1\right]\exp\left[i\left(\Omega_I + \pi J\right)t_2\right] \\
&+ \exp\left[i\left(-\Omega_I + \pi J\right)t_1\right]\exp\left[i\left(\Omega_I + \pi J\right)t_2\right] \\
&+ \exp\left[i\left(-\Omega_I - \pi J\right)t_1\right]\exp\left[i\left(\Omega_I - \pi J\right)t_2\right] \\
&+ \exp\left[i\left(-\Omega_I + \pi J\right)t_1\right]\exp\left[i\left(\Omega_I - \pi J\right)t_2\right]\Big\}. \quad (40.18)
\end{aligned}$$

By Fourier transforming (40.18) in two dimensions, we obtain four pairs of frequencies $(\omega_1, \omega_2)$, where $\omega_1$ and $\omega_2$ correspond to $t_1$ and $t_2$, respectively:

$$\begin{array}{ll} (-\Omega_I - \pi J, \Omega_I + \pi J) & (-\Omega_I + \pi J, \Omega_I + \pi J) \\ (-\Omega_I - \pi J, \Omega_I - \pi J) & (-\Omega_I + \pi J, \Omega_I - \pi J)\,. \end{array} \tag{40.19}$$

These frequencies are the coordinates of the COSY-I spectral peaks in the $(\omega_1, \omega_2)$ plane. Since $\pi J << |\omega_I|$ all these signals are close to $(-\Omega_I, \Omega_I)$, i.e. to the diagonal of the spectrum. These so-called "diagonal" peaks are shown in Figure 40.3. The coordinates of the other four diagonal peaks are obtained by interchanging I and S in (40.19).

The term in (40.15) which is proportional to $\varepsilon_S$ is calculated in an analogous manner:

$$\begin{aligned} & -i\,2\,\varepsilon_S\,q\left[\left(\bar{d}_1 - i\,\bar{b}_1\right)\left(d_2 + i\,b_2\right)\right] \\ & = \frac{i}{2}\varepsilon_S\,q\,\Big\{\exp\left[i\,(-\Omega_S + \pi J)\,t_1\right]\exp\left[i\,(\Omega_I + \pi J)\,t_2\right] \\ & \qquad - \exp\left[i\,(-\Omega_S + \pi J)\,t_1\right]\exp\left[i\,(\Omega_I - \pi J)\,t_2\right] \\ & \qquad - \exp\left[i\,(-\Omega_S - \pi J)\,t_1\right]\exp\left[i\,(\Omega_I + \pi J)\,t_2\right] \\ & \qquad + \exp\left[i\,(-\Omega_S - \pi J)\,t_1\right]\exp\left[i\,(\Omega_I - \pi J)\,t_2\right]\Big\}\,. \end{aligned} \tag{40.20}$$

By performing a two-dimensional Fourier transformation of (40.15) we obtain four signals with the coordinates

$$\begin{array}{ll} (-\Omega_S + \pi J, \Omega_I + \pi J) & (-\Omega_S + \pi J, \Omega_I - \pi J) \\ (-\Omega_S - \pi J, \Omega_I + \pi J) & (-\Omega_S - \pi J, \Omega_I - \pi J)\,. \end{array} \tag{40.21}$$

These signals are close to $(-\Omega_S, \Omega_I)$, and are thus "off-diagonal". Equation (40.20) and Figure 40.3 show that the second and third signals in (40.21) are upside down with respect to the first and the fourth. The coordinates of the other four cross-peaks in Figure 40.3 are obtained by interchanging I and S in (40.21).

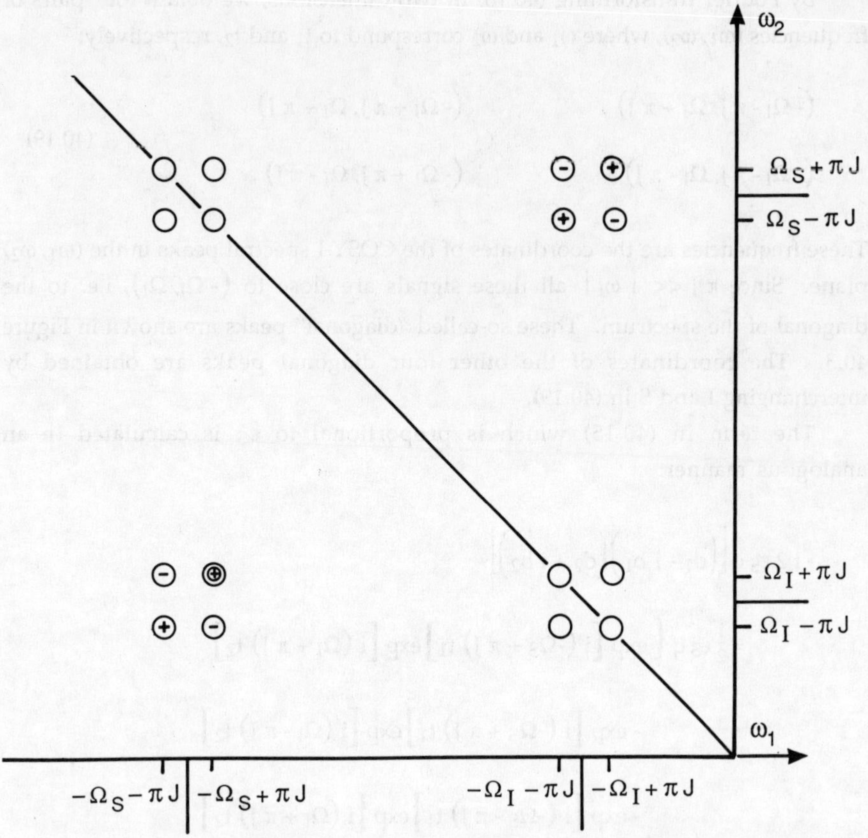


**Figure 40.3.** Two-dimensional spectrum of two weakly coupled spins 1/2 obtained by the version of COSY with pulse cycling (COSY-I). The position of the peaks are marked by circles. The shape of the peak marked by a double circle is given by (40.22) with $\omega_a = -\Omega_S + \pi J$ and $\omega_b = \Omega_I + \pi J$.

In order to determine not only the *positions* of the peaks but also their *shapes,* we Fourier transform the signal

$$Z(t) = \left\langle\left\langle M_{\perp}^{(I)} \right\rangle\right\rangle \exp\left(-t_1/T_2\right) \exp\left(-t_2/T_2\right) \exp\left(i\,\varphi\right)$$

which takes into account the effect of relaxation and of apparatus-dependent phase shifts.

We have seen in Section 36 that by multiplying the signal by a suitably chosen phase factor $z = \exp\left(i\,\alpha\right)$ we can give the spectrum various shapes, of which the absorption shape is the most convenient to the spectroscopist.

Consider the possibilities open to us in this respect in COSY-I. We use as an example the non-diagonal peak given by the first term in the sum (40.20):

$$F(\omega_1, \omega_2) = \frac{i}{8\pi^2} q\, \varepsilon_S \exp\left[i(\varphi + \alpha)\right]$$

$$\times \int_0^{+\infty} \exp(-t_1/T_2) \exp\left[i(\omega_a - \omega_1) t_1\right] dt_1 \int_0^{+\infty} \exp(-t_2/T_2) \exp\left[i(\omega_b - \omega_2) t_2\right] dt_2$$

where we have put $\omega_a = -\Omega_S + \pi J$ and $\omega_b = \Omega_I + \pi J$ for clarity. Using (34.3c) we obtain

$$\mathrm{Re}\, F(\omega_1, \omega_2) = \frac{q\, \varepsilon_S T_2^2}{8\pi^2}$$

$$\times \Big\{ -\left[\mathrm{abs}(\omega_a | \omega_1)\, \mathrm{dsp}(\omega_b | \omega_2) + \mathrm{dsp}(\omega_a | \omega_1)\, \mathrm{abs}(\omega_b | \omega_2)\right] \cos(\varphi + \alpha)$$

$$-\left[\mathrm{abs}(\omega_a | \omega_1)\, \mathrm{abs}(\omega_b | \omega_2) + \mathrm{dsp}(\omega_a | \omega_1)\, \mathrm{dsp}(\omega_b | \omega_2)\right] \sin(\varphi + \alpha) \Big\}. \quad (40.22)$$

We see therefore that the desired pure absorption lineshape of the type "abs abs" cannot be obtained. The same applies to diagonal peaks, as can be confirmed by performing similar calculations for peaks given by (40.18).

We now turn to the COSY-II experiment. Assume that the mixing pulse is $P_x$. Then at $t_2 = 0$ the density operator has the form (40.11a). We use (40.8) to calculate the evolution of the operator during time $t_2$, in the same way used in COSY-I for $\sigma_\Sigma$. After acting with the operator $\left[1 + (\leftrightarrow)\right]$ and discarding ineffective terms for calculating the transverse magnetization of spins I we obtain

$$\sigma_x(t_2) = -I_x\left(\varepsilon_I c_1 a_2 + 4\varepsilon_S S_z^2 \bar{b}_1 d_2\right) - I_y\left(\varepsilon_I c_1 c_2 + 4\varepsilon_S S_z^2 \bar{b}_1 b_2\right).$$

With this density operator we obtain

$$\left\langle\left\langle M_\perp^{(I)} \right\rangle\right\rangle = \mathrm{Tr}\left[q\left(I_x + i I_y\right) \sigma_x(t_2)\right] = -q\, \varepsilon_I c_1 \left(a_2 + i c_2\right) - q\, \varepsilon_S \bar{b}_1 \left(d_2 + i b_2\right)$$

where we have made use of (40.4) and (40.14). Taking into account the effect of relaxation and of apparatus-dependent phase shifts, we obtain the signal induced by that part of the total magnetization

$$Z = \exp\left(-t_1/T_2\right) \exp\left(-t_2/T_2\right) \exp\left(i\,\varphi\right) \left\langle\left\langle M_{\perp}^{(I)}\right\rangle\right\rangle$$

$$= -\,q\,\varepsilon_I \exp\left(i\,\varphi\right) \exp\left(-t_1/T_2\right) c_1 \exp\left(-t_2/T_2\right) \left(a_2 + i\,c_2\right)$$

$$-\,q\,\varepsilon_S \exp\left(i\,\varphi\right) \exp\left(-t_1/T_2\right) \bar{b}_1 \exp\left(-t_2/T_2\right) \left(d_2 + i\,b_2\right). \qquad (40.23)$$

We subject this signal to three successive mathematical operations:

1. Multiplication by the phase factor $\exp\left(i\,\alpha\right)$, chosen so that $\exp\left[i\,(\alpha + \varphi)\right] = -\,i$.
2. Cosine Fourier transformation with respect to $t_1$.
3. Full Fourier transformation with respect to $t_2$.

We begin by applying this treatment to the first of the two terms in (40.23)

$$F_1\left(\omega_1, \omega_2\right) = \frac{q\,\varepsilon_I}{4\pi^2} \int_0^{+\infty} \exp\left(-t_1/T_2\right) c_1 \cos\left(\omega_1 t_1\right) dt_1$$

$$\times \int_0^{+\infty} i \exp\left(-t_2/T_2\right) (a_2 + i\,c_2) \exp\left(-i\,\omega_2\,t_2\right) dt_2 \qquad (40.24)$$

where, on the strength of (40.9),

$$a_2 + i\,c_2 = \frac{1}{2}\left\{\exp\left[i\left(\Omega_I + \pi J\right) t_2\right] + \exp\left[i\left(\Omega_I - \pi J\right) t_2\right]\right\}. \qquad (40.24a)$$

The following trigonometric relationships facilitate the calculation of the integral with respect to $t_1$:

$$\sin\alpha \sin\beta = \frac{1}{2}\left[\cos\left(\alpha - \beta\right) - \cos\left(\alpha + \beta\right)\right]$$

$$\cos\alpha \cos\beta = \frac{1}{2}\left[\cos\left(\alpha + \beta\right) + \cos\left(\alpha - \beta\right)\right]$$

$$\cos\alpha \sin\beta = \frac{1}{2}\left[\sin\left(\alpha + \beta\right) - \sin\left(\alpha - \beta\right)\right]$$

enabling us to make the transformation

$$c_1 \cos\left(\omega_1 t_1\right) = \cos\left(\pi J t_1\right) \sin\left(\Omega_I t_1\right) \cos\left(\omega_1 t_1\right)$$

$$= \frac{1}{4}\left[\sin\left(\Omega_I + \pi J - \omega_1\right) t_1 + \sin\left(\Omega_I - \pi J - \omega_1\right) t_1\right]$$

$$- \frac{1}{4}\left[\sin\left(- \Omega_I - \pi J - \omega_1\right) t_1 + \sin\left(- \Omega_I + \pi J - \omega_1\right) t_1\right].$$

Using (34.3a) and (34.3b) we obtain

$$\int_0^{+\infty} \exp\left(- t_1/T_2\right) c_1 \cos\left(\omega_1 t_1\right) dt_1$$

$$= \frac{T_2}{4}\left[\operatorname{dsp}\left(\Omega_I + \pi J \mid \omega_1\right) + \operatorname{dsp}\left(\Omega_I - \pi J \mid \omega_1\right)\right]$$

$$- \frac{T_2}{4}\left[\operatorname{dsp}\left(- \Omega_I - \pi J \mid \omega_1\right) + \operatorname{dsp}\left(- \Omega_I + \pi J \mid \omega_1\right)\right]. \quad (40.25)$$

We discard the last two terms as reflected in the axis $\omega_1 = 0$ with respect to the spectrum given by the first two terms. This effect will be discussed in detail later.

The integral with respect to $t_2$ in (40.24) is calculated by substituting (40.24a) and applying (34.3a) and (34.3b)

$$i \int_0^{+\infty} \exp\left(- t_2/T_2\right) (a_2 + i\, c_2) \exp\left(- i\, \omega_2 t_2\right) dt_2$$

$$= - \frac{T_2}{2}\left[\operatorname{dsp}\left(\Omega_I + \pi J \mid \omega_2\right) + \operatorname{dsp}\left(\Omega_I - \pi J \mid \omega_2\right)\right]$$

$$+ i \frac{T_2}{2}\left[\operatorname{abs}\left(\Omega_I + \pi J \mid \omega_2\right) + \operatorname{abs}\left(\Omega_I - \pi J \mid \omega_2\right)\right]. \quad (40.26)$$

We now substitute the integrals (40.25) and (40.26) into (40.24), and calculate the real part of the Fourier transform

$$\text{Re } F_1(\omega_1, \omega_2) = \frac{q\, \varepsilon_I\, T_2^2}{32\pi^2}$$

$$\times \Big[ - \text{dsp}\left(\Omega_I + \pi J \,|\, \omega_1\right) \text{dsp}\left(\Omega_I + \pi J \,|\, \omega_2\right) - \text{dsp}\left(\Omega_I + \pi J \,|\, \omega_1\right) \text{dsp}\left(\Omega_I - \pi J \,|\, \omega_2\right)$$

$$- \text{dsp}\left(\Omega_I - \pi J \,|\, \omega_1\right) \text{dsp}\left(\Omega_I + \pi J \,|\, \omega_2\right) - \text{dsp}\left(\Omega_I - \pi J \,|\, \omega_1\right) \text{dsp}\left(\Omega_I - \pi J \,|\, \omega_2\right) \Big].$$

We thus have four diagonal peaks of purely dispersive character. The remaining four diagonal peaks, which are are close to $(\Omega_S, \Omega_S)$, are obtained by interchanging I and S in the above formula.

We now subject the second part of (40.23) to the same mathematical treatment. Bearing in mind that $\exp\left[i(\alpha + \varphi)\right] = -i$, we obtain

$$F_2(\omega_1\, \omega_2) = \frac{q\, \varepsilon_S}{4\pi^2} \int_0^{+\infty} \exp\left(-t_1/T_2\right) \bar{b}_1 \cos\left(\omega_1 t_1\right) dt_1$$

$$\times \int_0^{+\infty} i \exp\left(-t_2/T_2\right) \left(d_2 + i\, b_2\right) \exp\left(-i\, \omega_2 t_2\right) dt_2$$

where, on the strength of (40.9),

$$d_2 + i\, b_2 = -\frac{i}{2} \left\{ \exp\left[i\left(\Omega_I + \pi J\right) t_2\right] - \exp\left[i\left(\Omega_I - \pi J\right) t_2\right] \right\}$$

and

$$\bar{b}_1 \cos\left(\omega_1 t_1\right) = \frac{1}{4} \big[ \cos\left(\Omega_S - \pi J - \omega_1\right) t_1 - \cos\left(\Omega_S + \pi J + \omega_1\right) t_1$$

$$- \cos\left(\Omega_S + \pi J - \omega_1\right) t_1 + \cos\left(\Omega_S - \pi J + \omega_1\right) t_1 \big].$$

The same transformations as those used previously give the result

$$\mathrm{Re}\, F_2 (\omega_1 \omega_2) = \frac{q\, \varepsilon_S\, T_2^2}{32\pi^2}$$

$$\times \Big[ - \mathrm{abs} (\Omega_S + \pi J | \omega_1)\, \mathrm{abs} (\Omega_I + \pi J | \omega_2) + \mathrm{abs} (\Omega_S + \pi J | \omega_1)\, \mathrm{abs} (\Omega_I - \pi J | \omega_2)$$

$$+ \mathrm{abs} (\Omega_S - \pi J | \omega_1)\, \mathrm{abs} (\Omega_I + \pi J | \omega_2) - \mathrm{abs} (\Omega_S - \pi J | \omega_1)\, \mathrm{abs} (\Omega_I - \pi J | \omega_2) \Big]$$

corresponding to four non-diagonal peaks with the convenient purely absorptive lineshape.

We now examine the reason why COSY-I and COSY-II may give rise to two-dimensional spectra with different lineshapes. We know that the expressions which were subjected to two-dimensional Fourier transformation are products of the form $f_1 (t_1)\, f_2 (t_2)$. In COSY-I $f_1$ and $f_2$ are both complex functions. In order to obtain a purely absorptive spectrum using this method, the computer would need to form the product

$$[\mathrm{Re}\, \mathfrak{F}_1 f_1 (t_1)]\, [\mathrm{Re}\, \mathfrak{F}_2 f_2 (t_2)]$$

where $\mathfrak{F}_1$ and $\mathfrak{F}_2$ denote one-dimensional Fourier transformations with respect to $t_1$ and $t_2$, respectively. Without any intervention on the part of the spectroscopist, the first term corresponds to absorption lines, but the second gives absorption lines only when the value of $\alpha$ is suitably chosen. Therefore, the product of the two terms could in principle give purely absorptive signals. The problem is that there is no way of forming such a product, because NMR measurements do not give the values of $f_1 (t_1)$ and $f_2 (t_2)$ individually. The computer can only provide $\mathrm{Re} [ \mathfrak{F}_1 f_1 (t_1)\, \mathfrak{F}_2 f_2 (t_2) ]$ or $\mathrm{Im} [ \mathfrak{F}_1 f_1 (t_1)\, \mathfrak{F}_2 f_2 (t_2) ]$. The result is that COSY-I cannot give a purely absorptive spectrum.

In COSY-II the function $f_1 (t_1)$ is real and, depending on the kind of Fourier transformation (sine or cosine) with respect to $t_1$, can give absorption or dispersion peaks. By a suitable choice of the value of $\alpha$ we can also control the shape of lines given by $\mathrm{Re}\, \mathfrak{F}_2 f_2 (t_2)$. We see therefore that COSY-II has at its disposal two adjustable parameters, which independently influence the lineshapes in the $t_1$ and $t_2$ spaces. Table 40.2 shows that different combinations of these parameters allow us to obtain different forms of two-dimensional spectra (see Figure 40.4).

**Table 40.2.** Two-dimensional spectra of two weakly coupled spins 1/2, I and S, obtained by COSY-II for two values of the phase factor $z = \exp\left[i(\alpha + \varphi)\right]$ and different types of transformation with respect to $t_1$. The first term in the products abs dsp, dsp abs, abs abs and dsp dsp gives the lineshape with respect to $\omega_1$, and the second term with respect to $\omega_2$. The remaining spectral peaks are obtained by interchanging the subscripts I and S.

| Peak coordinates | | Transformation with respect to $t_1$ | | | |
|---|---|---|---|---|---|
| | | z = 1 | | z = - i | |
| | | cosine | sine | cosine | sine |
| diag | $(\Omega_I + \pi J, \Omega_I + \pi J)$ | - dsp abs | - abs abs | - dsp dsp | - abs dsp |
| | $(\Omega_I + \pi J, \Omega_I - \pi J)$ | - dsp abs | - abs abs | - dsp dsp | - abs dsp |
| | $(\Omega_I - \pi J, \Omega_I + \pi J)$ | - dsp abs | - abs abs | - dsp dsp | - abs dsp |
| | $(\Omega_I - \pi J, \Omega_I - \pi J)$ | - dsp abs | - abs abs | - dsp dsp | - abs dsp |
| cross | $(\Omega_S + \pi J, \Omega_I + \pi J)$ | abs dsp | - dsp dsp | - abs abs | dsp abs |
| | $(\Omega_S + \pi J, \Omega_I - \pi J)$ | - abs dsp | dsp dsp | abs abs | - dsp abs |
| | $(\Omega_S - \pi J, \Omega_I + \pi J)$ | - abs dsp | dsp dsp | abs abs | - dsp abs |
| | $(\Omega_S - \pi J, \Omega_I - \pi J)$ | abs dsp | - dsp dsp | - abs abs | dsp abs |

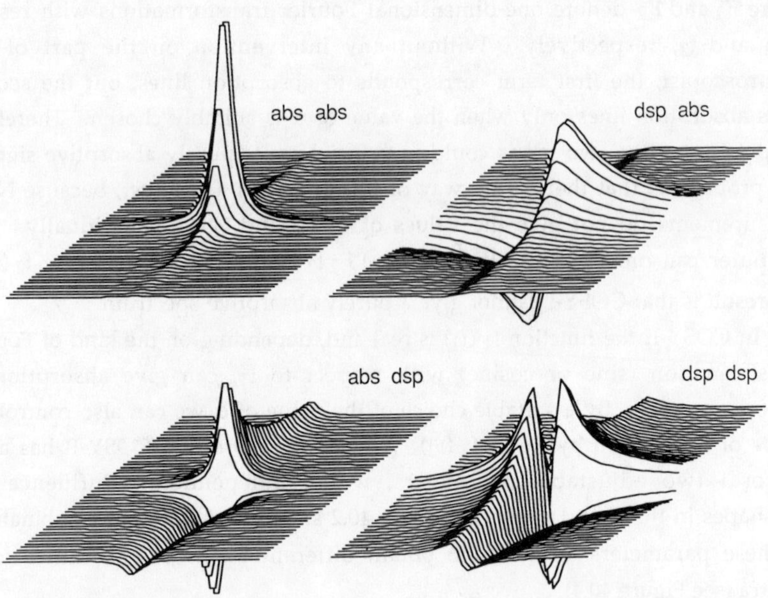


**Figure 40.4.** Peak shapes in two-dimensional spectra: abs abs; dsp abs; abs dsp; dsp dsp. For details see text.

The disadvantage of COSY-II is that it gives rise to two spectra, which are mirror images of one another with respect to the $\omega_1$ axis. In order not to allow the two spectra to overlap, the carrier frequency $\omega_e$ must be placed outside the spectral range. As we know from Section 35, this requires the use of powerful and very short pulses. COSY-I does not have this disadvantage, because repeating elementary experiments with mixing pulses of different phases amounts to "artificial" quadrature detection with respect to $t_1$, which gives the dependence of the signals on $t_1$ in the form of a circular function.

The advantage of COSY-II is that it reduces errors caused by the imperfections of the quadrature detector and the inaccuracies of phase setting between the $P_x$ pulse and the mixing pulse. These inaccuracies cause the signal to deviate from a perfect circular function, and false (aliased) lines appear in the spectrum as a result. The summing of free induction decays acquired with different phases of mixing pulse forming a cycle reduces the amplitude (intensity) of the aliased lines almost to zero.

Note that non-diagonal peaks arise from that part of the transverse magnetization of spins I which is proportional to $\varepsilon_S$ and from that part of the transverse magnetization of spins S which is proportional to $\varepsilon_I$. The appearance of the magnetization of spins of one kind proportional to the degree of polarization of spins of another kind means that transfer of polarization order (coherence) has taken place. To examine the mechanism of this process in detail, we will explain as an example the reason for the appearance of the term $-8\varepsilon_I I_z S_y b_1 \bar{b}_2$ in (40.13a). This term is effective in calculating the expectation value $\langle\langle S_y \rangle\rangle$, despite which its value is proportional to $\varepsilon_I$ and not to $\varepsilon_S$. The reason is that the term originates from the starting value of the density matrix $\varepsilon_I I_y$ as shown below:

$$\underset{(40.5)}{\varepsilon_I I_y} \rightarrow \underset{(40.10)}{-2\varepsilon_I I_y S_z b_1} \rightarrow \underset{(40.13)}{4\varepsilon_I I_z S_y b_1} \rightarrow \underset{(40.13a)}{-4\varepsilon_I S_y I_z^2 b_1 \bar{b}_2}$$

where the numbers of equations in which a given term appears are given below each term. The reason for the difference in numerical coefficient shown above and in (40.13a) is that the equation applies to a sum of four elementary experiments, while the above scheme refers to a single experiment. During time $t_1$ (corresponding to the first arrow) the operator $I_y$ gives rise to (among others) the operator $I_y S_z$. This is possible only because of the presence of J-coupling, and follows from (40.7b). However, the appearance of $S_z$ in the density matrix is not observed experimentally, because $S_z$ does not induce a voltage in the receiver coil. The role of the mixing pulse $P_\alpha$ (the second arrow) is to convert $S_z$ into $S_y$, which is observable. By precessing during time $t_2$ (the third arrow), $S_y$ induces a voltage in the receiver coil.

Consider how the spectrum would change if $J \to 0$. Of course, this is only possible in theory, since in practice the value of J for a given pair of protons is fixed. It turns out that, as long as the peaks are well separated from each other, their height will not change and only their mutual distance will decrease. Since the peaks have a certain width dependent on $T_2$ (or on $T_2^*$ if the inhomogeneity of the magnetic field is significant) for some value of $J \approx 1/T_2$ they will begin to overlap. The increasing overlap of the non-diagonal peaks will lead to them cancelling out since, as we have seen from (40.20) and Table 40.2, in each group of four non-diagonal peaks the sign of two is opposite to that of the other two. The peaks will therefore become smaller and smaller, and will finally disappear in the noise. By contrast, the overlap of diagonal peaks will lead to an increase of their intensity, since they have the same sign. In the limit we arrive at a conventional one-dimensional spectrum arranged along the diagonal.

## 41. The Spin Echo

We continue our discussion of pulsed NMR in liquids. However, we shall for the time being neglect chemical shifts and scalar interactions, and concentrate on the effects of the inhomogeneity of the external magnetic field and the effects of relaxation. This approach is justified when field inhomogeneity is so strong as to obscure the fine structure of the spectrum. The omission of spin-spin interactions enables us to consider a single spin as a quantum-mechanical system, and to describe the motion of the magnetization using the vector model described in Chapter 3.

In practice magnetic fields are not ideally homogeneous. This means that the value of the external field **B** is different in different parts of the sample, and only at some points is $B_0 = -\omega_e/\gamma$, where $\omega_e$ is the angular frequency of the carrier and of the rotating reference frame. To deal with this situation, we decompose magnetization **M** into a sum of elementary magnetic moments associated with different volume elements dV of the sample. The transverse components $\delta\mathbf{M}$ of these elementary moments precess at slightly different rates, and therefore individually change their orientation with respect to the rotating axes X' and Y', despite the fact that all started from a common position parallel to Y' immediately after the $\pi/2$ pulse. At time t after the pulse (the duration of which is taken as negligible in comparison with t) the phase angle $\varphi$ traversed by the individual magnetization vectors in the X'Y' frame is $\varphi = -\gamma t\,(B - B_0)$. This gives rise to the "fanning out" shown in Figure 41.1(b). Apart from spin-

spin relaxation, the fanning out of the magnetization is an additional (and generally decisive) reason for the decay of the free induction signal. The decay of the free induction signal will certainly be significant if the partial magnetizations, coming from two points of the sample corresponding to the greatest difference $\Delta B$ in field value B, reach the difference in phase equal to $\pi$.

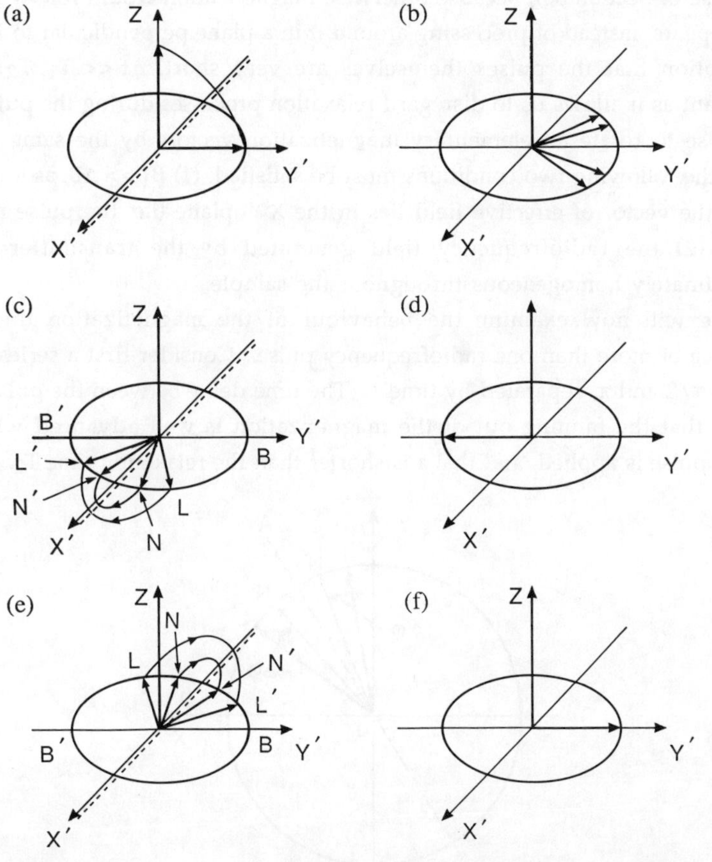


**Figure 41.1.** The generation of spin echoes, using coherent radiofrequency pulses the axes of which lie along X'. (a) The action of the $\pi/2$ pulse; (b) the "fanning out" of the magnetization; (c) the action of the first $\pi$ pulse; (d) the first echo; (e) the action of the second $\pi$ pulse; (f) the second echo. The axes of the pulses are marked with broken lines.

For this difference to appear in time equal to $T_2$ (for protons in water $T_2 = 2.7$ s) it is necessary for the span of the field intensity in the sample to be $\Delta B = 2\pi/\gamma T_2 = 8 \times 10^{-9}$ T. In most spectrometers, the length of the sample is of the order of 0.5 cm. Field inhomogeneity of ca. $8 \times 10^{-9}$ T per 0.5 cm is achievable in superconducting magnets, but usually not in cheaper iron core electromagnets or permanent magnets used for relaxation and diffusion measurements. As a result, the lineshape is distorted, often completely, by the inhomogeneity of the magnetic field. The shape of the free induction then depends on the shape of the sample. This effect gives rise to NMR imaging.

Finally, we should justify some of the assumptions which we have made. It is necessary for the pulses to start and terminate rapidly (non-adiabatically in the sense of Section 30), because otherwise magnetization would follow field $\mathbf{B_1}$ as it appears, instead of precessing around it in a plane perpendicular to $\mathbf{B_1}$. The assumption that the pulses themselves are very short, $\Delta t << T_1, T_2$, is also important as it allows us to disregard relaxation processes during the pulse. For the pulse to rotate all elementary magnetization vectors by the same desired angle, the following two conditions must be satisfied: (1) $B_1 >> \Delta B$, as a result of which the vector of effective field lies in the X'Y' plane (i.e. the pulse must be hard); (2) the radiofrequency field generated by the transmitter coil is approximately homogeneous throughout the sample.

We will now examine the behaviour of the magnetization under the influence of more than one radiofrequency pulse. Consider first a series of two pulses, $\pi/2$ and $\pi$, separated by time $\tau$. The time delay between the pulses is so chosen that the fanning out of the magnetization is well advanced when the second pulse is applied, and that $\tau$ is shorter than the relaxation time $T_2$.

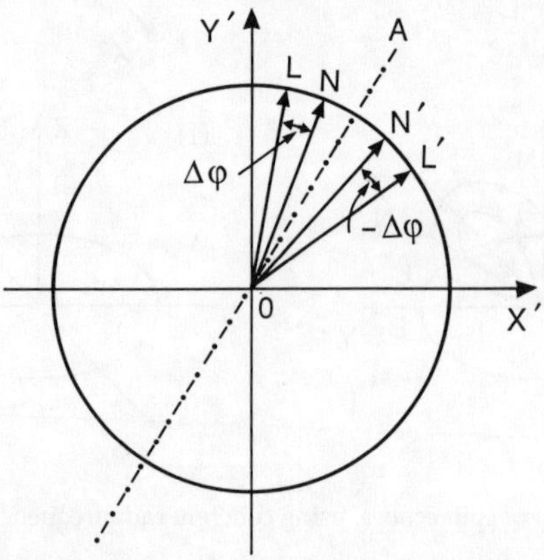


**Figure 41.2.** The action of a $\pi$ pulse on two chosen isochromats **L** and **N**. While precessing by the angle $\pi$ around the axis OA of the pulse, **L** and **N** move from their starting positions OL and ON to OL' and ON' symmetrical with respect to the OA axis. The result is a change in sign of the phase difference $\Delta\varphi$.

We already know what happens to the magnetization after the $\pi/2$ pulse. It remains to consider the action of the $\pi$ pulse. As before, we decompose the total magnetization into a sum of components coming from elementary magnetic moments in the different volume elements of the sample. We will call the component of the elementary magnetic moment in the X'Y' plane an "isochromat".

Consider two volume elements of the sample for which the value of the external magnetic field **B** is somewhat different. The isochromats **L** and **N** corresponding to these volume elements precess at different rates and after time $\tau$ differ in phase by $\Delta\varphi$. This is seen from Figures 41.1(c) and 41.2, which show the positions OL and ON of the isochromats **L** and **N** at time $\tau$, just before the application of the $\pi$ pulse. The second pulse causes precession by angle $\pi$ around axis OA, which is the axis of the pulse. As a result, vector OL moves to position OL' symmetrical with respect to OA and similarly vector ON moves to position ON'. Figures 41.1(c) and 41.2 show that the $\pi$ pulse causes the phase difference between **L** and **N** to change from $\Delta\varphi$ to $-\Delta\varphi$. This means that isochromat **N**, which, because of its faster precession, overtook isochromat **L** by the angle $\Delta\varphi$, now lags behind it by the same angle. We see that precession is clockwise. Figure 41.1(c) shows the action of the $\pi$ pulse for the special case when its axis coincides with X'. The angular velocity of both elementary vectors does not change as a result of the pulse, which means that after time $t = 2\tau$ from the first pulse they must coincide. Of course, this argument applies to all isochromats, which means that after $t = 2\tau$ all will "refocus" in the same direction (Figure 41.1(d)). This is accompanied by the induction of voltage of resonance frequency $\nu_0$ in the receiver coil. This momentary voltage is known as the spin echo (Figure 41.3).

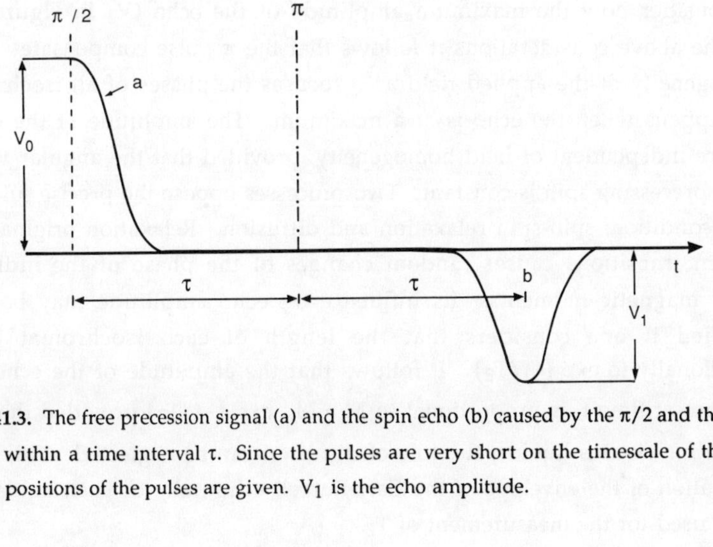


**Figure 41.3.** The free precession signal (a) and the spin echo (b) caused by the $\pi/2$ and the $\pi$ pulse applied within a time interval $\tau$. Since the pulses are very short on the timescale of the figure, only the positions of the pulses are given. $V_1$ is the echo amplitude.

The growth and decay of the spin echo is caused by the same factors as those of the free induction signal. This is why the echo is symmetric and looks as if it were composed of two free induction decays combined back-to-back.

There is no significant difference between the state of the sample at the maximum of the free precession signal (just after the $\pi/2$ pulse) and at the maximum of the echo, since at both these times the phases of all isochromats are equal. It follows that if at time $\tau$ after the maximum of the echo we apply another $\pi$ pulse, we shall obtain yet another spin echo. The pulse sequence suggested by Carr and Purcell (1954) produces a greater number of echoes. The sequence is composed of a $\pi/2$ pulse followed after time $\tau$ by a $\pi$ pulse; further $\pi$ pulses are applied at intervals of $2\tau$. The echo appears precisely in the middle of each $2\tau$ interval (see Figure 41.4).

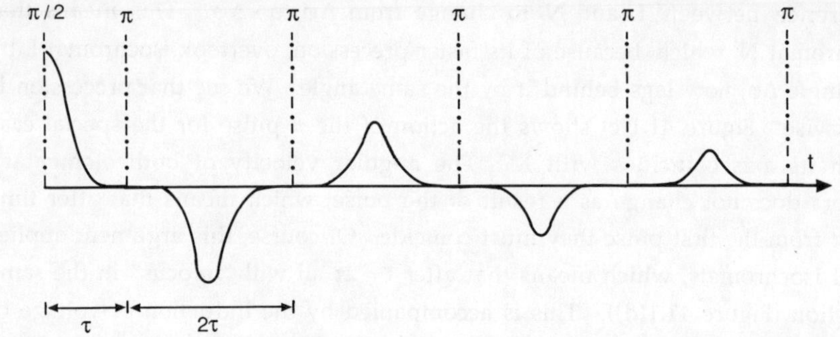

**Figure 41.4.** The Carr-Purcell echo sequence.

Consider now the maximum amplitude of the echo ($V_1$ in Figure 41.3). From the above considerations it follows that the $\pi$ pulse compensates for the inhomogeneity of the applied field as it focuses the phases of all isochromats. This happens when the echo is at a maximum. The amplitude of the echo is therefore independent of field homogeneity, provided that the angular velocity of each precessing spin is constant. Two processes oppose the precise fulfilment of this condition: spin-spin relaxation and diffusion. Relaxation originating in quantum transitions causes random changes of the phase of the individual nuclear magnetic moments. Its influence on echo amplitude may be easily quantified if one considers that the length of each isochromat decays proportionally to $\exp\left(-t/T_2\right)$. It follows that the amplitude of the echo, with maximum at time t, is proportional to $M = M_\infty \exp\left(-t/T_2\right)$ provided that, as is the case for viscous liquids, the role of diffusion can be neglected. This is also the equation of the envelope of the Carr-Purcell echo train for such liquids, and may be used for the measurement of $T_2$.

To summarize, of the processes causing the fanning out of the transverse component of the magnetization, some (those caused by the inhomogeneity of the field) are reversible and some (spin-spin relaxation and diffusion) are irreversible. The application of the $\pi$ pulse removes the former but has no effect on the latter.

We will now consider the role of molecular diffusion in the generation of spin echoes. The decomposition of the total magnetization into isochromats, originating in different macroscopic parts of the sample which differ in the value of field **B**, is no longer sufficient. In order to quantify the influence of diffusion we must go further and decompose the magnetization into elements which undergo their own diffusional motion. We therefore treat the magnetization of the sample as a sum of elementary magnetic moments belonging to particles undergoing individual diffusional motions, i.e. to molecules. We will treat the motion of these moments classically, just as we have done with the motion of partial magnetization vectors. We will also keep the term "isochromat" to describe the component perpendicular to the Z axis. Much attention will be given to these components since it is their sum which induces an electric voltage in the coil.

Immediately after the end of the $\pi/2$ pulse (call this instant $t = 0$) the length of an isochromat is $M_\infty/N_0$ where $N_0$ is the number of nuclei in 1 cm$^3$ of the sample. The fanning out of the magnetization begins at this moment, since the phases of the individual isochromats are time-dependent

$$\frac{d\varphi\,(t)}{dt} = -\gamma\left(B - B_0\right).$$

The quantity $d\varphi\,(t)/dt$ would be time-independent if the nucleus were to remain in the field with the same intensity B. However, in liquids of moderate viscosity we must take into account the fact that molecules change their location rapidly as a result of diffusion. The value of B is then a random function of time and the equalization of phase at $t = 2\tau$ is only partial. Calculate the sum of the isochromats at $t = 2\tau$ in the rotating frame of reference. Putting $\alpha = \varphi\,(2\tau)$ we have

$$M_{y'} = \sum \frac{M_\infty}{N_0} \exp\left(\frac{-2\tau}{T_2}\right) \cos\alpha = M_\infty \exp\left(\frac{-2\tau}{T_2}\right) < \cos\alpha >$$

$$M_{x'} = M_\infty \exp\left(-2\tau/T_2\right) < \sin\alpha >$$

where $< >$ denotes averaging over the nuclear assembly, and the summation is over all the isochromats. Since phases $+\alpha$ and $-\alpha$ are equally probable, $<\sin\alpha> = 0$, which means that $M_{x'} = 0$. It follows that the voltage $V_1$ induced in the receiver coil is proportional only to $M_{y'}$. The ratio of the amplitude of the echo $V_1$ to the amplitude of the preceding free precession signal or to the amplitude of the preceding echo is

$$\frac{V_1}{V_0} = \exp\left(\frac{-2\tau}{T_2}\right) < \cos\alpha >$$

from which we calculate the amplitude of the nth Carr-Purcell echo

$$V_n = k\,M_\infty \left[\exp\left(\frac{-2\tau}{T_2}\right) < \cos\alpha >\right]^n \tag{41.1}$$

where k is a constant depending on the apparatus used.

In order to calculate the mean $<\cos\alpha>$ we first calculate $<\alpha^2>$. Assume that the inhomogeneity of the field **B** is regular throughout the sample with a constant gradient **G**, so that **B** changes linearly along any direction parallel to **G**. It is sufficient to consider the component of the diffusional motion along the direction of the gradient **G**, since molecular displacement perpendicular to this direction does not affect the magnitude of the field **B** acting on a given nucleus.

The process of diffusion proceeds via a multitude of small jumps in the positive or negative direction at very short time intervals. Statistical mechanics derives the relationship

$$D = \xi^2/2\,s \tag{41.2}$$

linking the diffusion coefficient D, the mean length of the individual jump $\xi$ and the mean time s between the individual jumps. We neglect the duration of the jump itself. The displacement of the nucleus during time $t = js$, in the course of which the nucleus undergoes j jumps, is the sum of the individual displacements

$$\sum_{i=1}^{j} \xi\, a_i$$

where $a_i = \pm 1$ depending on whether the jump is in the direction of increasing or decreasing **B**. If at $t = 0$ the nucleus is at the field of intensity B (0), then at $t = js$ it will be at field

$$B(js) = B(0) + G\xi \sum_{i=1}^{j} a_i . \qquad (41.3)$$

Since the length of an individual jump $\xi$ is of the order of the diameter of the molecule, the time s during which the molecule "waits" for another jump is exceedingly short: in water it is of the order of $10^{-12}$ s. The number of jumps performed by the nucleus over time $\tau$ between the $\pi/2$ pulse and the $\pi$ pulse, normally at least $10^{-4}$ s, is thus very large. Denote this number by N/2. We have

$$\tau = \frac{1}{2} N s . \qquad (41.4)$$

The increase in phase of the magnetic moment is obtained by summing the increases gained at the individual "stopovers" as follows:

$$\varphi(\tau) = \sum_{j=1}^{N/2} s\gamma \left[ B(js) - B(0) \right] .$$

Substituting (41.3) into this sum we arrive at the double sum

$$\varphi(\tau) = \gamma s G \xi \sum_{j=1}^{N/2} \sum_{i=1}^{j} a_i .$$

By writing it as

$a_1$

$a_1 + a_2$

$a_1 + a_2 + a_3$

.

.

.

$a_1 + a_2 + a_3 + \ldots + a_{N/2}$

we see that the term $a_j$ is repeated $\frac{1}{2}N + 1 - j$ times. Therefore, by summing in columns, we can replace the double sum by a single sum

$$\varphi(\tau) = \gamma s G \xi \sum_{j=1}^{N/2} \left( \frac{1}{2} N + 1 - j \right) a_j .$$

The $\pi$ pulse applied at time $t = \tau$ changes the sign of the phase but does not affect the diffusional process itself. We denote the coefficients describing the direction of the jumps after the pulse by $b_i$ where $b_i = \pm 1$. With these symbols the phase at echo maximum, i.e. at time $t = 2\tau$, is

$$\alpha = \varphi(2\tau) = -\varphi(\tau) + \gamma s G \xi \sum_{j=1}^{N/2} \left(\frac{1}{2}N + 1 - j\right) b_j = \gamma s G \xi \sum_{j=1}^{N/2} \left(\frac{1}{2}N + 1 - j\right)(b_j - a_j)$$

from which we obtain

$$<\alpha^2> = \gamma^2 s^2 G^2 \xi^2 \sum_{j=1}^{N/2} \left(\frac{1}{2}N + 1 - j\right)^2 2 \qquad (41.5)$$

since $b_j^2 = a_j^2 = 1$ and, in view of mutual independence of $a_i$ and $b_i$, we have $<a_j b_j> = 0$.

By applying the well known results

$$1 + 2 + 3 + ... + n = \frac{1}{2} n (n + 1)$$

$$1^2 + 2^2 + 3^2 + ... + n^2 = \frac{1}{6} n (n + 1) (2n + 1)$$

and discarding terms containing N to a power less than 3 (which is justified since N is a very large number) we find that

$$\sum_{j=1}^{N/2} \left(\frac{1}{2}N + 1 - j\right)^2 = \frac{N^3}{24}. \qquad (41.6)$$

Substituting (41.6) into (41.5), and taking advantage of (41.2) and (41.4) we obtain

$$<\alpha^2> = \frac{1}{6}\gamma^2 G^2 D (2\tau)^3$$

where $2\tau$ is the time between the successive maxima in the Carr-Purcell train.

Assuming that the distribution of phases is Gaussian

$$P(\alpha) = \frac{1}{\sqrt{2\pi <\alpha^2>}} \exp\left(\frac{-\alpha^2}{2<\alpha^2>}\right)$$

we calculate the mean

$$\langle \cos \alpha \rangle = \int_{-\infty}^{+\infty} P(\alpha) \cos \alpha \, d\alpha = \exp\left(\frac{-\langle \alpha^2 \rangle}{2}\right) = \exp\left(-\frac{1}{12}\gamma^2 G^2 D (2\tau)^3\right).$$

Substituting this result into expression (41.1) for the amplitude of the nth echo at time $t = 2\tau n$ we obtain the relationship

$$V_n = k M_\infty \exp\left[\left(-\frac{1}{T_2} - \frac{\gamma^2 G^2 D}{12 f^2}\right) t\right] \tag{41.7}$$

where $f = n/t = 1/2\tau$ is the number of echoes per unit time. Equation (41.7) is also the equation of the echo envelope.

By choosing a sufficiently large f we can reduce at will the influence of field inhomogeneity and diffusion on the shape of the envelope. From envelopes measured for two different values of f we can determine the spin-spin relaxation time $T_2$ and the value of $G^2 D$. D is therefore experimentally accessible if the field gradient G is known.

Our discussion of the Carr-Purcell echo train has so far assumed that the pulses which follow the $\pi/2$ pulse satisfy the condition

$$\gamma B_1 \tau_p = \pi \tag{41.8}$$

where $\tau_p$ is the duration of the pulse (see (31.1)). In practice, this requirement can be only partially met because of the difficulty in achieving a homogeneous field $B_1$. We shall therefore consider the influence of the incomplete satisfaction of the condition (41.8) on the envelope of the echo train and describe the method of eliminating this effect as suggested by Meiboom and Gill (1958). Since it amounts to an improvement of the Carr-Purcell experiment, it is known as the Carr-Purcell-Meiboom-Gill sequence or CPMG for short.

We assume that radiofrequency pulses are coherent. Figure 41.1 describes the situation when the axes of all the pulses coincide with the X' axis. By comparing Figures 41.1(c) and 41.1(e) we see that the isochromats are rotated in the same sense by the first and the second $\pi$ pulse. Any imprecision in satisfying condition (41.8) will thus accumulate and, after a sufficiently large number of $\pi$ pulses, may take the elementary transverse vectors away from the X'Y' plane. This, in turn, will reduce the amplitude of the echoes and cause error in the measurement of $T_2$. The error is significant in liquids of low viscosity and long $T_2$ for which, in order to avoid the influence of diffusion, a large number of pulses per unit time is necessary.

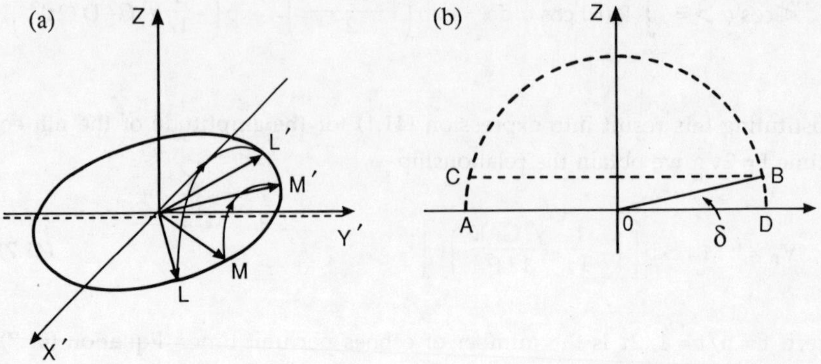


**Figure 41.5.** (a) The action of the π pulse phase-shifted by 90° with respect to the preceding π/2 pulse. The axis of the pulse is marked with a broken line. (b) The action of two successive π - δ pulses.

Meiboom and Gill (1958) pointed out that this difficulty may be avoided if the π pulses are shifted in phase by 90° with respect to the phase of the π/2 pulse. The action of the π/2 pulse and the fanning out of the magnetization is of course the same as in Figures 41.1(a) and 41.1(b), but the axis of the π pulse now coincides with the Y' axis and its action is as shown in Figure 41.5(a). The isochromats are moved to symmetrical positions on the other side of the Y' axis. Now the refocusing of the elementary transverse vectors always takes place on the +Y' axis. In this way the error caused by the imperfect fulfilment of condition (37.1) does not accumulate. This is seen in Figure 41.5(b), which shows a projection of a single isochromat onto the X'Z' plane. Assume that the pulse for which $\gamma B_1 \tau_p = \pi - \delta$ began when the tip of the isochromat was at position A. After the pulse, the vector is in position B, and from that moment onwards it precesses to point C during time 2τ. At that time another π - δ pulse is applied, which transfers the vector in question to point D, from where it precesses back to point A over time 2τ. In this way the imperfections of two successive pulses cancel one another. The CPMG pulse sequence makes it possible to measure $T_2$ longer than 10 s in liquids.

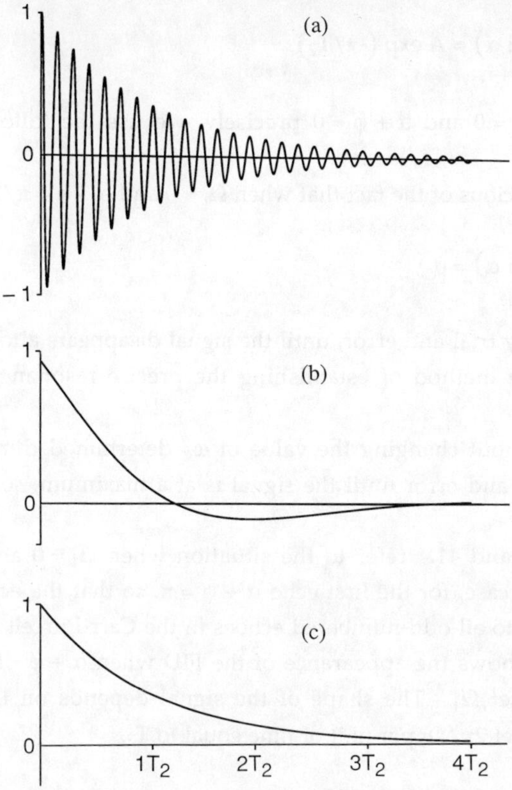


**Figure 41.6.** The form of the free precession signal (FID) at different offsets. (a) Far from resonance, $2\pi/\Omega_i << T_2$ (here $2\pi/\Omega_i = 0.15\ T_2$); (b) close to resonance, $2\pi/\Omega_i = 5\ T_2$; (c) exactly on resonance, $2\pi/\Omega_i >> T_2$ (here $2\pi/\Omega_i = 100\ T_2$). Note that far from resonance the damping function $\exp\left(-t/T_2\right)$ appears as the envelope of the signal.

Consider the form of signals obtained in the experiments discussed in this section. We assume for simplicity that the spectrum contains only one line. We then have only one value of offset $\Omega_i = \omega_i - \omega_e$ in the formula (36.10) for the signal $Z(t)$ obtained by the quadrature detector. Since we are interested in the amplitude, we ask the computer to display the real part of the signal multiplied by an arbitrary phase factor $\exp\left(i\,\alpha\right)$

$$\mathrm{Re}\, Z(t) \exp\left(i\,\alpha\right)$$

$$= A \exp\left(-t/T_2\right) \left[\cos\left(\Omega_i t\right) \cos\left(\varphi + \alpha\right) - \sin\left(\Omega_i t\right) \sin\left(\varphi + \alpha\right)\right].$$

If we set $\alpha + \varphi = 0$ and change the carrier frequency so that $\Omega_i = \omega_i - \omega_e = 0$ (the spectrometer is "on resonance"), we obtain the plot of the damping function

$$\mathrm{Re}\, Z(t) \exp(i\,\alpha) = A \exp(-t/T_2)\,.$$

In order to set $\Omega_i = 0$ and $\alpha + \varphi = 0$ precisely, we use the following two-step procedure.

**Step 1.** Conscious of the fact that when $\Omega_i = 0$ and $\alpha + \varphi = \pi/2$, then

$$\mathrm{Re}\, Z(t) \exp(i\,\alpha) = 0$$

we set $\Omega_i$ and $\alpha$ by trial and error, until the signal disappears altogether. This is the most accurate method of establishing the precise resonance value of the carrier frequency.

**Step 2.** Without changing the value of $\omega_e$ determined during step 1, we change $\alpha$ by trial and error until the signal is at a maximum, so that $\alpha + \varphi = 0$ and $\Omega_i = 0$.

Figures 41.3 and 41.4 refer to the situation when $\Omega_i = 0$ and the FID has $\alpha + \varphi = 0$. In this case, for the first echo $\alpha + \varphi = \pi$, so that the echo is negative. The same applies to all odd-numbered echoes in the Carr-Purcell sequence.

Figure 41.6 shows the appearance of the FID when $\alpha + \varphi \approx 0$ for different values of the offset $\Omega_i$. The shape of the signal depends on the number of periods of the offset $2\pi/\Omega_i$ per unit of time equal to $T_2$.

# Chapter 8. The Dipolar Interaction

## 42. Formulation of the Problem

Consider a system composed of two nuclear spins: spin $\mathbf{I}^{(1)}$ with gyromagnetic ratio $\gamma_1$ and spin $\mathbf{I}^{(2)}$ with gyromagnetic ratio $\gamma_2$. We assume that the two spins belong to a molecule immobilized in a crystal, and that other neighbouring magnetic dipoles are fairly far away, so that the pair can be considered as isolated. The crystal containing identically oriented spin pairs is placed in the magnetic field $\mathbf{B}_0$.

We adopt a laboratory coordinate system with the origin at the centre of spin (1) and the Z axis parallel to $\mathbf{B}_0$. The polar coordinates of a vector joining the nuclei (1) and (2) are denoted by (r, θ, ϕ). In other words, in terms of Figure 3.1 nucleus (1) is at point O and nucleus (2) at point A.

Nucleus (1), with a magnetic moment $\vec{\mu}_1 = \gamma_1 \hbar \, \mathbf{I}^{(1)}$, is a magnetic dipole and generates a magnetic field at the site of nucleus (2). As a result, nucleus (2) experiences the external magnetic field $\mathbf{B}_0$ *plus* a local field $\Delta\mathbf{B}$, which is normally much smaller than $\mathbf{B}_0$. The local field depends on the quantum state of spin (1). Similarly, the local field generated at the site of spin (1) depends on the quantum state of spin (2). The local field manifests itself as the splitting of lines in the NMR spectrum. For example, when $\mathbf{I}^{(2)} = 1/2$, the value of $\Delta\mathbf{B}$ at the site of spin (1) may take on one of two possible values, depending on whether spin (2) is in the state + 1/2 or the state - 1/2. Since both situations are possible in the sample, the spectral line of spin (1) will be split into two. The interaction of two spins via the local field caused by the nuclear dipolar moment is known as the dipolar interaction. This chapter is devoted to the calculation of NMR spectra for the situation in which the dipolar interaction is dominant.

Before proceeding further, we consider the size of dipolar interactions. Since the magnitude of the local field is of the order of $\mu_0 \, \mu / 4\pi \, r^3$, the field generated by a proton at a distance r = 2 Å (typical between atoms within a molecule) is of the order of $2 \times 10^{-4}$ tesla. By comparison, the typical 10 ppm chemical shift range of protons corresponds in a 9.4 tesla magnet to $9.4 \times 10^{-5}$ tesla. It follows that, even in high magnetic fields, dipolar interactions between protons are larger than chemical shift effects. Since the isolation of the pair of spins which we are considering is never perfect, the lines are further broadened by the dipolar interaction with protons belonging to neighbouring pairs. As a consequence, in most solid samples the weak effects of the chemical shift are hidden within the dipolar linewidth, resulting in an almost complete loss of chemical information. It is only with nuclei of large chemical shift range (such as $^{195}Pt$) in very high magnetic fields, and with nuclei of low gyromagnetic ratio, that the chemical shift, which is field-dependent, can compete with the dipole-dipole interaction.

## 43. The Dipolar Hamiltonian

According to classical electromagnetic theory, the energy of interaction between two magnetic point dipoles associated with spins (1) and (2) is

$$E_D = \frac{\mu_o}{4\pi}\left(\frac{\vec{\mu}_1 \cdot \vec{\mu}_2}{r^3} - 3\,\frac{(\vec{\mu}_1 \cdot \mathbf{r})(\vec{\mu}_2 \cdot \mathbf{r})}{r^5}\right) \tag{43.1}$$

where $\vec{\mu}_1$ and $\vec{\mu}_2$ are the two interacting dipole moments, $\mu_o$ is the permeability of vacuum and the dots stand for the scalar product. This formula is valid in the SI system of units (see Section 10), and for the definition (11.1) of the magnetic moment.

The classical expression for the interaction energy $E_D$ is transformed into an operator by the substitution $\vec{\mu}_1 = \gamma_1 \hbar\, \mathbf{I}^{(1)}$ and $\vec{\mu}_2 = \gamma_2 \hbar\, \mathbf{I}^{(2)}$ treating the coordinates of the spin vector as operators. The operator $\mathcal{H}_D$ obtained in this way is known as the dipolar Hamiltonian. It is convenient to introduce operators $I_+$ and $I_-$ for both spins in accordance with the definition (4.16), for example $I_+^{(i)} = I_x^{(i)} + i\, I_y^{(i)}$, because the rules of their operation (4.17) are very simple. We can then transform all scalar products appearing in (43.1) according to the formula

$$\mathbf{K} \cdot \mathbf{L} = \frac{1}{2} K_+ L_- + \frac{1}{2} K_- L_+ + K_z L_z \tag{43.2}$$

where $K_+ = K_x + i\, K_y$ and $K_- = K_x - i\, K_y$, and similarly for L. For example

$$\vec{\mu}_1 \cdot \mathbf{r} = \gamma_1 \hbar \left(\frac{1}{2} I_+^{(1)} r_- + \frac{1}{2} I_-^{(1)} r_+ + I_z z\right).$$

We use a laboratory coordinate system in which, as is usual, the Z axis is parallel to $\mathbf{B}_0$. In accordance with (3.3), in the polar coordinate system with the origin at spin (1) the coordinates of vector $\mathbf{r}$ are

$$r_+/r = \sin\theta \exp(i\,\phi)$$

$$r_-/r = \sin\theta \exp(-i\,\phi) \qquad (43.3)$$

$$z/r = \cos\theta\,.$$

After substituting (43.2) into (43.1) we group terms containing products $I_+^{(1)} I_+^{(2)}$, $I_+^{(1)} I_-^{(2)}$, $I_-^{(1)} I_+^{(2)}$, $I_z^{(1)} I_z^{(2)}$, etc., and express the coefficients appearing together with these products in terms of (43.3). The dipolar Hamiltonian $\mathcal{H}_D$ obtained in this way is given by the "alphabet" expression

$$\mathcal{H}_D = d\left[\,A + B + C + D + E + F\,\right] \qquad (43.4)$$

where

$$A = I_z^{(1)} I_z^{(2)} \left(1 - 3\cos^2\theta\right)$$

$$B = -\tfrac{1}{4}\left(I_+^{(1)} I_-^{(2)} + I_-^{(1)} I_+^{(2)}\right)\left(1 - 3\cos^2\theta\right)$$

$$C = -\tfrac{3}{2}\left(I_+^{(1)} I_z^{(2)} + I_z^{(1)} I_+^{(2)}\right)\sin\theta\cos\theta\exp\left(-i\,\phi\right)$$

$$D = -\tfrac{3}{2}\left(I_-^{(1)} I_z^{(2)} + I_z^{(1)} I_-^{(2)}\right)\sin\theta\cos\theta\exp\left(i\,\phi\right) \qquad (43.5)$$

$$E = -\tfrac{3}{4}\left(I_+^{(1)} I_+^{(2)}\right)\sin^2\theta\exp\left(-2i\,\phi\right)$$

$$F = -\tfrac{3}{4}\left(I_-^{(1)} I_-^{(2)}\right)\sin^2\theta\exp\left(2i\,\varphi\right)$$

$$d = \frac{\mu_0\,\gamma_1\,\gamma_2\,\hbar^2}{4\pi\, r^3}\,.$$

The constant d is known as the "dipolar coupling constant".

Each of the terms A to F contains a spin factor and a geometrical factor. We note that the time-averaged values of the terms C, D, E and F are all zero, because for the random thermal motion of molecules in liquids

$$\langle \exp(\pm i\,\phi)\rangle = \langle \exp(\pm 2i\,\phi)\rangle = 0\,.$$

These terms do not therefore lead to the splitting or broadening of NMR lines in liquids, and are only active in nuclear relaxation. Further, terms A and B contain the factor $(1 - 3\cos^2\theta)$. In Section 38 we have shown that for a random thermal motion of molecules the time average $\langle 3\cos^2\theta - 1\rangle = 0$, with the result that in liquids the whole dipolar interaction is averaged to zero. This may also be the case in some solids in which, provided that the temperature is not too low, molecules may reorient freely. However, in this chapter we consider only the case of motionless molecules.

## 44. Truncation of the Dipolar Hamiltonian

In order to calculate the NMR spectrum for the case when both interacting nuclei have the same spin quantum number I = 1/2, we first need to calculate the eigenvalues of the total Hamiltonian

$$\mathcal{H} = \mathcal{H}_Z + \mathcal{H}_D$$

where the Zeeman Hamiltonian has the form $\mathcal{H}_Z = \hbar\,\omega_1\,I_z^{(1)} + \hbar\,\omega_2\,I_z^{(2)}$ (known from Section 15), while $\mathcal{H}_D$ is given by (43.4). The exact way of doing so would be to diagonalize the sum of matrix representations. However, it is more appropriate to use the time-independent perturbation theory (Section 8) and treat $\mathcal{H}_D$ as a small perturbation on the Zeeman Hamiltonian. This method, albeit approximate, gives results which are more comprehensible and more easily compared with experiment. It is necessary to consider two distinct cases:

1. $\gamma_1 = \gamma_2$, which means that the two spins are identical. This is the so-called homonuclear case.
2. $\gamma_1 \neq \gamma_2$. In this case we must make an additional assumption concerning the size of the quantity $|\,B_o(\gamma_1 - \gamma_2)\,|$. The reason is that the use of the perturbation theory is only legitimate when all eigenvalues of $\mathcal{H}_Z$ are much larger than the eigenvalues of $\mathcal{H}_D$. We will see later that this condition reduces to the inequality $\hbar\,|\,B_o(\gamma_1 - \gamma_2)\,| >> d$, which is always satisfied when spins (1) and (2) belong to different nuclear species, such as $^1H$ and $^{19}F$. This is why this case is known as heteronuclear.

The eigenfunctions of the Zeeman Hamiltonian $\mathcal{H}_Z$

$$|++\rangle,\ |+-\rangle,\ |-+\rangle \text{ and } |--\rangle \tag{44.1}$$

have been calculated in Section 15, and their eigenvalues are listed in Table 15.1. Note that in the homonuclear case, when $\omega_1 = \omega_2$, one of the eigenvalues (which is equal to zero) is doubly degenerate, because it appears with eigenfunctions $|+-\rangle$ and $|-+\rangle$. In the heteronuclear case there is no such degeneracy.

In order to discover how to truncate the perturbing Hamiltonian $\mathcal{H}_D$, we must consider which of the terms in the sum (43.4) contribute to each of the elements of the matrix $\{\mathcal{H}_D\}$ represented in the *eigenbasis of the Hamiltonian* $\mathcal{H}_Z$ (44.1).

Consider first the term A containing the product of operators $I_z^{(1)} I_z^{(2)}$. We act with this product on all eigenfunctions of $\mathcal{H}_Z$. As was explained in Section 15, the operator $I_z^{(1)}$ acts only on the first quantum number in a ket and the operator $I_z^{(2)}$ acts only on the second quantum number. Following this principle we obtain

$$I_z^{(1)} I_z^{(2)} |++\rangle = \frac{1}{2}\frac{1}{2}|++\rangle = \frac{1}{4}|++\rangle$$

$$I_z^{(1)} I_z^{(2)} |+-\rangle = \frac{1}{2}\left(-\frac{1}{2}\right)|+-\rangle = -\frac{1}{4}|+-\rangle$$

$$I_z^{(1)} I_z^{(2)} |-+\rangle = \left(-\frac{1}{2}\right)\frac{1}{2}|-+\rangle = -\frac{1}{4}|-+\rangle$$

$$I_z^{(1)} I_z^{(2)} |--\rangle = \left(-\frac{1}{2}\right)\left(-\frac{1}{2}\right)|--\rangle = \frac{1}{4}|--\rangle.$$

We see that term A contributes only to the diagonal elements, because it "links" only identical eigenfunctions. For example

$$\langle ++|\, I_z^{(1)} I_z^{(2)} |++\rangle = \frac{1}{4}\langle ++|++\rangle = \frac{1}{4}$$

whereas

$$\langle --|\, I_z^{(1)} I_z^{(2)} |++\rangle = \frac{1}{4}\langle --|++\rangle = 0.$$

Consider now the term B. We have

$$\left(I_+^{(1)} I_-^{(2)} + I_-^{(1)} I_+^{(2)}\right) |++\rangle = 0$$

$$\left(I_+^{(1)} I_-^{(2)} + I_-^{(1)} I_+^{(2)}\right) |--\rangle = 0$$

because the state + 1/2 cannot be raised by $I_+$ and the state - 1/2 cannot be lowered by $I_-$. Acting with term B on the remaining two eigenfunctions we obtain

$$\left(I_+^{(1)} I_-^{(2)} + I_-^{(1)} I_+^{(2)}\right) |+-\rangle = |-+\rangle$$

$$\left(I_+^{(1)} I_-^{(2)} + I_-^{(1)} I_+^{(2)}\right) |-+\rangle = |+-\rangle .$$

We see that term B gives two non-diagonal elements "linking" the states $|+-\rangle$ and $|-+\rangle$:

$$\langle +-| B |-+\rangle \qquad \text{and} \qquad \langle -+| B |+-\rangle .$$

In an entirely analogous way we show that the terms C, D, E and F give only non-diagonal elements. Results of these calculations are given in Table 44.1.

**Table 44.1.** The contribution of the individual terms of the Hamiltonian $\mathcal{H}_D = d\,(A + B + C + D + E + F)$ to the various terms of the matrix $\{\mathcal{H}_D\}$ represented in the eigenbasis of the operator $\mathcal{H}_Z$.

| | $\|++\rangle$ | $\|+-\rangle$ | $\|-+\rangle$ | $\|--\rangle$ |
|---|---|---|---|---|
| $\langle ++\|$ | A | C | C | E |
| $\langle +-\|$ | D | A | B | C |
| $\langle -+\|$ | D | B | A | C |
| $\langle --\|$ | F | D | D | A |

The rules of truncation require that the diagonal and non-diagonal elements "linking" the states belonging to the same degenerate eigenvalue be left, and all remaining elements discarded (replaced by zeros). Truncation will thus be different for the heteronuclear case, when $\omega_1 \neq \omega_2$ and $\mathcal{H}_Z$ does not have degenerate eigenvalues, and different for the homonuclear case when such degeneration is present. It follows that in the heteronuclear case we need to leave only elements coming from the term A. The truncated dipolar Hamiltonian is thus

$$\mathcal{H}_D' = d\,A = d\left(1 - 3\cos^2\theta\right) I_z^{(1)} I_z^{(2)} \tag{44.2}$$

$$\left\{\mathcal{H}_D'\right\} = -\tfrac{1}{4}\, d\left(1 - 3\cos^2\theta\right) \begin{Bmatrix} -1 & 0 & 0 & 0 \\ 0 & 1 & 0 & 0 \\ 0 & 0 & 1 & 0 \\ 0 & 0 & 0 & -1 \end{Bmatrix}. \tag{44.3}$$

On the other hand, in the homonuclear case, in which the functions $|+-\rangle$ and $|-+\rangle$ belong to the same energy level, the truncated dipolar Hamiltonian takes on a different form

$$\mathcal{H}_D' = d\,(A + B) = d\left(1 - 3\cos^2\theta\right)\left[\, I_z^{(1)} I_z^{(2)} - \tfrac{1}{4}\left(I_+^{(1)} I_-^{(2)} + I_-^{(1)} I_+^{(2)}\right)\right] \tag{44.4}$$

$$\left\{\mathcal{H}_D'\right\} = -\tfrac{1}{4}\, d\left(1 - 3\cos^2\theta\right) \begin{Bmatrix} -1 & 0 & 0 & 0 \\ 0 & 1 & 1 & 0 \\ 0 & 1 & 1 & 0 \\ 0 & 0 & 0 & -1 \end{Bmatrix}. \tag{44.5}$$

Because of this difference, the two cases must be treated separately.

## 45. The Homonuclear Case

Consider the homonuclear case first. In order to diagonalize matrix (44.5) it is sufficient to diagonalize the matrix

$$\begin{Bmatrix} 1 & 1 \\ 1 & 1 \end{Bmatrix}$$

by forming two new eigenfunctions

$$|2\rangle = x_1^{(2)}\,|+-\rangle + x_2^{(2)}\,|-+\rangle$$

$$|3\rangle = x_1^{(3)}\,|+-\rangle + x_2^{(3)}\,|-+\rangle.$$

On the other hand, the eigenfunctions $|++\rangle$ and $|--\rangle$ are eigenfunctions of $\mathcal{H}_D'$ and remain unchanged. In accordance with the diagonalization procedure described in Section 6, the eigenvalues are obtained from the characteristic equation

$$\begin{vmatrix} 1-\lambda & 1 \\ 1 & 1-\lambda \end{vmatrix} = \lambda\,(2-\lambda) = 0\,.$$

It is clear that the two roots of the above equation are $\lambda_2 = 2$ and $\lambda_3 = 0$. It follows that the eigenvalues of $\mathcal{H}_D'$ which appear with eigenfunctions $|2\rangle$ and $|3\rangle$ are $-\frac{1}{2}\,d\left(1 - 3\cos^2\theta\right)$ and 0, respectively. The coefficients $x_1$ and $x_2$ are obtained from the set of homogeneous equations (6.17), which for the case in hand has the form

$$\begin{aligned} (1-\lambda)\,x_1 \quad &+ x_2 = 0 \\ x_1 \quad &+ (1-\lambda)\,x_2 = 0. \end{aligned} \tag{45.1}$$

Two sets of the coefficients required are obtained from these equations by substituting $\lambda = \lambda_2$ and $\lambda = \lambda_3$ in turn and solving for $x_1$ and $x_2$. However, these equations are not linearly independent, because their determinant vanishes. It is therefore sufficient to solve one of them, because solving the other will give the same answer.

Substituting $\lambda = \lambda_2 = 2$ into the first of equations (45.1) we obtain

$$-\,x_1^{(2)} + x_2^{(2)} = 0\,.$$

However, since the eigenfunction $|2\rangle$ is normalized, it is necessary that

$$\left(x_1^{(2)}\right)^2 + \left(x_2^{(2)}\right)^2 = 1$$

so that $x_1^{(2)} = 1/\sqrt{2}$ and $x_2^{(2)} = 1/\sqrt{2}$. We thus have $|2\rangle = \left(1/\sqrt{2}\right)\left(|+-\rangle + |-+\rangle\right)$. Similarly, by substituting $\lambda = \lambda_3 = 0$ we obtain $|3\rangle = \left(1/\sqrt{2}\right)\left(|+-\rangle - |-+\rangle\right)$.

These eigenfunctions of the Hamiltonian $\mathcal{H}_D'$ are simultaneously eigenfunctions of the Hamiltonian $\mathcal{H}_Z$. Table 45.1 gives all four functions which are eigenfunctions of both these Hamiltonians, together with their eigenvalues.

**Table 45.1.** The case of a homonuclear pair of spins. Eigenfunctions and eigenvalues of the Zeeman Hamiltonian $\mathcal{H}_Z = \hbar\,\omega_0 \left(I_z^{(1)} + I_z^{(2)}\right)$ and of the truncated dipolar Hamiltonian $\mathcal{H}_D' = d\,(A + B)$.

| Eigenfunction | Eigenvalue of $\mathcal{H}_Z$ | Eigenvalue of $\mathcal{H}_D'$ | Eigenvalue of $\mathcal{H}_Z + \mathcal{H}_D'$ |
|---|---|---|---|
| $\lvert 1\rangle = \lvert ++\rangle$ | $\hbar\,\omega_0$ | $\frac{d}{4}(1 - 3\cos^2\theta)$ | $\hbar\,\omega_0 + \frac{d}{4}(1 - 3\cos^2\theta)$ |
| $\lvert 2\rangle = \frac{1}{\sqrt{2}}(\lvert +-\rangle + \lvert -+\rangle)$ | 0 | $-\frac{d}{2}(1 - 3\cos^2\theta)$ | $-\frac{d}{2}(1 - 3\cos^2\theta)$ |
| $\lvert 3\rangle = \frac{1}{\sqrt{2}}(\lvert +-\rangle - \lvert -+\rangle)$ | 0 | 0 | 0 |
| $\lvert 4\rangle = \lvert --\rangle$ | $-\hbar\,\omega_0$ | $\frac{d}{4}(1 - 3\cos^2\theta)$ | $-\hbar\,\omega_0 + \frac{d}{4}(1 - 3\cos^2\theta)$ |

Figure 45.1 shows the corresponding energy levels according to column 4 of the above table.

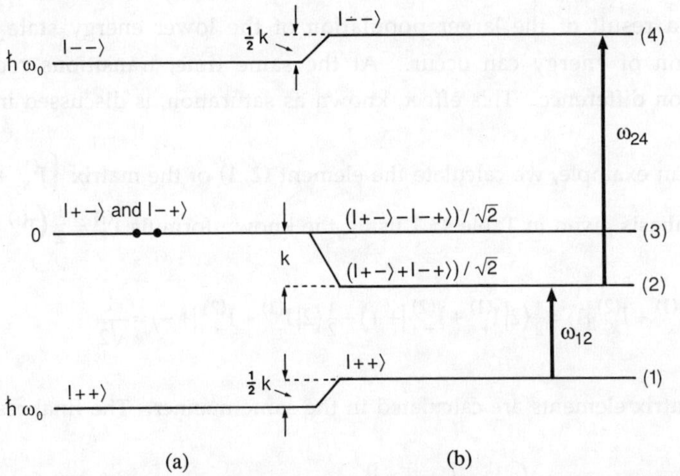


**Figure 45.1.** Energy levels of a homonuclear system of two spins 1/2. (a) Zeeman interaction alone; (b) Zeeman and dipolar interactions. Allowed transitions are marked with bold arrows. $k = \frac{1}{2} d\left(1 - 3\cos^2\theta\right)$. The states are numbered according to Table 45.1. Distances shown are not to scale because $k << \omega_0$.

Since we are interested in the spectrum, we now have to consider transitions between the calculated levels. In the continuous-wave method of NMR, transitions between states are caused by the oscillating magnetic field generated along the X' axis of the rotating frame, which is collinear with the coil

$$\mathbf{i}\,2B_1 \cos\left(\omega_e\, t\right)$$

where **i** is the unit vector along the X' axis. The interaction of the spins with this field is

$$\left(\vec{\mu}_1 + \vec{\mu}_1\right) \cdot \mathbf{i}\, 2B_1 \cos\left(\omega_e t\right) = -\gamma\hbar\left(I_x^{(1)} + I_x^{(2)}\right) 2B_1 \cos\left(\omega_e t\right)$$

and serves as a time-dependent perturbation (see Section 9) causing transitions between states (1) and (2) when $\omega_e \approx \omega_{12}$ and between states (2) and (4) when $\omega_e \approx \omega_{24}$. According to time-dependent perturbation theory (see Section 8), the probability that a transition will take place is proportional to the square of the matrix element "linking" the states, so that $\omega_{12} = \omega_{21} = \left|\langle 2|\, I_x^{(1)} + I_x^{(2)}\, |1\rangle\right|^2$ and $\omega_{24} = \omega_{42} = \left|\langle 4|\, I_x^{(1)} + I_x^{(2)}\, |2\rangle\right|^2$. In order to estimate these intensities we must calculate the matrix elements involved. Since the oscillating field causes transitions between two states with the same probability in either direction, it is only as a result of the larger population of the lower energy state that net absorption of energy can occur. At the same time, transitions reduce the population difference. This effect, known as saturation, is discussed in Section 29.

As an example, we calculate the element (2, 1) of the matrix $\left\{I_x^{(1)} + I_x^{(2)}\right\}$ in the eigenbasis given in Table 45.1 using the known formula $I_x^{(i)} = \frac{1}{2}\left(I_+^{(i)} + I_-^{(i)}\right)$

$$\langle 2|\, I_x^{(1)} + I_x^{(2)}\, |1\rangle = \tfrac{1}{2}\langle 2|\, I_+^{(1)} + I_+^{(2)}\, |{+}{+}\rangle + \tfrac{1}{2}\langle 2|\, I_-^{(1)} + I_-^{(2)}\, |{+}{+}\rangle = \frac{1}{\sqrt{2}}.$$

Other matrix elements are calculated in the same manner. The final result is

$$\left\{I_x^{(1)} + I_x^{(2)}\right\} = \frac{1}{\sqrt{2}}\begin{Bmatrix} 0 & 1 & 0 & 0 \\ 1 & 0 & 0 & 1 \\ 0 & 0 & 0 & 0 \\ 0 & 1 & 0 & 0 \end{Bmatrix}.$$

Inspection of this matrix tells us that the probabilities of transitions $|1\rangle \leftrightarrow |2\rangle$ and $|2\rangle \leftrightarrow |4\rangle$ are the same, and that the probability of all transitions from or to state $|3\rangle$ is zero.

We conclude that the spectrum of a homonuclear system of two spins coupled via the dipolar interaction (see Figure 45.2) consists of two lines of equal intensity with the angular frequencies

$$\omega_{12} = \omega_0 + \frac{3}{4} d\, \hbar^{-1} \left(1 - 3\cos^2\theta\right)$$

$$\omega_{24} = \omega_0 - \frac{3}{4} d\, \hbar^{-1} \left(1 - 3\cos^2\theta\right)$$

where d is defined in (43.5) and the transitions are shown in Figure 45.1. The spacing of the lines depends on the orientation of the crystal with respect to $B_0$. Note that the internuclear distance r can be obtained experimentally with a fairly good precision from the maximum value of the spacing, which is $3d\hbar^{-1}$. Furthermore, measurements carried out at a number of different crystal orientations may yield the orientation of the internuclear vector with respect to the crystal axis.

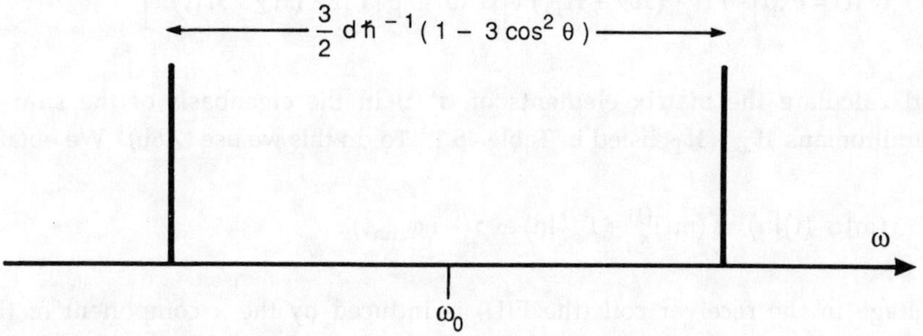


**Figure 45.2.** Spectrum of a homonuclear pair of spins 1/2. d is the dipolar coupling constant (43.5).

The splitting of the NMR line of a pair of two protons was discovered in gypsum, $CaSO_4 \cdot 2H_2O$, by Pake (1948), who also provided a theoretical explanation of the effect. This spectrum is therefore known as the "Pake doublet". The case of three protons located at apices of an equilateral triangle was solved by Andrew and Bersohn (1950) and that of four protons at apices of a regular tetrahedron by Bersohn and Gutowsky (1954). The larger the number of spins in the system, the higher the dimension of the Hilbert space $L = (2I + 1)^N$ and the more difficult the calculation of the spectrum.

We will now show how to derive the dipolar spectrum of a homonuclear pair of spins 1/2 in pulsed NMR. We begin with the density matrix at equilibrium

$$\sigma_\infty = \varepsilon \left(I_z^{(1)} + I_z^{(2)}\right) \tag{45.2}$$

where $\varepsilon = \gamma B_0 \hbar / 4kT$. We go over to the resonance rotating frame using the operator $\exp\left(i\, \hbar^{-1} \mathcal{H}_Z t\right)$, which commutes with the operators $\sigma_\infty$ and $\mathcal{H}_D'$ and thus does not change their form.

The $P_y$ pulse transforms the operator (45.2) into

$$\sigma'(0) = -\varepsilon\left(I_x^{(1)} + I_x^{(2)}\right).$$

Since in the rotating frame the interaction $\mathcal{H}_Z$ disappears (see Section 33), the evolution of $\sigma'$ proceeds solely under the operator $\mathcal{H}_D'$

$$\sigma'(t) = \exp\left(-i\hbar^{-1}\mathcal{H}_D' t\right)\sigma'(0)\exp\left(i\hbar^{-1}\mathcal{H}_D' t\right).$$

We now return to the laboratory frame using the operator $\exp\left(-i\hbar^{-1}\mathcal{H}_Z t\right)$

$$\sigma'(t) = \exp\left[-i\hbar^{-1}\left(\mathcal{H}_Z + \mathcal{H}_D'\right)t\right]\sigma'(0)\exp\left[i\hbar^{-1}\left(\mathcal{H}_Z + \mathcal{H}_D'\right)t\right]$$

and calculate the matrix elements of $\sigma'(t)$ in the eigenbasis of the sum of Hamiltonians $\mathcal{H}_Z + \mathcal{H}_D'$ listed in Table 45.1. To do this we use (7.6b). We obtain

$$\langle m|\sigma'(t)|n\rangle = \varepsilon\langle m|I_x^{(1)} + I_x^{(2)}|n\rangle\exp(-i\omega_{mn}t).$$

Voltage in the receiver coil (the FID) is induced by the x component of the magnetization $M_x = \langle\langle \mathcal{M}_x\rangle\rangle$, where $\mathcal{M}_x = q\left(I_x^{(1)} + I_x^{(2)}\right)$, $q = N^{(\rho)}\gamma\hbar$ and $N^{(\rho)}$ is the number of pairs per unit volume of the sample. We calculate $M_x$ according to the formula

$$M_x = \langle\langle \mathcal{M}_x\rangle\rangle = \mathrm{Tr}\left[\sigma(t)\,M_x\right] = \sum_{m,n}\langle m|\sigma(t)|n\rangle\langle n|\mathcal{M}_x|m\rangle$$

$$= -\varepsilon q\sum_{m,n}\langle m|I_x^{(1)} + I_x^{(2)}|n\rangle\langle n|I_x^{(1)} + I_x^{(2)}|m\rangle\exp(-i\omega_{mn}t)$$

$$= -\varepsilon q\sum_{m,n}\left|\langle m|I_x^{(1)} + I_x^{(2)}|n\rangle\right|^2\exp(-i\omega_{mn}t).$$

We see therefore that circular frequencies appear with the intensity $\left|\langle m|I_x^{(1)} + I_x^{(2)}|n\rangle\right|^2$, exactly the same as in the continuous-wave method. We thus obtain exactly the same spectrum. This illustrates the equivalence of the continuous-wave and the pulsed methods of NMR.

## 46. The Heteronuclear Case

Consider now the case when $\omega_1 \neq \omega_2$, for which the the eigenfunctions and eigenvalues of $\mathcal{H}_Z$ are listed in Table 15.1, and the eigenvalues of the truncated dipolar Hamiltonian $\mathcal{H}_D^{'}$ are given by (44.3). Table 46.1 gives the eigenfunctions and eigenvalues of their sum. Note that the meaning of symbols $|1\rangle$, $|2\rangle$, $|3\rangle$ and $|4\rangle$ is now different to that in Table 45.1.

**Table 46.1.** The case of a heteronuclear pair of spins. Common eigenfunctions of the Hamiltonian $\mathcal{H}_Z = \hbar\left(\omega_1 I_z^{(1)} + \omega_2 I_z^{(2)}\right)$ and of the truncated dipolar Hamiltonian (44.2) and the eigenvalues of their sum.

| Eigenfunction | Eigenvalue of $\mathcal{H}_Z + \mathcal{H}_D^{'}$ |
|---|---|
| $\|1\rangle = \|{+}{+}\rangle$ | $\frac{1}{2}\hbar\,(\omega_1 + \omega_2) + \frac{d}{4}(1 - 3\cos^2\theta)$ |
| $\|2\rangle = \|{+}{-}\rangle$ | $\frac{1}{2}\hbar\,(\omega_1 - \omega_2) - \frac{d}{4}(1 - 3\cos^2\theta)$ |
| $\|3\rangle = \|{-}{+}\rangle$ | $-\frac{1}{2}\hbar\,(\omega_1 - \omega_2) - \frac{d}{4}(1 - 3\cos^2\theta)$ |
| $\|4\rangle = \|{-}{-}\rangle$ | $-\frac{1}{2}\hbar\,(\omega_1 + \omega_2) + \frac{d}{4}(1 - 3\cos^2\theta)$ |

The energy levels of $\mathcal{H}_Z + \mathcal{H}_D^{'}$ are shown in Figure 46.1. In order to discover which transitions between these energy levels can occur as a result of the action of an oscillating radiofrequency field, we calculate the matrix of the operator $I_x^{(1)} + I_x^{(2)}$ using eigenvalues given in Table 46.1:

$$\left\{I_x^{(1)} + I_x^{(2)}\right\} = \frac{1}{2}\begin{Bmatrix} 0 & 1 & 1 & 0 \\ 1 & 0 & 0 & 1 \\ 1 & 0 & 0 & 1 \\ 0 & 1 & 1 & 0 \end{Bmatrix}.$$

We see that four transitions have non-zero probabilities: $|1\rangle \leftrightarrow |2\rangle$, $|1\rangle \leftrightarrow |3\rangle$, $|2\rangle \leftrightarrow |4\rangle$ and $|3\rangle \leftrightarrow |4\rangle$ with the frequencies

$$\omega_{21} = \omega_2 + \frac{d}{2\hbar}(1 - 3\cos^2\theta)$$

$$\omega_{31} = \omega_1 + \frac{d}{2\hbar}(1 - 3\cos^2\theta)$$

$$\omega_{42} = \omega_1 - \frac{d}{2\hbar}\left(1 - 3\cos^2\theta\right)$$

$$\omega_{43} = \omega_2 - \frac{d}{2\hbar}\left(1 - 3\cos^2\theta\right).$$

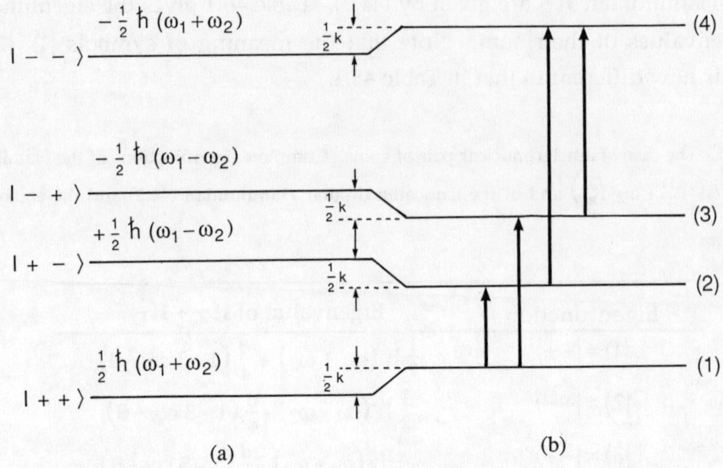


**Figure 46.1.** Energy levels of a heteronuclear system of two spins 1/2. (a) Zeeman interaction alone; (b) Zeeman and dipolar interactions. Allowed transitions are marked with bold arrows. $k = \frac{1}{2}d\left(1 - 3\cos^2\theta\right)$. The states are numbered according to Table 46.1. Distances shown are not to scale because $k << \left|\omega_1 - \omega_2\right|$.

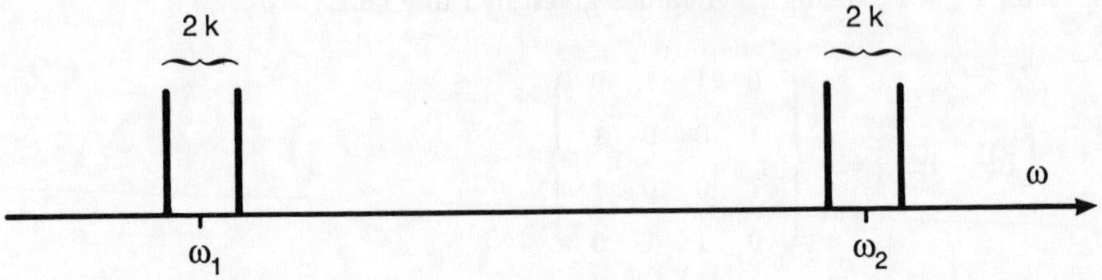


**Figure 46.2.** Spectrum of a heteronuclear pair of spins 1/2. The drawing is not to scale, because $|\omega_2 - \omega_1| >> d$, where d is the dipolar coupling constant (43.5). In fact, the two doublets are so far from each other that in order to observe both of them the spectrometer must be retuned. $k = \frac{1}{2}d\left(1 - 3\cos^2\theta\right)$.

The spectrum is shown in Figure 46.2. We see that the line from spin (1) is symmetrically split into two components of equal intensity. The distance between the two components is $d\,\hbar^{-1}\left(1 - 3\cos^2\theta\right)$. The same applies to the line belonging to spin (2).

## 47. Dipolar Spectrum of a Powdered Sample

In a powdered sample all values of θ are present at random, and it is of interest to consider the form of the spectrum resulting from a superposition of a large number of signals coming from variously oriented microcrystals, each producing spectral lines at a specific location determined by the orientation of the microcrystal with respect to the field $\mathbf{B}_0$. We shall perform the calculation for a homonuclear pair of spin 1/2 nuclei.

Introduce the function

$$p = \varepsilon\left(3\cos^2\theta - 1\right) \tag{47.1}$$

where $\varepsilon = \pm 1$. The value of p for a given angle θ determines the position of the spectral line. It is clear that for the line with $\varepsilon = 1$ and $\varepsilon = -1$ we have $-1 \le p \le 2$ and $-2 \le p \le 1$, respectively. We denote the normalized shape of this signal by g (p), so that for the first half-spectrum (from the line with $\varepsilon = 1$) we have

$$\int_{-1}^{+2} g_1(p)\, dp = 1\,.$$

Imagine that one of the interacting nuclei is placed at the centre of a sphere of unit radius, and extend the internuclear vector until it crosses the surface of the sphere. Since the crystallites are randomly oriented, the density of such cross-sectional points will be uniform throughout the surface of the sphere. We want to know what fraction of such points corresponds to an infinitely small range of the angle θ, from θ to θ + dθ. This region forms an annulus on the surface, as shown in Figure 38.1. Note that a similar annulus, corresponding to the region -θ - dθ lies on the other hemisphere (not shown). We have to add the areas of both annuli, because angles θ and - θ correspond to the same position of the spectral line. The sum of these areas is

$$2 \times 2\pi \sin\theta\, d\theta \tag{47.2}$$

where sin θ is the radius, and dθ the width of each annulus. The fraction of the surface of the sphere occupied by the two annuli is obtained by dividing (47.2) by the surface area of the sphere, $4\pi$. This fraction is therefore $\sin\theta \, d\theta$. On the other hand, the same fraction corresponds to the fraction of the mass of the powdered sample which gives spectral lines in the interval (p, p + dp). This fraction equals $g_1(p)\, dp$. In this way we arrive at the equation

$$g_1(p)\, dp = \sin\theta \, d\theta \,. \tag{47.3}$$

By differentiating (47.1) with respect to $\theta$ we obtain

$$\left|\frac{dp}{d\theta}\right| = 6 \cos\theta \sin\theta \,. \tag{47.4}$$

Introducing (47.4) into (47.3) we find that

$$g_1(p) = \frac{1}{6 \cos\theta} \,. \tag{47.5}$$

On the other hand, from (47.1) we have

$$\cos\theta = \sqrt{(p+1)/3} \tag{47.6}$$

so that the final result is

$$g_1(p) = \frac{1}{2\sqrt{3}} \frac{1}{\sqrt{p+1}} . \tag{47.7}$$

Considering the range of p (see above), the limiting values of $g_1(p)$ are

$$p \to -1 \qquad g_1(p) \to \infty \qquad \theta = \pi/2$$

$$p = 0 \qquad g_1(p) = \frac{1}{2\sqrt{3}} \qquad \theta = \arccos \frac{1}{\sqrt{3}} = 54^{o}\, 44'$$

$$p = 2 \qquad g_1(p) = \frac{1}{6} \qquad \theta = 0 \,.$$

The other half-spectrum (for $\varepsilon = -1$) is calculated in the same way. The resulting function

$$g_2(p) = \frac{1}{2\sqrt{3}} \frac{1}{\sqrt{1-p}}$$

is simply a reflection of $g_1$ (p) with respect to p = 0. The total spectrum, shown in Figure 47.1, is the sum of both half-spectra, g (p) = $g_1$ (p) + $g_2$ (p). In practice the dipolar spectrum is broadened further as a result of interactions with next-nearest-neighbour nuclei and of chemical shift interactions.

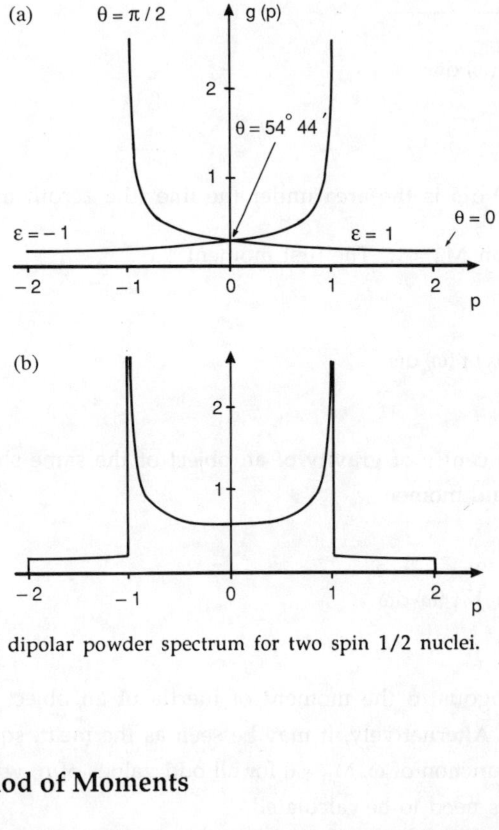


**Figure 47.1.** The dipolar powder spectrum for two spin 1/2 nuclei. (a) $g_1$ (p) and $g_2$ (p); (b) $g_1$ (p) + $g_2$ (p).

## 48. The Method of Moments

We have seen that the dipolar interaction within an isolated pair of protons in a powdered sample leads to a substantially broadened NMR spectrum. The situation is complicated still further when groups of more than two interacting nuclei are present, and when interactions with other spin systems have to be considered. In this case, each crystallite becomes an assembly of an enormous number of interlinked spins, and its spectrum is intractable by normal quantum-mechanical methods. It turns out that even then the method of moments, developed by Van Vleck (1948), can provide important information about the sample. This section describes the main idea of the method. For detailed derivation of the formulas we refer the reader to the book by Abragam (1983).

The nth moment of the lineshape $f(\omega)$ about $\omega_0$ is defined as

$$M_n = \frac{\int_0^{\infty} (\omega - \omega_0)^n f(\omega)\, d\omega}{\int_0^{\infty} f(\omega)\, d\omega} \tag{48.1}$$

where $M_o = \int_0^{\infty} f(\omega)\, d\omega$ is the area under the line (the zeroth moment). For a normalized function $M_0 = 1$. The first moment

$$M_1 = \int_0^{\infty} (\omega - \omega_0)\, f(\omega)\, d\omega \tag{48.2}$$

is then zero at the centre of gravity of an object of the same shape as the line ($\omega = \omega_0$). The second moment

$$M_2 = \int_0^{\infty} (\omega - \omega_0)^2 f(\omega)\, d\omega \tag{48.3}$$

is physically analogous to the moment of inertia of an object with the same shape as the line. Alternatively, it may be seen as the mean square linewidth. If $f(\omega)$ is an even function of $\omega$, $M_n = 0$ for all odd values of n, which means that only even moments need to be calculated.

When, as is often the case in the solid state, the NMR line is Gaussian

$$f(\omega) = \frac{1}{\sigma\sqrt{2\pi}} \exp\left(\frac{-(\omega - \omega_0)^2}{2\sigma^2}\right) \tag{48.4}$$

the second moment is easily seen to be equal to $\sigma^2$. On the other hand, for a Lorentzian line, the second or higher moments cannot be properly calculated, because the integrals in (48.1) diverge.

Using a diagonal sum method, Van Vleck (1948) calculated the value of each moment from the interatomic distances in the solid containing pairs j, k of nuclei linked via the dipolar interaction. The expression for the second moment, known as the Van Vleck formula, is

$$M_2 = \frac{3}{4}\gamma^4 \hbar^2 I(I+1) \sum_k \frac{(1 - 3\cos^2\theta_{jk})^2}{r_{jk}^6} \tag{48.5}$$

where $\mathbf{r}_{jk}$ is the internuclear vector, and $\theta_{jk}$ the angle between $\mathbf{r}_{jk}$ and $\mathbf{B}_0$. For a polycrystalline powder composed of randomly oriented crystals we can use the average value of 4/5 calculated in Section 38 for $(1 - 3\cos^2\theta_{jk})^2$. The final result for identical nuclei is thus

$$M_2 = \frac{3}{5}\gamma^4 \hbar^2 I(I+1) \sum_k \frac{1}{r_{jk}^6}. \tag{48.6}$$

However, the second moment due to the interaction of *unlike* spins is different from the above result by the factor

$$\frac{4}{9}\left(\frac{\gamma_S}{\gamma_I}\right)^2 \frac{S(S+1)}{I(I+1)}. \tag{48.7}$$

It follows that, even if the two nuclei have very similar gyromagnetic ratios and the same spin, the heteronuclear second moment differs by a factor of 4/9 from the homonuclear moment. The second moment is thus very sensitive to the kind of neighbour.

The method of moments has several important advantages. First of all, moments can be calculated without the knowledge of the eigenstates of the dipolar Hamiltonian. Secondly, since the second moment is inversely proportional to the sixth power of the internuclear distance, it is a very sensitive means of determining distances between atoms in solids. Thirdly, it can provide insights into the structure. For example, Richards and Smith (1951) demonstrated the presence of groups of *three* equivalent protons in solid hydrates of strong acids, such as nitric acid monohydrate, thus proving the existence of oxonium ions, $H_3O^+$, in such compounds. Fourthly, the method of moments is useful for the study of motion. This is because the moments are dramatically reduced when the dipolar interaction is partly or completely averaged out by an onset of a specific motion. Figure 48.1 shows the plot of the second moment of $^1H$ in solid benzene as a function of temperature (Andrew and Eades 1953). Below 90 K the rigid lattice value of the moment is observed. At 90-120 K the spectrum narrows dramatically as a result of the onset of reorientation of the molecules about their hexad axes in the crystal structure. Another decrease of the second moment, at the melting point of benzene of 278.7 K, corresponds to the onset of random isotropic motion of molecules. The proton-proton distance calculated from the rigid lattice value of $M_2$ using (48.6) is 2.495 ± 0.018 Å.

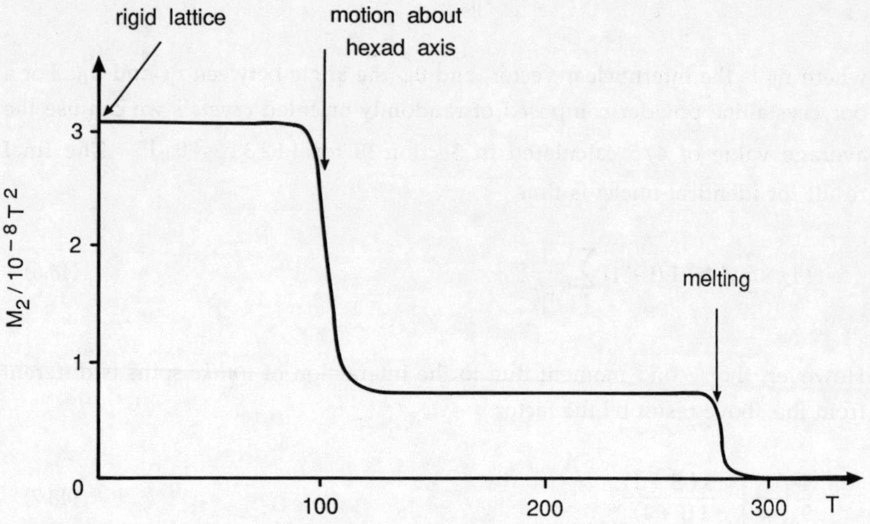


**Figure 48.1.** The second moment of protons in solid benzene as a function of temperature.

Finally, the method of moments is useful when we wish to distinguish between two line-broadening mechanisms: dipolar (which is field-invariant) and chemical shift anisotropy (which depends on the magnetic field). By measuring the second moment at two different magnetic fields we can therefore establish which mechanism controls the width of an NMR line.

# Chapter 9. Nuclear Magnetic Relaxation

## 49. Introduction

The macroscopic aspects of nuclear magnetic relaxation have already been discussed, but without inquiring into the causes of the effect or into its relationship with the structure of matter. In order to address these problems more fully, we shall outline the quantum theory of the interaction of nuclear magnetic moments with their environment and use it to derive the laws (described in Chapter 4) governing the motion of the macroscopic vector of magnetization during its approach to thermodynamic equilibrium.

The foundations of quantum theory of nuclear magnetic relaxation were laid by Bloembergen, Purcell and Pound (1948). Since then the theory has been greatly developed, both as regards the mathematical methods used and the scope of the applications. The arguments of the current section use the perturbation theory and are based on the paper by Solomon (1955), which adopts a general approach and is mathematically relatively simple. The density matrix formalism has also been used to describe relaxation (Redfield 1957; Abragam 1983). However, the discussion of these theories, which are applied mainly in very complex problems such as relaxation in a system of three and four spins, exceeds the scope of this book.

Solomon's theory assumes that motion of the molecules is random and isotropic. While it is mainly applied to liquids, it serves as a starting point for the theory of relaxation in gases and solids. The arguments of Bloembergen, Purcell and Pound, and those of Solomon, are based on the following model. Atomic nuclei possessing magnetic moments $\vec{\mu} = \gamma \hbar \mathbf{I}$ belong to molecules which undergo fast motion. However, motions of the molecules do not directly affect the spatial orientation of the nuclear magnetic moment: the only factor which can change this orientation is the interaction of the spin with the environment. For nuclei with no electric quadrupole moment, this reduces to the interaction with neighbouring magnetic moments of nuclear or electronic origin. In most cases, especially those involving protons, it is the dipolar interaction.

The potential energy of a spin can be considered as a sum of two contributions: (i) energy of interaction with the external field; and (ii) energy of interaction with the neighbouring magnetic moments or, in other words, with the "local field" generated by these dipoles at the site of the spin under consideration. The components of potential energy listed above will be referred to as energies of type (i) or (ii).

There is a very significant difference between the magnitude of these two effects. Energy (i) is ca. 5000 times greater than energy (ii) because the external field in which the experiments are carried out is normally of the order of 10 T, while the local field is rarely greater than 2 mT. Energy (i) does not depend on the orientation of the molecule since the direction of spin and the orientation of the molecule are independent. On the other hand, energy (ii) depends on the spatial orientation of the interacting dipoles. In particular, when they belong to the same molecule, energy (ii) depends on the orientation of the molecule. Through its motions the molecule can perform work, positive or negative, on behalf of the nucleus, only via interactions (ii). As we shall see, changes of energy (ii) can cause a change of energy (i). Thus interactions with neighbouring dipoles can lead to the transfer of energy to the lattice and to other spins. In order to consider the time dependence of energy (ii) we need to familiarize ourselves with certain elements of the theory of stochastic processes.

## 50. Random Processes and the Correlation Function

The aim of this section is to present an overview of the elements of the theory of random processes and describe the calculation of the correlation function. A rigorous discussion lies outside the scope of this book; we will limit ourselves to an intuitive treatment, which will deliberately compromise the requirements of precise derivation.

We first introduce the concept of a *random quantity*. This is a variable which can assume numerical values from a certain set of numbers, known as the field of values, in a way which cannot be predicted. An example is some time-independent physical property, such as the height of a mountain. As a result of imperfections in the measuring equipment, every time or almost every time we repeat the measurement, we obtain a different numerical value. The precise result of an individual measurement cannot be predicted in advance, except that it must lie between 0 and $+\infty$. The variable X is known as the random variable and the values x of variable X found as a result of individual measurements are known as numerical realizations. We cannot say anything about the magnitude of X unless we have at our disposal a sufficiently large set of its numerical realizations. In other words, a random quantity is determined by the set of its numerical realizations.

If a set of numerical realizations is sufficiently large, it can be described by a function which we call probability density. Consider a set $\Omega_x$ containing N numerical realizations of the variable X. The probability density is a function $\bar{P}(x)$ for which

$$n = \bar{P}(x)\, dx$$

where n is the number of realizations belonging to $\Omega_x$ and contained within the interval x, x + dx. $\bar{P}(x)$ is therefore the probability that the value of the realization is x.

The total number of realizations in the set $\Omega_x$ is

$$N = \int \bar{P}(x)\, dx$$

where the integration is over the entire set of values. (We have assumed that N is so large that the entire field of values is sufficiently densely covered by the numerical realizations x. Although, strictly speaking, P (x) can be defined even for small N, it then depends on the N numerical realizations used.)

A function defined as

$$P(x) = \frac{1}{N}\bar{P}(x) \qquad \text{with} \qquad \int P(x)\, dx = 1$$

is known as normalized probability density. In our further discussion we will only use P (x).

Introduce now the concept of a mean of a set of values. Let $\Omega$ be a set of numbers, not necessarily different from one another. Assume that the number $x_1$ appears in the set $n_1$ times, number $x_2$ appears $n_2$ times, etc. The number of elements of $\Omega$ is N where $N = \sum n_i$. The mean $<\Omega>$ of $\Omega$ is defined as

$$<\Omega> = \frac{x_1 n_1 + x_2 n_2 + \ldots}{N} = \sum x_i \frac{n_i}{N}$$

where the ratio $n_i/N$ tells us what fraction of the total set of numbers "belongs" to the number $x_i$.

When N approaches infinity we have

$$\frac{n_i}{N} \to P(x_i)\,dx$$

and the summation changes into integration over the set

$$<\Omega> = \int x\,P(x)\,dx\,. \tag{50.1}$$

Assume that $\Omega_x$ is an infinitely large set of numerical realizations of a random quantity X. Then the integral (50.1) over $\Omega_x$ is known as the mean value and denoted by the symbol $<X>$

$$<X> = \int x\,P(x)\,dx\,. \tag{50.2}$$

In many physical and statistical problems one encounters random quantities X and Y, the numerical realizations x and y of which appear in pairs. These quantities may be dependent on each other to a lesser or greater degree. Take, for example, the age and the height of a large group of people: the interdependence of these quantities is greater in children than in adults. The mutual dependence of two random quantities is known as a correlation. Denote infinite sets of realizations of X and Y by $\Omega_x$ and $\Omega_y$, respectively. If, in the forming of $x_i$, $y_i$ pairs there is a functional relationship $y_i = f(x_i)$, we say that the random quantities X and Y are completely interdependent (correlated). When, on the other hand, there is equal probability of any element of $\Omega_x$ appearing with any element of $\Omega_y$, we say that the values X and Y are completely independent. There are many possible relationships of partial dependence between these two extremes.

We shall now introduce a method used for the quantitative study of correlations. In this, a new random quantity is formed of which the numerical realizations are products x y and then the mean of this value is calculated. The new random variable is the product XY, and the quantity $<XY>$ is a measure of the correlation between X and Y. In order to demonstrate this we shall calculate $<XY>$ for two extreme cases of the complete independence and complete interdependence of X and Y. In accordance with the definition (50.2) of a mean we have

$$<XY> = \int\int x\,y\,P(x,y)\,dx\,dy = \int\int x\,y\,P(x)\,P(x\,|\,y)\,dx\,dy \tag{50.3}$$

where P (x, y) is the probability density of the appearance of the pair x, y. P (x, y) may be expressed as the product

$$P(x, y) = P(x)\, P(x \mid y)$$

in which P (x) is the probability density of the appearance of x as numerical realization of X, and P (x | y) is the probability density of y, a numerical realization of Y, appearing together with x. P (x | y) is known as the conditional probability density.

When the random quantities X and Y are independent, P (x | y) is independent of x and P (x | y) = P (y). In this case the mean takes the value

$$<XY> = \int x\, P(x)\, dx \int y\, P(y)\, dy = <X><Y>. \tag{50.4}$$

Equation (50.4) means that when two random quantities are independent the mean of their product is equal to the product of the mean values of these quantities. If, as often happens, $<X> = 0$ or $<Y> = 0$, then also $<XY> = 0$.

When X and Y are interdependent, then $<XY> = <x\, f(x)>$. In the special case of f (x) = x the mean is

$$<XY> = <x^2> = <y^2>. \tag{50.5}$$

We shall now define a random function of time, an important concept in the theory of nuclear relaxation. A random function of time is a function of t, the value of which at any moment is random. To illustrate this, consider the following example. A buoy is anchored at a certain distance from the shore in such a way that, when tossed by the waves, it can move in the vertical direction alone. Assume that a special instrument can continuously record the height of the buoy beginning with a certain time t = 0. The vertical position of the buoy is an example of a random function of time H (t), while the curve h (t) drawn by the instrument is an example of a "current realization" of this function.

Consider now the following experiment. We start again at time t = 0 with the buoy and the sea surface taking the same original positions and velocities, and again record the vertical motion of the buoy. We repeat this process many times. This results in a large number of current realizations, $h_1(t)$, $h_2(t)$, ... . Because of random factors which determine the motion of the buoy these realizations will not be identical. Thus the set of current realizations determines a random function of time (in our case the vertical position of the buoy) just as a set of numerical realizations determines a random quantity.

Moreover, by fixing the parameter t, for example at t = t', we obtain from the set of current realizations a set of numerical realizations $h_1$ (t'), $h_2$ (t'), etc. We see therefore that for any fixed moment the actual value of the random function is random.

In practice we often encounter random functions of time the general character of which is time-independent. Such functions are known as stationary functions and appear when the causes of random change are constant. For example, the vertical position of the buoy is a stationary function of time because the force of the wind making the waves is constant. In this situation the parameters describing the vertical motion of the buoy, such as the mean position, mean velocity, mean square velocity, etc., do not change. There is, of course, a more rigorous definition of a stationary function, but its discussion exceeds the scope of this book.

The above definition of a stationary random function leads to the conclusion that the mean values of such a function and the mean values of its powers are constant. In the theory of nuclear magnetic relaxation we come across a certain kind of random function, which we will call composite random functions. These are obtained by combining an ordinary function G (Ω) with a random function Ω (t) to give G [Ω (t)]. When the random function Ω (t) is stationary, the composite function G [Ω (t)] is also stationary.

Given a random function H (t) described by a set of current realizations $h_1$ (t) we choose two arbitrary times $t_a$ and $t_b$ and form a set of products

$$h_1(t_a)\, h_1(t_b),\; h_2(t_a)\, h_2(t_b),\; \ldots\,.$$

This set determines the product of random values H ($t_a$) H ($t_b$). The mean value of the product is given by (50.3) after the substitution h ($t_a$) = x and h ($t_b$) = y. Let P (x) be the probability density of the value x being measured at $t_a$ and P (x | y) the probability density that a given current realization which at time $t_a$ had the value x has the value y at time $t_b$. Since H (t) is stationary, P (x | y) does not depend on $t_a$ but only on the difference $\tau = t_b - t_a$. We express this by writing P (x | y) = P (x | y, τ). It follows that the formula (50.3) applied to the product in question is

$$\langle H(t_a)\, H(t_b) \rangle = \langle H(t_a)\, H(t_a + \tau) \rangle$$

$$= \int x\, y\, P(x)\, P(x \mid y, \tau)\, dx\, dy = R(\tau)\,. \tag{50.6}$$

The mean is a function of τ alone, and we denote it by R (τ). It is known as the autocorrelation function. The prefix "auto" is given to distinguish this case from the mutual correlation function, which arises when we place the product of two different random functions under the sign of the mean

$$R_{mut} = \langle H(t)\, M(t+\tau) \rangle .$$

In the theory of relaxation we come across random functions the values of which are complex numbers. For such functions the correlation function is defined as

$$R(\tau) = \langle H(t)\, H^*(t+\tau) \rangle .$$

Thus defined, the correlation function gives real values for stationary $H(t)$. If that were not so, we would have $\langle H(t)\, H^*(t+\tau) \rangle \neq \langle H^*(t)\, H(t+\tau) \rangle$, which would mean that $H(t)$ is not stationary, since the times $t$ and $t+\tau$ are not equivalent.

Consider some properties of $R(\tau)$. We can imagine a time interval $\tau$ so small that the realizations of random functions (for example the realization of the position of the buoy) at moments $\tau$ and $t+\tau$ are extremely close, i.e. $h_1(t) = h_1(t+\tau)$. Then from (50.5) we find

$$R(\tau) = \langle H(t)\, H^*(t+\tau) \rangle = \langle |H(t)|^2 \rangle .$$

Consider the other extreme, and assume that the interval $\tau$ between the two times is very large. Then the value of the realization at $t+\tau$ is independent of the value at t. From (50.4) we get therefore

$$R(\tau) = \langle H(t)\, H^*(t+\tau) \rangle = \langle H(t) \rangle \langle H^*(t+\tau) \rangle = |\langle H(t) \rangle|^2$$

since if $H(t)$ is stationary then $\langle H(t) \rangle = \langle H(t+\tau) \rangle$.

The above considerations lead to the conclusion that for $\tau \to 0$ we have $\lim R(\tau) = \langle |H(t)|^2 \rangle$ and that for $\tau \to \infty$ we have $\lim R(\tau) = |\langle H(t) \rangle|^2$. It follows that

$$|\langle H(t) \rangle|^2 < R(\tau) < \langle |H(t)|^2 \rangle .$$

It is convenient to operate on functions for which $\langle H(t) \rangle = 0$, since then

$$0 < R(\tau) < \langle |H(t)|^2 \rangle .$$

In Section 51 we will show that the correlation function describing Brownian motion of a particle in a viscous fluid covers the values from $<|H(t)|^2>$ to 0 as follows:

$$R(\tau) = <|H(t)|^2> \exp\left(-|\tau|/\tau_c\right) \tag{50.7}$$

where $\tau_c$ is a positive number characteristic for the given random function. This parameter is known as the *correlation time,* and describes the ability of the system to "forget" its previous states.

The correlation function is symmetric with respect to $\tau$. To prove it we invoke the stationary character of H (t)

$$R(-\tau) = <H(t)\, H^*(t-\tau)> = <H(t'+\tau)\, H^*(t')> = R(\tau) \tag{50.8}$$

where $t' = t - \tau$. In the light of this result the values of a stationary random function are formally equally dependent on the future as on the past.

In Section 51 we will come across functions of the type $F(\Omega) = F(\theta, \phi)$ which can assume complex values and are determined on the surface of a sphere. In the polar coordinate system the variables $\theta$ and $\phi$ determine the position of a point $\Omega$ on the surface of a sphere of a certain radius. If we assume that the angles $\theta$ and $\phi$ are random functions of time $\theta = \theta(t)$, $\phi = \phi(t)$, we obtain a composite random function of time $F(t) = F[\theta(t), \phi(t)]$. We find its autocorrelation function from (50.6) by substituting $x = F(\Omega_0)$, $y = F(\Omega)$, $P(x)\,dx = P(\Omega_0)\,d\Omega_0$, $P(x\,|\,y, \tau) = P(\Omega_0\,|\,\Omega, \tau)$:

$$<F(t)\, F^*(t+\tau)> = \int\!\!\int F(\Omega_0)\, F(\Omega)^*\, P(\Omega_0)\, P(\Omega_0\,|\,\Omega, \tau)\, d\Omega_0\, d\Omega \tag{50.9}$$

where integration is over the surface of the sphere. $P(\Omega_0\,|\,\Omega, \tau)$ denotes the probability density of finding a moving point $[\theta(t), \phi(t)]$ at time $t + \tau$ at $\Omega$ if at time t it was at $\Omega_0$.

## 51. Correlation Function for Molecular Diffusion

The energy of interaction between two nuclear spins belonging to the same molecule plays a particularly important role in the theory of relaxation. This energy is the perturbation which causes the quantum transitions described in Section 9. In Section 43 we have shown that the Hamiltonian of dipolar interaction of two spins, spin (1) and spin (2), with gyromagnetic ratios $\gamma_1$ and $\gamma_2$

respectively, can be written as a function of six terms (43.5) containing the following five functions

$$F_0(t) = d\left(1 - 3\cos^2\theta\right)$$

$$F_{\pm 1}(t) = -\frac{3}{2}\, d \sin\theta \cos\theta \exp\left(\pm i\,\phi\right) \qquad (51.1)$$

$$F_{\pm 2}(t) = -\frac{3}{4}\, d \sin^2\theta \exp\left(\pm 2\, i\,\phi\right)$$

where $d = \mu_0 \gamma_1 \gamma_2 \hbar^2 / 4\pi r^3$ and r, θ and φ are the polar coordinates of nucleus (2) with $Z \| \mathbf{B}_0$ and nucleus (1) at the origin.

The distance between the two nuclei is constant, r = b, since they belong to the same molecule. Thus the right-hand sides of equations (51.1) are solely functions of the variables θ and φ, which determine the direction of the internuclear vector from (1) to (2). If the molecule is involved in a rotational Brownian motion as is the case in liquids and in some crystals, then the angles θ and φ are random functions of time, θ = θ (t) and φ = φ (t), which means that the functions (51.1) are also composite random functions of time.

Note that (51.1) can be expressed using spherical harmonics (see Section 3) as follows

$$F_0(\Omega) = 2\, d\, Y_2^{(0)}(\Omega)$$

$$F_{\pm 1}(\Omega) = -\frac{1}{2}\, d\, Y_2^{(\pm 1)}(\Omega) \qquad (51.2)$$

$$F_{\pm 2}(\Omega) = -\frac{1}{4}\, d\, Y_2^{(\pm 2)}(\Omega)\,.$$

This representation will be useful in our further calculations.

Consider a spherical surface with the centre at the site of nucleus (1) and with unit radius. The variables θ and φ can, for convenience, be treated as the coordinates of the point at which the (1) - (2) line crosses the surface. This point will be referred to as the "moving point", because it travels on the surface as the result of rotational motions of the molecule.

Assume that the Brownian reorientation of the molecule is isotropic, i.e. that it occurs in all directions with equal probability. It follows that the probability density P (Ω) of finding the moving point at Ω on the surface is the same everywhere, i.e. P (Ω) = const. Since the normalization condition

$\int P(\Omega)\, d\Omega = 1$ must also be met (integration is over the surface of a sphere), thus

$$P(\Omega) = \frac{1}{4\pi}. \tag{51.3}$$

We also assume that the random functions $\theta(t)$ and $\phi(t)$ are stationary.

We begin our discussion of the properties of functions (51.1) by showing that for all t

$$< F_o(t) > = < F_{\pm 1}(t) > = < F_{\pm 2}(t) > = 0. \tag{51.4}$$

It is sufficient to prove the above for an arbitrarily chosen time since, as we know, mean values of stationary random functions are time-independent. Note that $P\left[ F_0(\Omega) \right] = P(\Omega)$; since $d\Omega = \sin\theta\, d\theta\, d\phi$ we obtain

$$< F_o(t) > = \int\int F_o(\Omega)\, P(\Omega)\, d\Omega = \frac{d}{4\pi} \int\int \left(1 - 3\cos^2\theta\right) \sin\theta\, d\theta\, d\phi = 0.$$

We can similarly calculate mean values of the remaining functions (51.1) and find that they are all zero. Equations (51.4) lead to the conclusion that the autocorrelation functions of $F_0$, $F_{\pm 1}$, $F_{\pm 2}$ approach zero as $\tau$ increases.

We shall now perform detailed calculations of autocorrelation functions. Since the results of these calculations will be used only in Section 56, on first reading the rest of the present section may be omitted, together with Sections 52 and 53, and the reader may proceed directly to Section 54.

The starting point for our calculations is equation (50.9) with $P(\Omega_o) = 1/4\pi$

$$< F_\varepsilon(t)\, F_\varepsilon^*(t + \tau) > = \frac{1}{4\pi} \int\int F_\varepsilon(\Omega_o)\, F_\varepsilon^*(\Omega)\, P(\Omega_0 \mid \Omega, \tau)\, d\Omega_0\, d\Omega. \tag{51.5}$$

The subscript $\varepsilon$ takes the values 0, $\pm 1$ and $\pm 2$ depending to which of functions (51.1) the formula is applied. The first step is to find a function $P(\Omega_0 \mid \Omega, \tau)$, which is the probability density of finding the moving point at position $\Omega$ at time $t + \tau$ if at time t the point was at position $\Omega_0$. $P(\Omega_0 \mid \Omega, \tau)$ can also be treated as the probability density of the moving point passing from $\Omega_0$ to $\Omega$ over time $\tau$.

We need to make one more assumption about the motion of the molecule, which will enable us to calculate the conditional probability density $P(\Omega_0 \mid \Omega, \tau)$. We assume that the moving point travels on the surface by making a large number of small jumps. It is well known that such motion of molecules is the cause of diffusion. The concentration of the diffusing particles f (x, y, z, t) fulfils the following differential equation, known as Fick's law (Atkins 1990)

$$\frac{\partial f(x, y, z, t)}{\partial t} = D\,\Delta f(x, y, z, t) \tag{51.6}$$

where D is the diffusion coefficient, and Δ is the Laplace operator defined as

$$\Delta = \frac{\partial^2}{\partial x^2} + \frac{\partial^2}{\partial y^2} + \frac{\partial^2}{\partial z^2}.$$

In spherical coordinates (51.6) becomes

$$\frac{\partial f(r, \theta, \phi, t)}{\partial t} = D\,\Delta f\left(r, \theta, \phi, t\right) \tag{51.7}$$

in which Δ is the Laplace operator in polar coordinates, derived as in Section 3 in another context

$$\Delta = \frac{1}{r^2}\frac{\partial}{\partial r}\left(r^2\frac{\partial}{\partial r}\right) + \frac{1}{r^2 \sin\theta}\frac{\partial}{\partial\theta}\left(\sin\theta\,\frac{\partial}{\partial\theta}\right) + \frac{1}{r^2\sin^2\theta}\frac{\partial^2}{\partial\phi^2}. \tag{51.8}$$

The concentration f (r, θ, ϕ, t) can also be interpreted as the probability density of finding a single diffusing particle at position (r, θ, ϕ) at moment t. Assuming the diffusive character of the motion of the molecule and the "moving point" associated with it, we can determine $P(\Omega_0 \mid \Omega, \tau)$ as the solution of equation (51.7) satisfying the three following conditions:

**Condition 1** follows from the simple fact that the "moving point" cannot leave the surface of the sphere. Thus the solution f (r, θ, ϕ, t) which we are seeking will not depend on r and may be written as f (Ω, t) where Ω denotes the pair of variables θ and ϕ. Introducing r = 1 into (51.7) is equivalent to discarding the first term in the Laplace operator (51.8) and (51.7) becomes

$$\frac{\partial f(\Omega, t)}{\partial t} = D_r\,\Delta_r\,f(\Omega, t) \tag{51.9}$$

in which $\Delta_r$ denotes the rest of the Laplace operator, known as the Legendre operator (3.9). Since equation (51.9) applies only to reorientation (rotation) of the molecule, and not to translation, we have given the diffusion coefficient the subscript r. $D_r$ is known as the coefficient of rotational diffusion.

**Condition 2** is the boundary condition

$$\int f(\Omega, t)\, d\Omega = 1 \tag{51.10}$$

where integration over the surface of a sphere expresses the certainty that the moving point is to be found somewhere on its surface. In other words, this is the normalization condition.

**Condition 3** is the initial condition

$$f(\Omega, 0) \begin{cases} = 0 & \text{for } \Omega \neq \Omega_0 \\ \neq 0 & \text{for } \Omega = \Omega_0 \end{cases}$$

which, using Dirac's δ function (see Appendix 4) and condition 2, can be rewritten as

$$f(\Omega, 0) = \delta(\Omega - \Omega_0)\,. \tag{51.11}$$

Equation (51.11) means that at $t = 0$ the moving point is at $\Omega_0$.

We know from Section 3 that the eigenfunctions of the Legendre operator are the spherical harmonics $Y_\ell^{(m)}(\Omega)$ with eigenvalues $-\ell(\ell+1)$ where $\ell$ is a positive integer

$$\Delta_r Y_\ell^{(m)}(\Omega) = -\ell(\ell+1)\, Y_\ell^{(m)}(\Omega)\,. \tag{51.12}$$

In order to exploit this property of $\Delta_r$ we shall express the desired function $f(\Omega, t)$ as a series of spherical harmonics. For some given value $t = t'$ this takes the form

$$f(\Omega, t') = \sum_{\ell=0}^{\infty} \sum_{m=-\ell}^{+\ell} b_\ell^{(m)}\, Y_\ell^{(m)}(\Omega)\,.$$

For other values of t the values of coefficients $b_\ell^{(m)}$ are different, so that we can write generally

$$f(\Omega, t) = \sum_{\ell} \sum_{m} b_\ell^{(m)}(t)\, Y_\ell^{(m)}(\Omega)\,. \tag{51.13}$$

The problem of solving the equation of rotational diffusion reduces therefore to finding the coefficients $b_\ell^{(m)}(t)$. Substituting (51.13) into (51.9) we obtain

$$\sum_\ell \sum_m Y_\ell^{(m)}(\Omega) \frac{d}{dt} b_\ell^{(m)}(t) = D_r \sum_\ell \sum_m b_\ell^{(m)}(t)\, \Delta_r Y_\ell^{(m)}(\Omega) .$$

Using (51.12) we have

$$\sum_\ell \sum_m \left( \frac{d}{dt} b_\ell^{(m)}(t) + D_r \ell(\ell+1)\, b_\ell^{(m)}(t) \right) Y_\ell^{(m)}(\Omega) = 0 .$$

The above relationship applies for all $\theta, \phi, \tau$. Since these variables are independent, coefficients appearing with $Y_\ell^{(m)}(\Omega)$ must all vanish. We arrive at the following differential equations for functions $b_\ell^{(m)}(t)$:

$$\frac{d}{dt} b_\ell^{(m)}(t) + D_r \ell(\ell+1)\, b_\ell^{(m)}(t) = 0 . \tag{51.14}$$

The general solutions of these equations are

$$b_\ell^{(m)}(t) = C_\ell^{(m)} \exp\left[ -\ell(\ell+1) D_r t \right] . \tag{51.15}$$

This can be easily verified by differentiation. $C_\ell^{(m)}$ are time-independent constants. Substituting (51.15) into (51.13) we find the general solution of the equation of rotational diffusion

$$f(\Omega, t) = \sum_\ell \sum_m C_\ell^{(m)} Y_\ell^{(m)}(\Omega) \exp\left[ -\ell(\ell+1) D_r t \right] . \tag{51.16}$$

The constants $C_\ell^{(m)}$ are determined from the initial condition (51.11) as follows: We express the function $\delta(\Omega - \Omega_0)$ as a series of spherical harmonics (see Appendix 4) and write

$$f(\Omega, 0) = \sum_\ell \sum_m \delta_\ell^{(m)} Y_\ell^{(m)}(\Omega) \tag{51.17}$$

where

$$\delta_\ell^{(m)} = \left(N_\ell^{(m)}\right)^{-1} Y_\ell^{(m)*}(\Omega_0)\,.$$

Putting t = 0 in the solution (51.16), and comparing the coefficients $Y_\ell^{(m)}$ with the coefficients in equation (51.17), we find that $C_\ell^{(m)} = \delta_\ell^{(m)}$. Substituting these values into (51.16), we find the final form of the solution of the diffusion equation

$$P(\Omega_0 \,|\, \Omega, t) = \sum_\ell \sum_m \left(N_\ell^{(m)}\right)^{-1} Y_\ell^{(m)*}(\Omega_0)\, Y_\ell^{(m)}(\Omega) \exp\left[-\ell(\ell+1) D_r t\right]. \quad (51.18)$$

Having obtained the desired result, we can return to the calculation of the autocorrelation function. We substitute (51.18) and (51.2) into (51.5), replace t by τ and then, using the orthogonality of the spherical functions (3.22), we find, for example, for $\varepsilon = \pm 1$

$$< F_{\pm 1}(t)\, F_{\pm 1}^*(t+\tau) > = < F_{\pm 1}(0)\, F_{\pm 1}^*(\tau) > = \frac{d^2}{16\pi} N_2^{(1)} \exp\left[-\ell(\ell+1) D_r |\tau|\right]$$

with $\ell = 2$, or

$$< F_{\pm 1}(t)\, F_{\pm 1}^*(t+\tau) > = < |F_{\pm 1}(t)|^2 > \exp\left(-6D_r |\tau|\right)$$

$$= < |F_{\pm 1}(t)|^2 > \exp\left(-|\tau|/\tau_c\right) \quad (51.19a)$$

since from (3.22) it follows that $N_2^{(1)} = 4\pi < |Y_2^{(\pm 1)}|^2 >$. Similarly we obtain the remaining autocorrelation functions

$$< F_{\pm 2}(t)\, F_{\pm 2}^*(t+\tau) > = < |F_{\pm 2}(t)|^2 > \exp\left(-|\tau|/\tau_c\right) \quad (51.19b)$$

$$< F_0(t)\, F_0(t+\tau) > = < |F_0(t)|^2 > \exp\left(-|\tau|/\tau_c\right) \quad (51.19c)$$

where

$$\tau_c = \left[\ell(\ell+1) D_r\right]_{\ell=2}^{-1} = \left(6 D_r\right)^{-1}. \quad (51.20)$$

The constant $\tau_c$ is known as the *correlation time.*

The means of the squares of random functions are obtained from (51.2) and (3.22) as follows:

$$<|F_0(t)|^2> = \frac{1}{4\pi}\,4\,d^2 N_2^{(0)} = \frac{4}{5}\,d^2$$

$$<|F_{\pm 1}(t)|^2> = \frac{1}{4\pi}\,\frac{1}{4}\,d^2 N_2^{(1)} = \frac{3}{10}\,d^2 \qquad (51.21)$$

$$<|F_{\pm 2}(t)|^2> = \frac{1}{4\pi}\,\frac{1}{16}\,d^2 N_2^{(2)} = \frac{3}{10}\,d^2$$

(for definition of d consult (51.1)).

In the theory of nuclear magnetic relaxation we encounter Fourier transforms known as spectral densities of the autocorrelation function

$$J_\varepsilon(\omega) = \int_{-\infty}^{+\infty} <F_\varepsilon(t)\,F_\varepsilon^*(t+\tau)> \exp\left(-i\,\omega\,\tau\right)\,d\tau\,. \qquad (51.22)$$

Using (51.19) and performing the integration in a manner similar to that used in Section 34 for the damped circular function, we find

$$J_\varepsilon(\omega) = <|F_\varepsilon(t)|^2> \frac{2\tau_c}{1+\omega^2\tau_c^2}\,. \qquad (51.23)$$

Note that spectral density depends on $\omega$ and $\tau_c$ but not on $\tau$.

From the Einstein formula, $<x^2> = 2\,Dt$ for the mean square of the path traversed by a diffusing particle along X, it follows that for isotropic diffusion on a plane $<r^2> = <x^2+y^2> = 4\,Dt$. Treating the surface of the sphere in the vicinity of point $\Omega_0$ as planar, we may write $<\theta^2+\phi^2> = 4\,Dt$. Comparing this with $\tau_c = (6\,D_r)^{-1}$ we see that the correlation time $\tau_c$ is approximately equal to the average time needed for the change of orientation of the molecule by $\sqrt{2/3}$ radians.

## 52. Correlation Time and Dielectric Relaxation

Debye's theory of dielectrics considers the decay of the electrical dipole moment upon switching off the electric field which brought about the polarization. The decay is caused by the reorientation of molecules possessed of a permanent electric moment. The contribution of a single molecule to the electric moment of the sample is proportional to cos θ where θ is the angle between the direction of the electric field which brought about the polarization and the direction of the electric dipole moment of the molecule. This is why the theory of dielectric relaxation is greatly concerned with the calculation of the correlation function cos θ, which, using spherical harmonics, can be represented as $\cos\theta = -Y_1^0(\theta,\phi)$. In this case $\ell = 1$, which means that the decay of the correlation function for cos θ and the associated decay of the polarization are governed by the parameter

$$\tau_d = \left[\ell\,(\ell+1)\,D_r\right]^{-1}_{\ell=1} = \left(2\,D_r\right)^{-1} .$$

known as the Debye's time of dielectric relaxation. On the other hand, the correlation time $\tau_c$ known from Section 51 is

$$\tau_c = \left[\ell\,(\ell+1)\,D_r\right]^{-1}_{\ell=2} = \left(6\,D_r\right)^{-1}$$

which gives

$$\tau_c = \frac{1}{3}\,\tau_d .$$

This result, derived by Bloembergen, Purcell and Pound (1948), gives us a rare opportunity to relate the correlation time to macroscopic parameters characterizing the liquid. The use of this formula poses certain difficulties, in that the dielectric relaxation time is not directly measurable, because of the interaction of molecular electric dipoles with the vector of electric polarization, which hinders the reorientation of the molecules.

## 53. The Einstein-Debye Model of the Liquid

The second method of relating the correlation time $\tau_c$ to macroscopic quantities applies only to liquids, and is based on the assumption that the molecules behave like macroscopic spheres suspended in a very viscous liquid. Of course, such a model is only a rough approximation and cannot be expected to give accurate results. The assumption made allows us to disregard the inertia of the molecule and leads to the following expression for the diffusion coefficient

$$D_r = kT/f \tag{53.1}$$

where f is the moment of force causing a unit angular velocity of the molecule

$$f = \frac{\text{torque}}{\text{angular velocity}}.$$

According to Stokes' law for the motion of a macroscopic sphere in a viscous medium,

$$f = 8\,\pi\,\eta\,a^3 \tag{53.2}$$

where $\eta$ is the viscosity coefficient of the medium and a is the radius of the sphere. Substituting (53.1) and (53.2) into (51.20) we obtain

$$\tau_c = \frac{4\,\pi\,\eta\,a^3}{3\,kT} \tag{53.3}$$

where a is now the radius of the molecule, k the Boltzmann constant and T the absolute temperature.

This method of relating the diffusion coefficient to viscosity, developed by Einstein, was used by Debye in the theory of electric relaxation. When used to calculate the times $T_1$ and $T_2$ of nuclear relaxation, the method gives a poor agreement with experiment. Better agreement between theory and experiment is obtained by introducing the coefficients of microviscosity, as calculated by Gierer and Wirtz (1953).

## 54. Relaxation in a System of Two Spins

This section is concerned with relaxation in substances in which nuclear spins with quantum number 1/2 are present in pairs consisting of spins (1) and (2). Each pair will be treated as an isolated spin system.

The eigenfunctions of Zeeman energy and the energy levels for an isolated pair of such spins have been calculated in Section 15 and are listed in Table 15.1. We denote the populations of these levels by $N_{++}$, $N_{+-}$, $N_{-+}$ and $N_{--}$. Clearly, their sum is equal to the total number of pairs, N, in the sample.

The eigenvalues of Zeeman energy are shown in Figure 54.1(a) together with all possible transitions, the probabilities of which are denoted by $w_0$, $w_1$, $w_1'$ and $w_2$. Probabilities of transitions are given as a number of transitions per pair per second. For example, if the probability of transition between states $|1\rangle$ and $|2\rangle$ is $w_1'$, then the number of transitions from state $|1\rangle$ to state $|2\rangle$ per second is $N_{++}\,w_1'$, and the number of transitions from state $|2\rangle$ to state $|1\rangle$ per second is $N_{+-}\,w_1'$. Assume that the transitions $|1\rangle \leftrightarrow |2\rangle$ and $|3\rangle \leftrightarrow |4\rangle$ have the same probability $w_1'$, because they involve spin (2) only.

We calculate the rate of change of the population of a given state by taking into account the decrease caused by quantum transitions to all other states and the increase caused by all possible transitions to that state. We obtain

$$\frac{dN_{++}}{dt} = -\left(w_1 + w_1' + w_2\right) N_{++} + w_1' N_{+-} + w_1 N_{-+} + w_2 N_{--} + \text{constant}$$

$$\frac{dN_{+-}}{dt} = w_1' N_{++} - \left(w_0 + w_1 + w_1'\right) N_{+-} + w_0 N_{-+} + w_1 N_{--} + \text{constant}$$

$$\frac{dN_{-+}}{dt} = w_1 N_{++} + w_o N_{+-} - \left(w_o + w_1 + w_1'\right) N_{-+} + w_1' N_{--} + \text{constant} \tag{54.1}$$

$$\frac{dN_{--}}{dt} = w_2 N_{++} + w_1 N_{+-} + w_1' N_{-+} - \left(w_1 + w_1' + w_2\right) N_{--} + \text{constant}\,.$$

The constants appearing in equations (54.1) represent the contribution from spontaneous emission and can be calculated from the equilibrium condition. However, we do not need to know them at this stage.

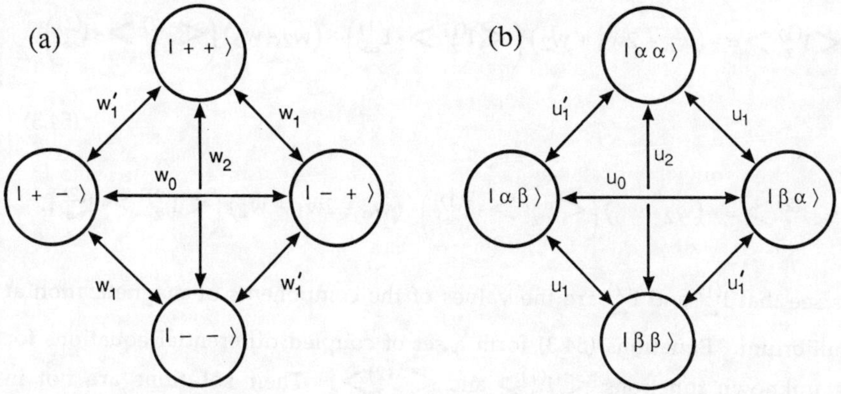


**Figure 54.1.** Quantum transitions (a) between eigenstates of operator $I_z^{(1)} + I_z^{(2)}$ and (b) between eigenstates of operator $I_x^{(1)} + I_x^{(2)}$.

When $\gamma_1 \neq \gamma_2$, because of the difference in Larmor frequency, we can measure $\langle I_z^{(1)} \rangle$ and $\langle I_z^{(2)} \rangle$ separately. These quantities are proportional to the occupancy of the relevant spin, so that

$$\left(N_{++} + N_{+-}\right) - \left(N_{-+} + N_{--}\right) = k \langle I_z^{(1)} \rangle \tag{54.2a}$$

$$\left(N_{++} + N_{-+}\right) - \left(N_{+-} + N_{--}\right) = k \langle I_z^{(2)} \rangle \tag{54.2b}$$

where k is a proportionality coefficient, the same in both equations, since we have assumed that $I^{(1)} = I^{(2)} = 1/2$. By differentiating both sides of (54.2) and using (54.1) we find[1]

$$\frac{d}{dt} \langle I_z^{(1)} \rangle = -\left(w_0 + 2w_1 + w_2\right) \langle I_z^{(1)} \rangle - \left(w_2 - w_0\right) \langle I_z^{(2)} \rangle + \text{constant}$$

$$\frac{d}{dt} \langle I_z^{(2)} \rangle = -\left(w_2 - w_0\right) \langle I_z^{(1)} \rangle - \left(w_0 + 2w_1' + w_2\right) \langle I_z^{(2)} \rangle + \text{constant}\,.$$

[1] Hint: in order to derive the first of the two equations we need to add and subtract $w_0 N_{++}$, $w_2 N_{+-}$, $w_2 N_{-+}$ and $w_0 N_{--}$.

By choosing appropriately the constants $I_\infty^{(1)}$ and $I_\infty^{(2)}$ we rewrite the above as

$$\frac{d}{dt}\left< I_z^{(1)} \right> = -\left(w_0 + 2w_1 + w_2\right)\left(\left< I_z^{(1)} \right> - I_\infty^{(1)}\right) - \left(w_2 - w_0\right)\left(\left< I_z^{(2)} \right> - I_\infty^{(2)}\right)$$

(54.3)

$$\frac{d}{dt}\left< I_z^{(2)} \right> = -\left(w_2 - w_0\right)\left(\left< I_z^{(1)} \right> - I_\infty^{(1)}\right) - \left(w_0 + 2w_1' + w_2\right)\left(\left< I_z^{(2)} \right> - I_\infty^{(2)}\right).$$

We see that $I_\infty^{(1)}$ and $I_\infty^{(2)}$ are the values of the components of magnetization at equilibrium. Equations (54.3) form a set of coupled differential equations for the unknown functions $\left< I_z^{(1)} \right>$ and $\left< I_z^{(2)} \right>$. Their solutions are not in general single-exponential functions. An example of such composite solutions will be given in the next section; here we will discuss the cases in which the solutions are exponential.

**Case A.** The spins (1) and (2) are identical, i.e. $\gamma_1 = \gamma_2$. Then the only experimentally accessible quantities are the sums $\left< I_z^{(1)} \right> + \left< I_z^{(2)} \right>$ and $\left< I_x^{(1)} \right> + \left< I_x^{(2)} \right>$. At the same time, it follows from Figure 54.1 that $w_1' = w_1$ and $u_1' = u_1$. Adding the right- and left-hand sides of equations (54.3), we find the differential equation for the function $\left< I_z^{(1)} \right> + \left< I_z^{(2)} \right>$

$$\frac{d}{dt}\left(\left< I_z^{(1)} \right> + \left< I_z^{(2)} \right>\right)$$

$$= -2\left(w_1 + w_2\right)\left[\left< I_z^{(1)} \right> + \left< I_z^{(2)} \right> - \left(I_\infty^{(1)} + I_\infty^{(2)}\right)\right]. \quad (54.4)$$

The solution is the exponential function

$$\left< I_z \right> = \left< I_z^{(1)} \right> + \left< I_z^{(2)} \right> = \left(\left< I_z \right>_{t=0} - I_\infty\right)\exp\left(-t/T_1\right) + I_\infty$$

where

$$I_\infty = I_\infty^{(1)} + I_\infty^{(2)}$$

(54.5)

$$1/T_1 = 2\left(w_1 + w_2\right).$$

It should be mentioned that non-exponential relaxation may take place even if the spin system under consideration consists of identical nuclei. This has been predicted theoretically by Hubbard (1958) for a group of three protons coupled via the dipolar interaction. Systems composed of two protons may also exhibit non-exponential behaviour if relaxation is caused by two different mechanisms, for example the dipolar interaction and the chemical shift anisotropy. This effect, known as the "interference of interactions" was predicted theoretically by Blicharski (1967 and 1970) and confirmed experimentally by Blicharski and Nosel (1972). See also Werbelow and Grant (1977). Deviations from exponentiality are usually small, and their observation requires high experimental precision.

**Case B.** The relaxation of one of the spins, say spin (2), is caused by a strong interaction with the environment, but does not depend on the presence of spin (1). If the result of this interaction is that $\langle I_z^{(2)} \rangle = \langle I_\infty^{(2)} \rangle$ at all times, then from (54.3) we obtain

$$\frac{d}{dt} \langle I_z^{(1)} \rangle = -\left(w_0 + 2w_1 + w_2\right)\left(\langle I_z^{(1)} \rangle - I_\infty^{(1)}\right)$$

which means that longitudinal relaxation of spin (1) is exponential with the relaxation time

$$1/T_1 = w_0 + 2\,w_1 + w_2 \,. \tag{54.6}$$

Case B applies to aqueous solutions of paramagnetic salts in which the electron spin of the ion plays the role of spin (2). Relaxation times of paramagnetic ions are several orders of magnitude shorter than the relaxation time of $^1H$. Case B applies also when spin (2) belongs to a nucleus with a strong quadrupole moment. The interaction of the quadrupole moment with electric field gradients in the molecule normally leads to very fast relaxation.

We shall now calculate the spin-spin relaxation time. We interpret this relaxation in terms of quantum transitions between the eigenstates of operators $I_x$ or $I_y$. It is sufficient to explain the train of thought using $I_x$ only, because the consideration of quantum transitions between the states of $I_y$ leads to the same result.

The operator $I_x$ has the same eigenvalues as operator $I_z$ but with different eigenfunctions, since the operators $I_x$ and $I_z$ do not commute. We will denote the eigenfunctions of $I_x$ by $\psi$. We thus have

$$I_x^{(1)} \psi_\alpha^{(1)} = \frac{1}{2} \psi_\alpha^{(1)} \qquad I_x^{(1)} \psi_\beta^{(1)} = -\frac{1}{2} \psi_\beta^{(1)}$$

$$I_x^{(2)} \psi_\alpha^{(2)} = \frac{1}{2} \psi_\alpha^{(2)} \qquad I_x^{(2)} \psi_\beta^{(2)} = -\frac{1}{2} \psi_\beta^{(2)}$$

where, in order to distinguish the eigenfunctions of $I_x$ from the eigenfunctions of $I_z$, we have put $\alpha = 1/2$ and $\beta = -1/2$.

Functions $\psi_\alpha^{(1)}$ and $\psi_\beta^{(1)}$ are orthonormal, and so are $\psi_\alpha^{(2)}$ and $\psi_\beta^{(2)}$. Since the operators $I_z$ and $I_x$ do not commute, none of these functions are the eigenfunctions of energy. The eigenfunctions of the operator $I_x^{(1)}$ can be represented as a linear combination of the eigenfunctions of $I_z^{(1)}$ as follows:

$$\psi_\alpha^{(1)} = \frac{1}{\sqrt{2}} \left(\varphi_+^{(1)} + \varphi_-^{(1)}\right)$$
$$\psi_\beta^{(1)} = \frac{1}{\sqrt{2}} \left(\varphi_+^{(1)} - \varphi_-^{(1)}\right). \qquad (54.7)$$

Expansion of a wavefunction into a series has been discussed in Section 6.

The eigenfunctions of the operator $\gamma_1 I_x^{(1)} + \gamma_2 I_x^{(2)}$ given in Table 54.1 are formed in the same way as the eigenfunctions of $\gamma_1 I_z^{(1)} + \gamma_2 I_z^{(2)}$ described in Section 15. For example, one of these functions is the product $\psi_\alpha^{(1)} \psi_\alpha^{(2)}$, which we denote by $|\alpha\alpha\rangle$.

We go through the second row of Table 54.1 as an example. We have

$$\left(\gamma_1 I_x^{(1)} + \gamma_2 I_x^{(2)}\right) |\alpha\beta\rangle$$
$$= \gamma_1 I_x^{(1)} |\alpha\beta\rangle + \gamma_2 I_x^{(2)} |\alpha\beta\rangle = \frac{1}{2} \gamma_1 |\alpha\beta\rangle - \frac{1}{2} \gamma_2 |\alpha\beta\rangle = \frac{1}{2} (\gamma_1 - \gamma_2) |\alpha\beta\rangle .$$

Calculations of $\langle I_x^{(1)} \rangle$ and $\langle I_x^{(2)} \rangle$ are very similar to those we did for $\langle I_z^{(1)} \rangle$ and $\langle I_z^{(2)} \rangle$ and give the result

$$\frac{d}{dt} \langle I_x^{(1)} \rangle = -(u_0 + 2u_1 + u_2) \langle I_x^{(1)} \rangle - (u_2 - u_0) \langle I_x^{(2)} \rangle$$
$$\frac{d}{dt} \langle I_x^{(2)} \rangle = -(u_2 - u_0) \langle I_x^{(1)} \rangle - (u_0 + 2u_1' + u_2) \langle I_x^{(2)} \rangle \qquad (54.8)$$

where $u_0$, $u_1$, $u_1'$ and $u_2$ are the transition probabilities between the states of $\gamma_1 I_x^{(1)} + \gamma_2 I_x^{(2)}$ defined in Figure 54.1(b).

**Table 54.1.** Eigenfunctions of the operator $\gamma_1 I_x^{(1)} + \gamma_2 I_x^{(2)}$ for a system composed of two spins 1/2.

| Definition | Eigenvalue | Occupancy |
|---|---|---|
| $\|1\rangle = \|\alpha\alpha\rangle$ | $\frac{1}{2}(\gamma_1 + \gamma_2)$ | $N_{\alpha\alpha}$ |
| $\|2\rangle = \|\alpha\beta\rangle$ | $\frac{1}{2}(\gamma_1 - \gamma_2)$ | $N_{\alpha\beta}$ |
| $\|3\rangle = \|\beta\alpha\rangle$ | $-\frac{1}{2}(\gamma_1 - \gamma_2)$ | $N_{\beta\alpha}$ |
| $\|4\rangle = \|\beta\beta\rangle$ | $-\frac{1}{2}(\gamma_1 + \gamma_2)$ | $N_{\beta\beta}$ |

The different structure of equations (54.3) and (54.8) derives from the fact that at equilibrium the transverse component of magnetization vanishes. We will show that $u_2 = u_0$ and therefore equations (54.8) take the form

$$\frac{d}{dt}\langle I_x^{(1)} \rangle = -2\,(u_1 + u_2)\,\langle I_x^{(1)} \rangle$$
$$\frac{d}{dt}\langle I_x^{(2)} \rangle = -2\,(u_1' + u_2)\,\langle I_x^{(2)} \rangle. \tag{54.9}$$

The solutions of these differential equations are exponential functions. For the first of them we have

$$\langle I_x^{(1)} \rangle = \langle I_x^{(1)} \rangle_{t=0} \exp\left(-t/T_2^{(1)}\right)$$

with

$$1/T_2^{(1)} = 2\,(u_1 + u_2)\,.$$

This equation describes transverse relaxation of nuclei (1). The solution of the second equation is very similar, and the relaxation time is

$$1/T_2^{(2)} = 2\,(u_1' + u_2)\,.$$

We see therefore that for both spins transverse relaxation is exponential in character, to the point that in most cases $T_2^{(2)} = T_2^{(1)}$ because, as we will show for low-viscosity liquids, $u_1 = u_1'$.

**Case A: two identical spins.** By adding equations (54.9) we find that

$$\frac{d}{dt}\left(\left\langle I_x^{(1)}\right\rangle + \left\langle I_x^{(2)}\right\rangle\right) = -2\left(u_1 + u_2\right)\left(\left\langle I_x^{(1)}\right\rangle + \left\langle I_x^{(2)}\right\rangle\right). \qquad (54.10)$$

The solution of the first of these equations is the exponential function

$$\langle I_x \rangle = \left\langle I_x^{(1)}\right\rangle + \left\langle I_x^{(2)}\right\rangle = \langle I_x \rangle_{t=0} \exp\left(-t/T_2\right)$$

where

$$1/T_2 = 2\left(u_1 + u_2\right). \qquad (54.11)$$

**Case B: fast relaxing spin (2).** We have at all times $\left\langle I_x^{(2)}\right\rangle = 0$, and from (54.8) we obtain

$$\frac{d}{dt}\left\langle I_x^{(1)}\right\rangle = -\left(u_o + 2u_1 + u_2\right)\left\langle I_x^{(1)}\right\rangle.$$

The solution of this equation is exponential with

$$1/T_2 = u_o + 2\,u_1 + u_2\,. \qquad (54.12)$$

## 55. The Overhauser Effect

Consider a situation in which a sample containing spin pairs (1) and (2) is at equilibrium with a radiofrequency field of frequency appropriate to the resonance of spins (2). Assume, for example, that the sample is subjected to a radiofrequency field generated by a coil carrying an alternating electric current of frequency $\omega_e = |\gamma_2|\, B_o$. After a sufficiently long time from the moment the current is switched on, an equilibrium will establish itself with $dI_z^{(1)}/dt = 0$ and $dI_z^{(2)}/dt = 0$. The first of equations (54.3) then becomes

$$\left(w_0 + 2w_1 + w_2\right)\left(<I_z^{(1)}> - I_\infty^{(1)}\right) + \left(w_2 - w_0\right)\left(<I_z^{(2)}> - I_\infty^{(2)}\right) = 0\,. \qquad (55.1)$$

The radiofrequency acting on the sample greatly enhances the probability of transitions between the states of spin (2). This manifests itself as the equalization of the populations of these two states, which means that $<I_z^{(2)}> = 0$ after the equilibrium with the radiofrequency is established. This corresponds to saturation, considered in Section 29. From (55.1) we then have

$$<I_z^{(1)}> = I_\infty^{(1)}\left(1 + \chi\, q^2\right) \qquad (55.2)$$

where

$$\chi = \frac{w_2 - w_0}{w_0 + 2w_1 + w_2} \qquad\qquad q^2 = \frac{I_\infty^{(2)}}{I_\infty^{(1)}}\,. \qquad (55.3)$$

We see therefore that saturation of spins (2) may cause a change in the magnetization of spins (1), in comparison with the situation in which spins (2) are not saturated. Depending on whether this change is an increase or a decrease, we call this phenomenon the positive or negative nuclear Overhauser effect (NOE). NOE is the more pronounced the larger the quotient $q^2$. From the Langevin-Curie formula (16.5) we find that $q^2 = (\gamma_2/\gamma_1)^2$ if for both spins $I = 1/2$.

The factor $\chi$ depends on the degree of isolation of the two spin quantum systems. This is because the numerator in $\chi$ depends on transitions involving both spins ($w_2$ and $w_0$ in Figure 54.1), while the denominator contains also the probability $w_1$ of transitions involving spin (1) alone. If relaxation of spin (1) is largely governed by an interaction with a strong magnetic moment not belonging to the pair, the probability $w_1$ may be much larger than $w_0$ and $w_2$, and the value of $\chi$ may be reduced as a result. Simultaneous transitions of both spins can be imagined only as the result of the interaction between these spins, because accidental coincidence of such transitions as a result of independent interactions is extremely improbable.

If the pair composed of (1) and (2) is well isolated and relaxation is due to the dipolar interaction, the value of $\chi$ can be calculated from (56.7). For low-viscosity liquids in which $(\omega_1 + \omega_2)^2 \tau_c^2 << 1$, we have $\chi = 1/2$. For viscous liquids or solutions of large molecules for which $(\omega_1 + \omega_2)^2 \tau_c^2 > 1$, we have $w_2 - w_0 < 1$ and NOE is negative.

Large positive NOE is very useful when spins (1) give a weak NMR signal because of their low gyromagnetic ratio. In this case irradiation of spins (2) with larger $\gamma$ makes it possible to measure the spectrum of spins (1) with greater sensitivity. In practice spins (2) may be protons, free radicals and paramagnetic ions. When spins (2) are electrons, the value of q may be very large. Polarization of nuclear spins based on NOE and related effects is known as dynamic orientation. Further details can be found in Abragam (1983), Jeffries (1963), Slichter (1989) and Homans (1989).

From equations (54.3) one can predict another interesting phenomenon, known as the transient Overhauser effect. Assume for simplicity that $w_1' = w_1$, which is true for low-viscosity liquids. Solving the set of differential equations (54.3) with the initial conditions

$$< I_z^{(1)} >_{t=0} = I_\infty^{(1)}$$

$$< I_z^{(2)} >_{t=0} - I_\infty^{(2)} \equiv A$$

we find

$$< I_z^{(1)} > - I_\infty^{(1)} = \frac{1}{2} A \left\{ \exp\left[-2(w_1 + w_2)\, t\right] - \exp\left[-2(w_1 + w_0)\, t\right] \right\}$$

$$< I_z^{(2)} > - I_\infty^{(2)} = \frac{1}{2} A \left\{ \exp\left[-2(w_1 + w_2)\, t\right] + \exp\left[-2(w_1 + w_0)\, t\right] \right\}. \tag{55.4}$$

We see that relaxation of spins (2) causes a change of magnetization of spins (1), although after time t = 0 the sample is not being irradiated. The transient Overhauser effect was first observed by Solomon (1955) in liquid HF. Stationary and transient NOE play an important role in $^{13}C$ NMR spectroscopy of organic compounds.

## 56. Calculation of the Longitudinal Relaxation Time $T_1$

Since spins (1) and (2) belong to molecules which undergo thermal motions, the coordinates $(r, \theta, \phi)$ are random functions of time. When the spins belong to the same molecule, we take r = b = const.

For our further calculations it is convenient to write the dipolar Hamiltonian (43.5) in the following form

$$\mathcal{H}_D(t) = \left[ I_z^{(1)} I_z^{(2)} - \frac{1}{4}\left( I_+^{(1)} I_-^{(2)} + I_-^{(1)} I_+^{(2)} \right) \right] F_0(t) + \left( I_-^{(1)} I_z^{(2)} + I_z^{(1)} I_-^{(2)} \right) F_1(t)$$

$$+ \left( I_+^{(1)} I_z^{(2)} + I_z^{(1)} I_+^{(2)} \right) F_{-1}(t) + I_-^{(1)} I_-^{(2)} F_2(t) + I_+^{(1)} I_+^{(2)} F_{-2}(t) \qquad (56.1)$$

where

$$F_0(t) = d\left(1 - 3\cos^2\theta\right) \qquad F_1(t) = -\frac{3}{2} d \sin\theta \cos\theta \exp\left(i\,\phi\right)$$

$$F_{-1}(t) = F_1(t)^* \qquad F_2(t) = -\frac{3}{4} d \sin^2\theta \exp\left(2\,i\,\phi\right) \qquad (56.2)$$

$$F_{-2}(t) = F_2(t)^* \qquad d = \frac{\mu_0 \gamma_1 \gamma_2 \hbar^2}{4\pi b^3}.$$

Consider two energy eigenstates, $|n\rangle$ and $|m\rangle$. They are eigenfunctions of the unperturbed Zeeman Hamiltonian, chosen from among those listed in Table 15.1. The probability that the quantum system, which at time 0 finds itself in state $|n\rangle$, changes under the influence of perturbation $\mathcal{H}'(t)$ to state $|m\rangle$ during time t is

$$W_{nm} = a_{nm}\, a_{nm}^* \qquad (56.3)$$

where

$$a_{nm} = \frac{1}{i\hbar} \int_0^t \langle m|\, \mathcal{H}'(t') |n\rangle \exp\left(-i\,\omega_{nm} t'\right) dt'$$

$$\qquad (56.4)$$

$$\omega_{nm} = \frac{E_n - E_m}{\hbar}.$$

These relationships were derived in Section 9. The perturbation Hamiltonian $\mathcal{H}'(t)$ is given by (56.1). It contains the quantities $F_0(t)$, $F_{-1}(t)$, $F_1(t)$, $F_{-2}(t)$ and $F_2(t)$, which are all composite random functions of time. The realizations of these random functions are of course different for different pairs of spins in the sample, so that the probability of transition is generally different for each pair. We are thus interested in the average value of this probability for all spins

$$< W_{nm} > = < a_{nm}\, a_{nm}^* >.$$

In order to obtain the probability of transition per unit of time needed for the calculation of relaxation times this value must be differentiated with respect to time

$$w_{nm} = \frac{d}{dt} < W_{nm} > = \left< a^*_{nm} \frac{d}{dt} a_{nm} \right> + \left< a_{nm} \frac{d}{dt} a^*_{nm} \right> . \qquad (56.5)$$

Note that the quantity $w_{nm}$ is not directly accessible experimentally, but only its mean value. Consider as an example the two-fold measurement of magnetization M in the time interval t. Because the accuracy of measurement is then optimal, t is usually chosen to be of the same order of magnitude as the required relaxation time. As a result, the measurement cannot provide $w_{nm}$, but only its average value in the time interval from 0 to t

$$< w_{nm} > = \frac{1}{t} \int_0^t w_{nm} \, dt .$$

Only in the simplest case when $w_{nm}$ = const do we have $< w_{nm} > = w_{nm}$. We will later demonstrate that this case applies to transitions between energy states.

As an example we shall calculate the probability $w_2$ of a transition between states 1 and 4 in Figure 54.1(a). On the strength of (56.3) and (56.4) we have for n = 4 and m = 1

$$a_{41} = \frac{1}{i\hbar} \int_0^t \langle ++| (\mathcal{H}'(t') |--\rangle \exp \left[ i \left( \omega_1 + \omega_2 \right) t' \right] dt'$$

where $\omega_1 = - \gamma_1 B_0$ and $\omega_2 = - \gamma_2 B_0$. Taking the form of $\mathcal{H}'(t')$ given by (56.1), and performing the operations indicated by the operators we find

$$\langle ++| (\mathcal{H}'(t') |--\rangle = \langle ++| (I^{(1)}_+ I^{(2)}_+ F_{-2}(t) |--\rangle = F_{-2}(t) \langle ++| (I^{(1)}_+ I^{(2)}_+ |--\rangle = F_{-2}(t)$$

which leads to

$$a_{41} = \frac{1}{i\hbar} \int_0^t F_{-2}(t') \exp \left[ i \left( \omega_1 + \omega_2 \right) t' \right] dt' .$$

Introducing this result into (56.5) we obtain

$$w_2 = \frac{1}{\hbar^2}\int_0^t < F_{-2}(t)\, F_{-2}^*(t') > \exp\left[ i\left(\omega_1 + \omega_2\right)\left(t - t'\right)\right] dt'$$

$$+ \frac{1}{\hbar^2}\int_0^t < F_{-2}(t')\, F_{-2}^*(t) > \exp\left[ - i\left(\omega_1 + \omega_2\right)\left(t - t'\right)\right] dt' . \qquad (56.6)$$

If we now introduce $\tau = t' - t$ we find that the autocorrelation function

$$R_{22}(\tau) = < F_{-2}(t)\, F_{-2}^*(t + \tau) >$$

appears in the above equation. Taking advantage of the relationship $R(\tau) = R(-\tau)$ (see (50.8)), and changing the direction of integration in the second term of (56.6), we find that

$$w_2 = \frac{1}{\hbar^2}\int_{-t}^{+t} R_{22}(\tau) \exp\left[ - i\left(\omega_1 + \omega_2\right)\tau\right] d\tau .$$

We limit our arguments almost entirely to liquids, although this does not exclude solids such as solid benzene (Andrew and Eades 1953), in which molecular motion causes fast reorientation of the pairs of spins. We can assume that the correlation function decays very fast, so that after time $\tau = t$ it is practically zero. The decay of the correlation function is described by formula (51.19b), and if one considers that for most liquids correlation times $\tau_c$ are in the range of $10^{-13}$ to $10^{-8}$ s and $t \geq 10^{-4}$ s, our assumption is clearly justified. We can thus widen the limits of integration without changing the value of the integral. We then obtain a time-independent quantity

$$w_2 = \frac{1}{\hbar^2}\int_{-\infty}^{+\infty} R_{22}(\tau) \exp\left[ - i\left(\omega_1 + \omega_2\right)\tau\right] d\tau = \frac{1}{\hbar^2} J_2\left(\omega_1 + \omega_2\right)$$

which is the spectral density known from Section 51. On the strength of (51.23) spectral density takes the form

$$w_2 = \frac{2}{\hbar^2} < | F_2(t) |^2 > \frac{\tau_c}{1 + \left(\omega_1 + \omega_2\right)^2 \tau_c^2} . \qquad (56.7a)$$

The above equation shows that the transition probability is proportional to the spectral density of the correlation function of the perturbation at point $\omega$, corresponding to the frequency of the transition. We can also say that from the spectrum of Brownian motions described by the correlation function, the system chooses the frequency appropriate for a given transition. The probabilities of the remaining transitions are calculated in an analogous manner:

$$w_0 = \frac{1}{8\hbar^2} < |F_0(t)|^2 > \frac{\tau_c}{1 + (\omega_1 - \omega_2)^2 \tau_c^2} \tag{56.7b}$$

$$w_1 = \frac{1}{2\hbar^2} < |F_1(t)|^2 > \frac{\tau_c}{1 + \omega_1^2 \tau_c^2} \tag{56.7c}$$

$$w_1' = \frac{1}{2\hbar^2} < |F_1(t)|^2 > \frac{\tau_c}{1 + \omega_2^2 \tau_c^2}. \tag{56.7d}$$

Substituting the above quantities into equation (54.6) for $1/T_1$, and using (51.21), we have for the case when spins (1) and (2) are different

$$\frac{1}{T_1} = \frac{1}{10}\left(\frac{\mu_0}{4\pi}\right)^2 \frac{\gamma_1^2 \gamma_2^2 \hbar^2}{b^6}\left(\frac{\tau_c}{1 + (\omega_1 - \omega_2)^2 \tau_c^2} + \frac{3\tau_c}{1 + \omega_1^2 \tau_c^2} + \frac{6\tau_c}{1 + (\omega_1 + \omega_2)^2 \tau_c^2}\right) \tag{56.8}$$

where $T_1$ is the relaxation time of spins (1). When the two spins are the same, i.e. when $\gamma_1 = \gamma_2 = \gamma$, we use (54.5) to find

$$\frac{1}{T_1} = \frac{6}{20}\left(\frac{\mu_0}{4\pi}\right)^2 \frac{\gamma^4 \hbar^2}{b^6}\left(\frac{\tau_c}{1 + \omega^2 \tau_c^2} + \frac{4\tau_c}{1 + 4\omega^2 \tau_c^2}\right) \tag{56.9}$$

where $\omega = -\gamma B_0$.

## 57. Calculation of the Spin-Spin Relaxation Time $T_2$

In order to determine the spin-spin relaxation time we need to know the probabilities shown in Figure 54.1(b). They concern transitions between the eigenstates of the operator $\gamma_1 I_x^{(1)} + \gamma_2 I_x^{(2)}$. These states are not the eigenstates of energy, since the operators $I_x^{(1)} + I_x^{(2)}$ and $I_z^{(1)} + I_z^{(2)}$ do not commute.

We shall first calculate the quantities $b_{ij}$ in equation (9.16). These are the coefficients in the expansion of the eigenstates of the operator $I_x^{(1)} + I_x^{(2)}$ into eigenfunctions of the energy operator $I_z^{(1)} + I_z^{(2)}$, for example

$$|\alpha\alpha\rangle = b_{11}\,|++\rangle + b_{12}\,|+-\rangle + b_{13}\,|-+\rangle + b_{14}\,|--\rangle \tag{57.1}$$

and similarly for the remaining states $|\alpha\beta\rangle$, $|\beta\alpha\rangle$ and $|\beta\beta\rangle$. The first subscript in $b_{ij}$ denotes the number of the function being expanded, and the second the number of the eigenfunction with which the coefficient appears. On the strength of (54.7) we find

$$|\alpha\alpha\rangle = \tfrac{1}{2}\,|++\rangle + \tfrac{1}{2}\,|+-\rangle + \tfrac{1}{2}\,|-+\rangle + \tfrac{1}{2}\,|--\rangle . \tag{57.2}$$

Comparing the right-hand sides of (57.1) and (57.2) we have $b_{11} = b_{12} = b_{13} = b_{14} = 1/2$. The remaining coefficients, shown in Table 57.1, are calculated in an identical manner.

**Table 57.1.** Coefficients $b_{ij}$ in the expansion of the eigenfunctions of the operator $I_x^{(1)} + I_x^{(2)}$ into a series of eigenfunctions of energy.

| | j | | | |
|---|---|---|---|---|
| i | 1 | 2 | 3 | 4 |
| 1 | $+\frac{1}{2}$ | $+\frac{1}{2}$ | $+\frac{1}{2}$ | $+\frac{1}{2}$ |
| 2 | $+\frac{1}{2}$ | $-\frac{1}{2}$ | $+\frac{1}{2}$ | $-\frac{1}{2}$ |
| 3 | $+\frac{1}{2}$ | $+\frac{1}{2}$ | $-\frac{1}{2}$ | $-\frac{1}{2}$ |
| 4 | $+\frac{1}{2}$ | $-\frac{1}{2}$ | $-\frac{1}{2}$ | $+\frac{1}{2}$ |

The calculation of the probabilities $u_0$, $u_1$, $u_1'$ and $u_2$ will be illustrated by the calculation of $u_2$. We therefore calculate the coefficients $A_{n\ell}$ of the transitions between states $|\alpha\alpha\rangle$ and $|\beta\beta\rangle$. The general form of these coefficients is given by (9.19). When using Table 57.1 to calculate them, we deliberately omit the factor $\exp\left(-i\,\omega_j\,t\right)$ which appears in (9.19) since, as we will see, it does not affect the result of our calculations.

We have

$$A_{14} = \frac{1}{4}\Big( a_{11} - a_{12} - a_{13} + a_{14} + a_{21} - a_{22} - a_{23} + a_{24}$$

$$+ a_{31} - a_{32} - a_{33} + a_{34} + a_{41} - a_{42} - a_{43} + a_{44} \Big) . \qquad (57.3)$$

The quantities $a_{ij}$ are calculated from equation (56.4) in which instead of symbols $\langle m|$ and $|n\rangle$ we substitute the energy eigenfunctions given in Table 54.1. We take the dipolar Hamiltonian (56.1) as the perturbation Hamiltonian $\mathcal{H}'(t')$. As an example, we only give four components of (57.3)

$$a_{11} = \frac{1}{i\hbar} \int \langle + + | \mathcal{H}'(t') | + + \rangle dt' = \frac{1}{4i\hbar} \int F_0(t')\, dt'$$

$$a_{12} = \frac{1}{i\hbar} \int \langle + - | \mathcal{H}'(t') | + + \rangle \exp\left(- i\, \omega_2 t'\right) dt'$$

$$= \frac{1}{2i\hbar} \int F_1(t') \exp\left(- i\, \omega_2 t'\right) dt'$$

$$a_{14} = \frac{1}{i\hbar} \int \langle - - | \mathcal{H}'(t') | + + \rangle \exp\left[- i\left(\omega_1 + \omega_2\right) t'\right] dt'$$

$$= \frac{1}{i\hbar} \int F_2(t') \exp\left[- i\left(\omega_1 + \omega_2\right) t'\right] dt'$$

$$a_{23} = \frac{1}{i\hbar} \int \langle - + | \mathcal{H}'(t') | + - \rangle \exp\left[- i\left(\omega_1 - \omega_2\right) t'\right] dt'$$

$$= -\frac{1}{4i\hbar} \int F_0(t') \exp\left[- i\left(\omega_1 - \omega_2\right) t'\right] dt'$$

where integration is between 0 and t. The reader may calculate the remaining components of the sum $A_{14}$ to find

$$A_{14} = \frac{1}{4i\hbar} \int \Big\{ \Big[ 1 + \tfrac{1}{4} \exp\big(-i(\omega_1 - \omega_2)t'\big) + \tfrac{1}{4} \exp\big(-i(\omega_2 - \omega_1)t'\big)\Big] F_0(t')$$

$$- \Big[\exp(-i\,\omega_1 t') + \exp(-i\,\omega_2 t')\Big] F_1(t') + \Big[\exp(i\,\omega_1 t') + \exp(i\,\omega_2 t')\Big] F_{-1}(t')$$

$$+ \exp\Big[-i(\omega_1 + \omega_2)t'\Big] F_2(t') + \exp\Big[i(\omega_1 + \omega_2)t'\Big] F_{-2}(t') \Big\}\, dt' .$$

The remaining coefficients are calculated in a similar fashion

$$A_{13} = \frac{1}{4i\hbar} \int \Big\{ \tfrac{1}{4}\Big[ - \exp\big(i(\omega_1 - \omega_2)t'\big) + \exp\big(-i(\omega_1 - \omega_2)t'\big) F_0(t')$$

$$+ \exp\big(-i\,\omega_2 t'\big) F_1(t') + \exp\big(i\,\omega_2 t'\big) F_{-1}(t')$$

$$- \exp\Big[-i(\omega_1 + \omega_2)t'\Big] F_2(t') + \exp\Big[i(\omega_1 + \omega_2)t'\Big] F_{-2}(t') \Big\}\, dt'$$

$$A_{23} = \frac{1}{4i\hbar} \int \Big\{ \Big[ 1 - \tfrac{1}{4} \exp\big(i(\omega_1 - \omega_2)t'\big) - \tfrac{1}{4} \exp\big(-i(\omega_1 - \omega_2)t'\big)\Big] F_0(t')$$

$$- \Big[\exp(-i\,\omega_1 t') - \exp(-i\,\omega_2 t')\Big] F_1(t') + \Big[\exp(i\,\omega_1 t') - \exp(i\,\omega_2 t')\Big] F_{-1}(t')$$

$$- \exp\Big[-i(\omega_1 + \omega_2)t'\Big] F_2(t') - \exp\Big[i(\omega_1 + \omega_2)t'\Big] F_{-2}(t') \Big\}\, dt' .$$

$A_{32}$ is obtained from $A_{23}$ by exchanging $\omega_1$ and $\omega_2$.

We will now calculate the mean probability of transition per unit of time

$$u_2 = \frac{1}{t} \int_0^t \frac{d}{dt} \left\langle A_{14} A_{14}^* \right\rangle dt . \qquad (57.4)$$

The derivative of the product $\langle A_{14} A_{14}^* \rangle$ is a sum of terms, which can generally be expressed as

$$\frac{d}{dt}\left\langle \left( \int_0^t F_s(t') \exp\left(i\,\omega_p t'\right) dt' \right) \left( \int_0^t F^*_{s'}(t'') \exp\left(-i\,\omega_{p'} t''\right) dt' \right) \right\rangle$$

$$= \left( \int_{-t}^{0} R_{ss'}(\tau) \exp\left(-i\,\omega_p \tau\right) d\tau + \int_0^t R_{ss'}(\tau) \exp\left(-i\,\omega_{p'} \tau\right) d\tau \right) \exp\left[i\left(\omega_p - \omega_{p'}\right) t\right]$$

where $R_{ss'}(\tau)$ denotes the correlation function $\langle F_s(t)\, F^*_{s'}(t+\tau) \rangle$ and $\tau = t'' - t'$.

Consider first the terms in which $s = s'$ and $\omega_p = \omega_{p'}$: we will call these "quadratic" terms. Relying on the arguments of Section 56, we can widen the limits of integration in these terms and thus obtain the density of the autocorrelation function

$$\int_{-t}^{+t} R_{ss}(\tau) \exp\left(-i\,\omega_p \tau\right) d\tau = \int_{-\infty}^{+\infty} R_{ss}(\tau) \exp\left(-i\,\omega_p \tau\right) = J_s(\omega_p) \qquad (57.5)$$

which is time-independent. We can therefore omit the averaging over time seen in (57.4) in the quadratic terms.

The terms in which $\omega_p \neq \omega_{p'}$ (mixed terms) are periodic functions of time and have zero time average provided that $|\omega_p - \omega_{p'}| >> 2\pi/t$. Since the observation time t is normally quite long, these terms can be discarded.

It is obvious that the omission of the exponentials above does not affect the value of the quadratic terms, since $\exp\left(-i\,\omega_j t\right) \exp\left(i\,\omega_j t\right) = 1$. The number of the quadratic terms depends on whether spins (1) and (2) are identical or different, i.e. on whether $\omega_1 - \omega_2 = 0$ or $|\omega_1 - \omega_2| >> 2\pi/t$. This is why the distinction between these two cases must be made at a sufficiently early stage of the calculation, before mixed terms are discarded.

**A. The case of identical spins: $\gamma_1 = \gamma_2$**

In the term $A_{14}$ we assume $\omega_1 - \omega_2 = \omega$, we sum similar terms and, after substitution into (57.4) and discarding mixed terms, we apply the relationship (57.5) to the quadratic terms. We obtain

$$u_2 = \frac{1}{16\hbar^2}\left[\frac{9}{4} J_0(0) + 8 J_1(\omega) + 2 J_2(2\omega)\right]$$

or, on the strength of (51.23),

$$u_2 = \frac{1}{8\hbar^2}$$

$$\times\left(\frac{9}{4}< |F_0(t)|^2 > \tau_c + \frac{8\tau_c}{1+\omega^2\tau_c^2} < |F_1(t)|^2 > + \frac{2\tau_c}{1+4\omega^2\tau_c^2} < |F_2(t)|^2 >\right).$$

In a similar way we calculate

$$u_0 = \frac{1}{8\hbar^2}\left(\frac{1}{4} < |F_0(t)|^2 > \tau_c + \frac{2\tau_c}{1+4\omega^2\tau_c^2} < |F_2(t)|^2 >\right)$$

$$u_1 = u_1' = \frac{1}{8\hbar^2}\left(\frac{2\tau_c}{1+\omega^2\tau_c^2} < |F_1(t)|^2 > + \frac{2\tau_c}{1+4\omega^2\tau_c^2} < |F_2(t)|^2 >\right).$$

Then, applying relationships (51.21) and (54.11), we finally obtain

$$\frac{1}{T_2} = 2\left(u_1 + u_2\right) = \frac{3}{20}\left(\frac{\mu_0}{4\pi}\right)^2 \frac{\gamma^4\hbar^2}{b^6}\left(3\tau_c + \frac{5\tau_c}{1+\omega^2\tau_c^2} + \frac{2\tau_c}{1+4\omega^2\tau_c^2}\right). \qquad (57.6)$$

**B. The case of different spins**

Assuming that $\omega_1 - \omega_2 >> 2\pi/t$, where t is the observation time, and discarding the mixed terms in the sum (57.4), we find

$$u_2 = \frac{1}{8\hbar^2}\left[\left(\tau_c + \frac{1}{8}\frac{\tau_c}{1+(\omega_1-\omega_2)^2\tau_c^2}\right) < |F_0(t)|^2 >\right.$$

$$\left. + \left(\frac{2\tau_c}{1+\omega_1^2\tau_c^2} + \frac{2\tau_c}{1+\omega_2^2\tau_c^2}\right) < |F_1(t)|^2 > + \frac{2\tau_c}{1+(\omega_1+\omega_2)^2\tau_c^2} < |F_2(t)|^2 >\right].$$

Similarly

$$u_0 = u_2$$

$$u_1 = \frac{1}{8\hbar^2}\Big[\frac{1}{8}\frac{\tau_c}{1+(\omega_1-\omega_2)^2\tau_c^2} < |F_0(t)|^2 >$$

$$+\frac{2\tau_c}{1+\omega_2^2\tau_c^2} < |F_1(t)|^2 > + \frac{2\tau_c}{1+(\omega_1+\omega_2)^2\tau_c^2} < |F_2(t)|^2 >\Big].$$

We obtain $u_1'$ from $u_1$ simply by swapping $\omega_1$ and $\omega_2$. Note that $u_1 = u_1'$ when $\omega_1^2\tau_c^2 << 1$ and $\omega_2^2\tau_c^2 << 1$. Substituting these probabilities in (54.12) and using (51.21) we obtain $1/T_2$ for spins (1) as

$$\frac{1}{T_2} = u_0 + 2u_1 + u_2 = \left(\frac{\mu_0}{4\pi}\right)^2 \frac{\gamma_1^2\gamma_2^2\hbar^2}{20\, b^6}$$

$$\times\left(4\tau_c + \frac{\tau_c}{1+(\omega_1-\omega_2)^2\tau_c^2} + \frac{3\tau_c}{1+\omega_1^2\tau_c^2} + \frac{6\tau_c}{1+\omega_2^2\tau_c^2} + \frac{6\tau_c}{1+(\omega_1+\omega_2)^2\tau_c^2}\right). \quad (57.7)$$

## 58. Relaxation Due to Intermolecular Interaction

In cases where the dipolar interaction is the only interaction, experimentally measured $1/T_1$ contains two contributions

$$\frac{1}{T_1} = \left(\frac{1}{T_1}\right)_{rot} + \left(\frac{1}{T_1}\right)_{trans}.$$

The first was calculated in Section 56 with the assumption that the distance $r = b$ of the interacting spins (1) and (2) is time-independent. The factor which brings about the time dependence of the interaction is the reorientation (rotation) of the molecule. The quantity $(1/T_1)_{trans}$, corresponding to the interaction of spin (1) with spins (2) belonging to nearby molecules, remains to be calculated. It is evident that the factor which introduces the time dependence of this interaction is above all the diffusional displacement of molecules, while reorientation is much less important and may be neglected. The calculations given in this section are based on the work of Bloembergen,

Purcell and Pound (1948) and are limited to liquids in the case of extreme narrowing, for which $T_1 = T_2$.

Consider a spherical layer of radius r and thickness dr with spin (1) at the centre of the sphere. The layer follows spin (1), which, carried by the molecule to which it belongs, undergoes a diffusional motion. Since, as we know, the correlation time is the mean time required for a significant change of the magnitude of the interaction, we assume that for all spins (2) in the spherical layer this time is approximately equal to the time required for the molecule carrying spin (2) to move away from its original position in the layer by a distance equal to the radius of the layer. The diffusion of the spherical layer and of the molecule containing spin (2) is independent, and we will demonstrate that this time is

$$\tau_c = \frac{r^2}{12\,D} \tag{58.1}$$

where D is the constant of translational diffusion.

If two independently diffusing points X and Y, with coordinates at time t denoted by $x_1$, $x_2$, $x_3$ and $y_1$, $y_2$, $y_3$, were at time $t = 0$ at the origin of the laboratory reference frame, then at time t the mean square of the distance between these points is

$$\langle r^2 \rangle = \left\langle \sum_i (x_i - y_i)^2 \right\rangle = \sum_i \langle x_i^2 + y_i^2 \rangle$$

since the mean of the mixed terms is zero. From the Einstein formula we have $\langle x_i^2 \rangle = \langle y_i^2 \rangle = 2\,Dt$ and thus $\langle r^2 \rangle = 12\,Dt$, which is identical to (58.1).

Introduce the correlation time given by (58.1) into the expression for $1/T_1$ given in (56.9) and neglect $\omega^2\,\tau_c^2$ and $4\omega^2\,\tau_c^2$ supposing that $\omega^2\,\tau_c^2 << 1$, as is the case for low-viscosity liquids and small molecules. We then obtain the contribution to $1/T_1$ from the interaction of spin (1) with a single spin (2). We multiply this contribution by the number of spins (2) in the spherical layer, $4\,\pi\,r^2\,N_0\,dr$ where $N_0$ is the number of spins (2) in a unit of volume of the liquid, and integrate with respect to r between the closest possible distance between the two nuclei $r = 2a'$ and infinity. We then obtain for $\gamma_1 = \gamma_2$

$$\left(\frac{1}{T_1}\right)_{trans} = \frac{3}{2}\hbar^2\,\gamma^4\left(\frac{\mu_o}{4\pi}\right)^2 \int_{2a'}^{\infty} \frac{r^2}{12\,D}\,\frac{1}{r^6}\,4\,\pi\,r^2\,N_0\,dr = \frac{\mu_o^2\,\hbar^2\,\gamma^4\,N_0}{64\,\pi\,a'\,D}. \tag{58.2}$$

Similarly for $\gamma_1 \neq \gamma_2$ we have from (56.8)

$$\left(\frac{1}{T_1}\right)_{trans} = \frac{\mu_o^2\, \hbar^2\, \gamma_1^2\, \gamma_2^2\, N_o}{96\, \pi\, a'\, D}. \tag{58.3}$$

When the quantum number $I^{(2)}$ of spin (2) is greater than 1/2, the right-hand-side of (58.3) must be multiplied by $\frac{4}{3}\, I^{(2)}\left(I^{(2)}+1\right)$ (Abragam 1983).

The fact that the distance 2a' of closest approach cannot be determined precisely is one of the main shortcomings of the method. For the proton-proton interaction in water, fair agreement with experiment is obtained by taking a' = a (where a is the radius of the molecule, in itself an ill-defined quantity).

A further simplification of the formulae is achieved by treating the molecules of the liquid as spheres suspended in a viscous liquid. We can then, as in Section 53, use the relationship D = kT/f, in which D is now the coefficient of translational diffusion and f is the ratio of the force to the linear velocity of the molecule caused by the force. In turn, the quantity f is given by Stokes' law as a function of the viscosity of the liquid $\eta$, $f = 6\pi\eta a$. Substituting $D = kT/6\pi\eta a$ into (58.2), and taking a' = a, we obtain the relationship

$$\left(\frac{1}{T_1}\right)_{trans} = \frac{3\, \mu_o\, \hbar^2\, \gamma^4\, \eta\, N_o}{32\, kT}$$

in which neither a nor a', both quantities of doubtful meaning, are present. This is, however, only an apparent way out of the problem since the equality a' = a has no physical justification.

# Appendices

## Appendix 1. Complex Numbers

The theory of complex numbers was developed by the Astronomer Royal of Ireland, Sir William Rowan Hamilton (1805-1865). It is enormously important for quantum mechanics in general, and for the understanding of nuclear magnetic resonance in particular.

A complex number is an ordered pair (a, b) of two real numbers. Thus (5, 3), (7, 0) and $(\pi, \sqrt{17})$ are all complex numbers. For reasons which will soon become apparent, when we write z = (a, b), a is known as the real part and b as the imaginary part of the complex number. Two complex numbers are equal if *both* their real parts and their imaginary parts are equal. Thus $(a_1, b_1) = (a_2, b_2)$ if $a_1 = a_2$ and $b_1 = b_2$. Unlike for ordinary numbers, we cannot define a "smaller" or "greater" complex number, so that the symbols ">" and "<" have no meaning.

Addition, subtraction and multiplication of complex numbers $z_1 = (a_1, b_1)$ and $z_2 = (a_2, b_2)$ is defined as follows

$$z_1 + z_2 = (a_1 + a_2, b_1 + b_2)$$

$$z_1 - z_2 = (a_1 - a_2, b_1 - b_2) \qquad \text{(A1.1)}$$

$$z_1 \cdot z_2 = (a_1 a_2 - b_1 b_2, a_1 b_2 + a_2 b_1) .$$

It is easy to show that with these definitions the commutative and associative laws of addition and multiplication, as well as the distributive law, all hold:

$$z_1 + z_2 = z_2 + z_1$$

$$z_1 + (z_2 + z_3) = (z_1 + z_2) + z_3 = z_1 + z_2 + z_3 \qquad \text{(A1.2)}$$

$$z_1 \cdot (z_2 \cdot z_3) = (z_1 \cdot z_2) \cdot z_3 = z_1 \cdot z_2 \cdot z_3 .$$

We see that the rules of addition, subtraction and multiplication of complex numbers for which the second member of the pair is zero, such as (a, 0), are exactly the same as for ordinary numbers. For example, (5, 0) · (3, 0) = (15, 0). Because of this, such complex numbers are called "real numbers" and are written just like ordinary numbers. For example, (5, 0) = 5 and (15, 0) = 15. Despite appearances, this does not lead to confusion and is in fact very convenient. We shall therefore make no difference between real and ordinary numbers. By contrast, complex numbers in which the first member of the pair is zero, such as (0, b) are known as "imaginary numbers".

Among the infinite number of pairs which constitute complex numbers, two pairs are very special: (1, 0) corresponding to unity and the pair (0, 1). To see the meaning of the latter we multiply it by itself using the definition of multiplication (A1.1). We have

$$(0, 1) \cdot (0, 1) = (0, 1)^2 = (-1, 0)\,. \qquad \text{(A1.3)}$$

We see that the complex number (0, 1), given the symbol i and known as the *imaginary unit*, may be regarded as the square root of - 1. The reason for this appellation is that i is the solution of the algebraic equation $x^2 + 1 = 0$, which has no solution among real numbers.

Note that multiplication of a real number by the imaginary unit converts it into an imaginary number

$$i \cdot (a, 0) = (0, 1) \cdot (a, 0) = (0, a).$$

It is convenient to write complex numbers not in the form of pairs (a, b) but as a sum a + i b of real and imaginary parts (this is known as the "abbreviated notation"). Since i = (0, 1), we use the definitions (A1.1) to show that the two notations are exactly equivalent:

$$a + i\,b = (a, 0) + (0, 1) \cdot (b, 0) = (a, 0) + (0 - 0, 0 + b)$$

$$= (a, 0) + (0, b) = (a + 0, 0 + b) = (a, b)\,. \qquad \text{(A1.4)}$$

*Because of this equivalence, in any operation involving sums and products we may treat a, b and i as though they were ordinary numbers, provided that $i^2$ is always replaced by - 1.*

The real part of a complex number z = a + i b is often written as a = Re z, and the imaginary part as b = Im z. So, z = Re z + i Im z.

It is enormously convenient to represent complex numbers geometrically as points on the *Argand diagram* (XY plane) in which the X axis is real and the Y axis imaginary (Figure A1.1). A complex number (a, b) may then be thought of as a vector with coordinates (a, b) (Figure A1.1), square length $r^2 = a^2 + b^2$ and phase angle $\varphi = \arctan(b/a)$.

The *complex conjugate* of a + i b is defined as

$$z^* = a - i\,b\,. \tag{A1.5}$$

It is clear that $z + z^* = 2\,\mathrm{Re}\,z$, and $z - z^* = 2i\,\mathrm{Im}\,z$ or, in view of $1/i = -i$

$$\mathrm{Im}\,z = \frac{z - z^*}{2i} = \frac{-i\,(z - z^*)}{2}\,.$$

Therefore, the necessary and sufficient condition for z to be real is that $z = z^*$.

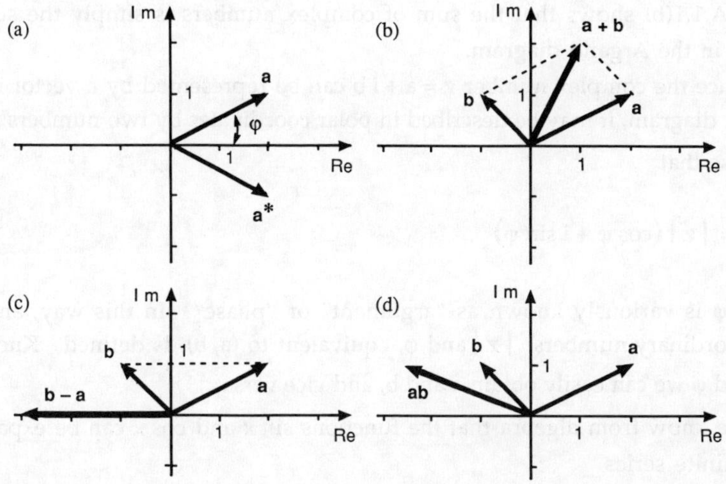


**Figure A1.1.** The Argand diagram. (a) The complex number (2 + i) and its complex conjugate, (2 - i); (b) the sum (2 + i) + (- 1 + i); (c) the difference (- 1 + i) - (2 + i); (d) multiplication (- 1 + i) · (2 + i) resulting in the addition of phase angles and the multiplication of moduli.

The square of the absolute value of a complex number z = (a, b) is defined as

$$|z|^2 = a^2 + b^2 \tag{A1.6}$$

and the absolute value as

$$|z| = \sqrt{a^2 + b^2}\,.$$

$|z|$ is also known as modulus or length of a complex number.

From (A1.6) it follows that

$$|z|^2 = z\,z^* .$$

The addition and multiplication of complex numbers $z_1 = a_1 + i\,b_1$ and $z_2 = a_2 + i\,b_2$ in the abbreviated notation goes as follows

$$z_1 + z_2 = (a_1 + a_2) + i\,(b_1 + b_2)$$

$$z_1 \cdot z_2 = (a_1 a_2 - b_1 b_2) + i\,(a_1 b_2 + a_2 b_1) .$$

Figure A.1.1(b) shows that the sum of complex numbers is simply the sum of vectors in the Argand diagram.

Since the complex number $z = a + i\,b$ can be represented by a vector in the Argand diagram, it may be described in polar coordinates by two numbers, $|z|$ and $\varphi$, so that

$$z = |z|\,(\cos\varphi + i\sin\varphi)$$

where $\varphi$ is variously known as "argument" or "phase". In this way, another pair of ordinary numbers, $|z|$ and $\varphi$, equivalent to (a, b), is defined. Knowing $|z|$ and $\varphi$ we can easily obtain a and b, and vice versa.

We know from algebra that the functions sin x and cos x can be expanded into infinite series

$$\sin x = x - \frac{x^3}{3!} + \frac{x^5}{5!} - \frac{x^7}{7!} + \ldots$$

$$\cos x = 1 - \frac{x^2}{2!} + \frac{x^4}{4!} - \frac{x^6}{6!} + \ldots . \qquad \text{(A1.7)}$$

On the other hand, the expansion of the exponential number is

$$\exp x = 1 + \frac{x}{1!} + \frac{x^2}{2!} + \frac{x^3}{3!} + \ldots . \qquad \text{(A1.8)}$$

Expressing $\cos\varphi + i\sin\varphi$ according to (A1.7) and comparing with (A1.8) we obtain the famous relationship known as Euler's equation

$$\cos\varphi + i \sin\varphi = \exp(i\varphi)\,. \tag{A1.9}$$

Euler's equation allows us to express a complex number in a very useful way

$$z = |z| \exp(i\varphi)\,. \tag{A1.10}$$

We use it to derive the product of two complex numbers, $z_1 = |z_1| \exp(i\varphi_1)$ and $z_2 = |z_2| \exp(i\varphi_2)$. By applying the rule of multiplication of exponentials, $\exp(x_1)\exp(x_2) = \exp(x_1 + x_2)$, we obtain

$$z_1 z_2 = |z_1|\,|z_2| \exp\left[i(\varphi_1 + \varphi_2)\right]. \tag{A1.11}$$

The reader may confirm that (A1.11) agrees with the definition of a product of complex numbers given in (A1.1). We conclude that *in order to multiply complex numbers we multiply their moduli and add their phases.* In other words, multiplication of two complex numbers *rotates* $z_1$ through the angle $\varphi_2$ while multiplying its magnitude by the factor $r_2$ (Figure A1.1(c)).

Since complex conjugation is equivalent to substituting - i for i, we have for $z = |z| \exp(i\varphi)$

$$z^* = |z| \exp(-i\varphi)$$

and, since $\exp(i\varphi)\exp(-i\varphi) = \exp 0 = 1$, we have

$$|z| = z z^* \qquad \text{and} \qquad \left|\exp(i\varphi)\right| = 1\,.$$

A complex number with a time-dependent argument

$$z(t) = |z| \exp(i\omega t)$$

plays a very important role in NMR. This number is represented on the Argand diagram by a vector of length $|z|$ rotating at the angular velocity $\omega$, the rotation being anticlockwise if $\omega > 0$ or clockwise if $\omega < 0$. In this book we call such a function a "circular function", although this name is not in general use. The reason for this terminology is a desire to distinguish the rotation of a vector of constant length from other periodic motions. Angular velocity $\omega$ is expressed in radians per second, so that $|\omega| = 2\pi\nu$, where $\nu$ is the number of revolutions per second (frequency). The real number $|z|$ which is the modulus of a circular function is known as its amplitude. A circular function can also be expressed in the form

$$z(t) = |z| \left[\cos(\omega t) + i \sin(\omega t)\right].$$

Note that multiplication of a circular function by a constant complex number $|r| \exp(i\varphi)$ changes its amplitude and phase

$$|r| \exp(i\varphi)\, z(t) = |r|\,|z| \exp\left[i(\omega t + \varphi)\right].$$

We finally note that because of the way equality of two complex numbers has been defined (see above), any equation involving complex numbers is equivalent to *two* simultaneous equations for real numbers. As a consequence, any measurement of a complex physical quantity requires two simultaneous measurements, one for the real and one for the imaginary part.

## Appendix 2. Scalar and Vector Products

Consider two vectors

$$\mathbf{A} = A_x\,\mathbf{i} + A_y\,\mathbf{j} + A_z\,\mathbf{k}$$
$$\mathbf{B} = B_x\,\mathbf{i} + B_y\,\mathbf{j} + B_z\,\mathbf{k} \qquad \text{(A2.1)}$$

where A and B are their coordinates and **i**, **j** and **k** are unit vectors along the axes X, Y and Z, respectively. Two distinct types of products are defined. The scalar product (also known as "dot product") is given by

$$\mathbf{C} = \mathbf{A} \cdot \mathbf{B} = A_x B_x + A_y B_y + A_z B_z = A\,B \cos\theta \qquad \text{(A2.2)}$$

where θ is the smaller of the angles between **A** and **B**. Note that **A · B** is a scalar and not a vector.

The definition of the vector product (also known as "cross-product") is

$$\mathbf{A} \times \mathbf{B} = \begin{vmatrix} \mathbf{i} & \mathbf{j} & \mathbf{k} \\ A_x & A_y & A_z \\ B_x & B_y & B_z \end{vmatrix}$$

$$= \mathbf{i}\left(A_y B_z - A_z B_y\right) + \mathbf{j}\left(A_z B_x - A_x B_z\right) + \mathbf{k}\left(A_x B_y - A_y B_x\right). \qquad \text{(A2.3)}$$

It is clear that $\mathbf{A} \times \mathbf{B}$ is a vector, and that $\mathbf{A} \times \mathbf{B} = -\mathbf{B} \times \mathbf{A}$.

The vector product is: (i) perpendicular to both **A** and **B** (and thus perpendicular to the plane they define); (ii) its magnitude (length) is $D = A\,B \sin\theta$; (iii) its direction agrees with the direction in which a right-handed screw would move if it were placed with its axis parallel to **D** and turned in the direction in which the vector **A** would have to be turned while holding the vector **B** immobile, so as to decrease the angle θ. We define θ as the angle between the two vectors. We have for example

$$\mathbf{i} \times \mathbf{j} = \mathbf{k} \qquad \text{and} \qquad \mathbf{j} \times \mathbf{i} = -\mathbf{k}.$$

## Appendix 3. Calculation of Traces

The *trace* of a matrix A with elements $a_{ij}$ is defined as the sum of its diagonal elements

$$\mathrm{Tr}\,A = \sum_i a_{ii}.$$

The most important properties of traces are outlined below.

**Theorem 1.** The trace of a matrix is invariant with respect to a reversible transformation, i.e. $\mathrm{Tr}\left\{S\,A\,S^{-}\right\} = \mathrm{Tr}\,A$ where $S^{-}S = \{1\}$.

*Proof.* The theorem is proved as follows

$$\mathrm{Tr}\left\{S\,A\,S^{-}\right\} = \sum_{ijk} s_{ij}\, a_{jk}\, \bar{s}_{ki} = \sum_{jk} a_{jk} \sum_i \bar{s}_{ki}\, s_{ij}$$

$$= \sum_{jk} a_{jk}\, \delta_{kj} = \sum_j a_{jj} = \mathrm{Tr}\,A. \qquad \text{q.e.d.}$$

*Conclusion.* The trace of a matrix which is a representation of an operator does not depend on the choice of basis. The trace is therefore a characteristic property of an operator.

**Theorem 2.** $\mathrm{Tr}\{A\,B\} = \sum_{ij} a_{ij}\, b_{ji} = \sum_{ji} b_{ji}\, a_{ij} = \mathrm{Tr}\{B\,A\}$.

*Conclusion*. $\mathrm{Tr}\{A\,B\,C\} = \mathrm{Tr}\{B\,C\,A\} = \mathrm{Tr}\{C\,A\,B\}$. In other words, a cyclic permutation of operators does not affect the trace of their product.

**Theorem 3.** The trace of all the coordinates of the spin operator is zero, i.e. $\mathrm{Tr}\{I_k\} = 0$ for k = x, y, z.

*Proof*. As was explained in Section 3 for the angular momentum, all three operators of spin have the same eigenvalues: m = - I, - I + 1, ..., 0, ..., I - 1, I. The representation of an operator $I_k$ in the basis of its eigenfunctions is thus a diagonal matrix with these values on the diagonal. Therefore

$$\mathrm{Tr}\{I_k\} = \sum_{-I}^{+I} m = 0. \qquad \text{q.e.d.}$$

It is instructive to prove Theorem 3 again using a different method. Consider, for example, the coordinate $I_z$. By rotating the coordinate system around the X axis by the angle π, the coordinate $I_z$ becomes $-I_z$. We have on the one hand $\mathrm{Tr}\{-I_z\} = -\mathrm{Tr}\{I_z\}$ and on the other hand we know that the trace is an invariant of rotation. Therefore $\mathrm{Tr}\{I_z\}$ must vanish. It follows that $\mathrm{Tr}\{I_x\} = 0$ and $\mathrm{Tr}\{I_y\} = 0$, because $I_z$ becomes $I_x$ or $I_y$ upon appropriate rotations.

**Theorem 4.** The product of two different coordinates of the same spin is traceless:

$$\mathrm{Tr}\{I_k\, I_\ell\} = 0 \text{ for } k \neq \ell\,.$$

*Proof*. We rotate the coordinate system by the angle π around the axis ℓ. The rest of the proof is similar to that of Theorem 3.

**Theorem 5.** $\mathrm{Tr}\{I_k\, I_\ell\, I_m\} = 0$ for k, ℓ, m = x, y, z.

*Proof*.
Case 1. All the coordinates are different, for example k = x, ℓ = y and m = z. We rotate the coordinate system by the angle π/2 around the k axis, whereupon the product $I_\ell\, I_m$ changes sign.
Case 2. ℓ = m. We rotate the coordinate system by the angle π around the ℓ axis, whereupon $I_k$ changes sign.

Case 3. $k = \ell = m$. The proof is the same as for $\mathrm{Tr}\left\{ I_k \right\}$.

**Theorem 6.** The trace of the product of the coordinates of two different spins is zero:

$$\mathrm{Tr}\left\{ I_k^{(1)} \; I_\ell^{(2)} \right\} = 0 .$$

*Proof.* When $k \neq \ell$ the proof is the same as for the coordinates of the same spin. For $k = \ell = z$ we represent the operator $I_z^{(1)} I_z^{(2)}$ in the basis of its eigenfunctions $\varphi_m^{(1)} \varphi_n^{(2)}$, where $\varphi_m^{(1)}$ is an eigenfunction of the operator $I_z^{(1)}$, and $\varphi_n^{(2)}$ an eigenfunction of the operator $I_z^{(2)}$. In this way we obtain a diagonal matrix of dimension $(2I + 1)^2$. The eigenvalues $mn$, where $m, n = -I, ..., +I$ are on the diagonal of the matrix. We have therefore

$$\sum_{m,n} m\, n = \left(\sum m\right)\left(\sum n\right) = 0 .$$

The operators $I_x^{(1)} I_x^{(2)}$ and $I_y^{(1)} I_y^{(2)}$ may be obtained from the operator $I_z^{(1)} I_z^{(2)}$ by rotating the coordinate system. It follows that the trace of these operators must also be zero.

*Conclusion.* $\mathrm{Tr}\,\mathcal{H}_D = 0$. As seen from (43.5), the dipolar Hamiltonian is composed entirely of terms containing products of the type $I_k^{(1)} I_\ell^{(2)}$, which means that its trace must vanish.

**Theorem 7.** If a quantum system is composed of a single spin with spin quantum number I, then

$$\mathrm{Tr}\left\{ I_z^2 \right\} = \frac{1}{3}\, I\, (I + 1)\, (2I + 1) .$$

*Proof.* We represent the operator $I_z^2$ in the basis of its eigenfunctions and sum the diagonal terms

$$\mathrm{Tr}\left\{ I_z^2 \right\} = \sum_{-I}^{+I} m^2 = \sum_{0}^{2I} (m - I)^2 .$$

We substitute the well known expressions for the sum of natural numbers and the sum of their squares

$$\sum_{0}^{2I} m = I\,(2I+1)$$

$$\sum_{0}^{2I} m^2 = \frac{1}{3}\, I\,(2I+1)\,(4I+1)\,. \qquad \text{q.e.d.}$$

*Conclusion.* $\mathrm{Tr}\left\{ I_x^2 \right\} = \mathrm{Tr}\left\{ I_y^2 \right\} = \frac{1}{3}\, I\,(I+1)\,(2I+1)$ for a single spin.

**Theorem 8.** For a quantum system composed of N spins $I_z^{(i)}$, each with spin quantum number I, we have

$$\mathrm{Tr}\left\{ I_z^{(i)} \right\}^2 = \frac{1}{3}\, I\,(I+1)\,(2I+1)^N\,.$$

*Proof.* We represent the operator $\left(I_z^{(i)}\right)^2$ in the basis of eigenfunctions which are products of the eigenvalues of the z coordinate of spin for the individual spins

$$\left| m_1\, m_2 \ldots m_q \ldots m_N \right\rangle = \varphi_{m_1}^{(1)}\, \varphi_{m_2}^{(2)} \ldots \varphi_{m_q}^{(q)} \ldots \varphi_{m_N}^{(N)}\,.$$

Since each of the quantum numbers m can independently assume 2I + 1 values, there are $(2I+1)^N$ such combinations of quantum numbers. We sum the diagonal elements over all combinations as follows

$$\mathrm{Tr}\left\{ I_z^{(q)} \right\}^2 = \sum_{m_1} \ldots \sum_{m_q} \ldots \sum_{m_N} \left\langle m_1 \ldots m_q \ldots m_N \right| \left\{ I_z^{(q)} \right\}^2 \left| m_1 \ldots m_q \ldots m_N \right\rangle$$

$$= (2I+1)^{N-1} \sum_{m_q} \left\langle m_q \right| \left( I_z^{(q)} \right)^2 \left| m_q \right\rangle$$

$$= (2I+1)^{N-1} \sum_{-I}^{+I} \left[ m^{(q)} \right]^2 = \frac{1}{3}\, I\,(I+1)(2I+1)^N$$

where in the last step we made use of Theorem 7. In a similar way one obtains

$$\mathrm{Tr}\left\{\left(I_z^{(1)}\right)^2\left(I_z^{(2)}\right)^2\right\}=(2I+1)^{N-2}\left[\tfrac{1}{3}I(I+1)(2I+1)\right]^2 .$$

*Conclusion*. For $I_z=\sum_i^N I_z^{(i)}$ we have

$$\mathrm{Tr}\left\{I_z^2\right\}=\sum_{i=1}^{N}\mathrm{Tr}\left\{I_z^{(i)}\right\}^2=\frac{1}{3}\,N\,I\,(I+1)\,(2I+1)^N .$$

## Appendix 4. Dirac's δ Function

This function, denoted by $\delta\,(x - x')$, has rather unusual properties:

$$\delta\,(x-x')=0 \qquad \text{for } x\neq x'$$

$$\delta\,(x-x')=\infty \qquad \text{for } x=x' \tag{A4.1}$$

$$\int_a^b \delta\,(x-x')\,dx=1$$

when $a < x' < b$. For any smooth function f

$$\int_a^b f\,(x)\,\delta\,(x-x')\,dx=f\,(x')\int_a^b \delta\,(x-x')\,dx=f\,(x') \tag{A4.2}$$

so δ "projects out" the value of f at $x = x'$. The identities

$$\delta\,(x)=\delta\,(-x) \tag{A4.3}$$

$$x\,d\delta/dx=-\,\delta\,(x) \tag{A4.4}$$

$$x\,\delta\,(x)=0 \tag{A4.5}$$

can all be proved by multiplying both sides by $f\,(x)$ and integrating.

Suppose that functions $\varphi_n\,(x)$ form a complete orthonormal set. We may then expand an arbitrary function

$$\Psi = \sum_n c_n \varphi_n \tag{A4.6}$$

where $c_n = \langle \varphi_n | \Psi \rangle \equiv \int \varphi_n^* \, \Psi \, dx'$. Substituting this into (A4.6) yields

$$\Psi(x) = \sum_n \varphi_n(x) \int \varphi_n^*(x') \, \Psi(x') \, dx' = \int \left( \sum_n \varphi_n(x) \, \varphi_n^*(x') \right) \Psi(x') \, dx' . \tag{A4.7}$$

Comparing (A4.7) with the definition of the δ function, we obtain

$$\sum_n \varphi_n(x) \, \varphi_n^*(x') = \delta(x - x') \tag{A4.8}$$

known as the "closure relation".

Consider the Dirac δ function on the surface of a sphere of unit radius. A point on the sphere is determined by a pair of spherical variables (θ, ϕ) which we denote by Ω for brevity. On the surface of the sphere the function $\delta(\Omega - \Omega')$ has the following properties:

$$\delta(\Omega - \Omega') = \begin{cases} 0 & \text{for } \Omega \neq \Omega' \\ +\infty & \text{for } \Omega = \Omega' \end{cases} \tag{A4.9}$$

$$\int \delta(\Omega - \Omega') \, d\Omega = 1 \tag{A4.10}$$

where the integration is over the entire surface of the sphere.

Our task is to express the function δ as a series

$$\delta(\Omega - \Omega') = \sum_{\ell=0}^{\infty} \sum_{m=-\ell}^{+1} \delta_\ell^{(m)} \, Y_\ell^{(m)}(\Omega) .$$

The problem reduces to finding the coefficients $\delta_\ell^{(m)}$. Multiply both sides of the above equation by $Y_\ell^{(m)*}(\Omega)$ and integrate over the surface of the sphere. Using the theorem of the orthogonality of spherical functions (3.22) we obtain

$$N_\ell^{(m)} \, \delta_\ell^{(m)} = \int Y_\ell^{(m)*}(\Omega) \, \delta(\Omega - \Omega') \, d\Omega .$$

But, on the strength of (A4.9), $\delta(\Omega - \Omega') \neq 0$ only in the infinitely small vicinity of $\Omega'$ in which the spherical function may be considered to be constant: $Y_\ell^{(m)*}(\Omega) = Y_\ell^{(m)*}(\Omega')$. We have therefore

$$\delta_\ell^{(m)} = \left(N_\ell^{(m)}\right)^{-1} Y_\ell^{(m)*}(\Omega') \int \delta(\Omega - \Omega')\, d\Omega = \left(N_\ell^{(m)}\right)^{-1} Y_\ell^{(m)*}(\Omega') .$$

## Appendix 5. Sinusoidal Operators

We know from algebra that the functions sin x and cos x can be expanded into infinite series

$$\sin x = x - \frac{x^3}{3!} + \frac{x^5}{5!} - \frac{x^7}{7!} + \dots$$

$$\cos x = 1 - \frac{x^2}{2!} + \frac{x^4}{4!} - \frac{x^6}{6!} + \dots .$$

It is convenient to define functions in which x is an operator. By substituting $x = a\,G$, where G is an operator and a is a number, we obtain the operators $\sin(a\,G)$ and $\cos(a\,G)$ defined in terms of the following series

$$\sin(a\,G) = a\,G - \frac{a^3 G^3}{3!} + \frac{a^5 G^5}{5!} - \frac{a^7 G^7}{7!} + \dots \tag{A5.1}$$

$$\cos(a\,G) = 1 - \frac{a^2 G^2}{2!} + \frac{a^4 G^4}{4!} - \frac{a^6 G^6}{6!} + \dots . \tag{A5.2}$$

In two-dimensional NMR spectroscopy (see Section 40) we encounter these series with $G = I_z$, where $I_z$ is the Z coordinate of spin 1/2. The following relationship holds for $I_z$ and for n = 2, 4, 6, ...

$$(I_z)^n = \{1\}\left(\frac{1}{2}\right)^n \tag{A5.3}$$

where $\{1\}$ is an L-dimensional unit matrix. For example, in the basis of the functions given in Table 15.1 we have

$$I_z = \frac{1}{2}\left\{\begin{matrix} 1 & 0 & 0 & 0 \\ 0 & 1 & 0 & 0 \\ 0 & 0 & -1 & 0 \\ 0 & 0 & 0 & -1 \end{matrix}\right\}.$$

Substituting $G = I_z$ in (A5.1) we have

$$\sin\left(a\, I_z\right) = 2I_z\left(\frac{1}{2}a - \frac{\frac{1}{2}a^3 I_z^2}{3!} + \frac{\frac{1}{2}a^5 I_z^4}{5!} - \frac{\frac{1}{2}a^7 I_z^6}{7!} + \dots\right).$$

Using (A5.3) we find that

$$\sin\left(a\, I_z\right) = 2I_z\left(\frac{1}{2}a - \frac{\left(\frac{1}{2}a\right)^3}{3!} + \frac{\left(\frac{1}{2}a\right)^5}{5!} - \frac{\left(\frac{1}{2}a\right)^7}{7!} + \dots\right).$$

Therefore

$$\sin\left(a\, I_z\right) = 2I_z \sin\left(\frac{1}{2}a\right). \tag{A5.4}$$

In an analogous way we use (A5.2) to calculate

$$\cos\left(a\, I_z\right) = \{1\} - \frac{\left(\frac{1}{2}a\right)^2}{2!}\{1\} + \frac{\left(\frac{1}{2}a\right)^4}{4!}\{1\} - \frac{\left(\frac{1}{2}a\right)^6}{6!}\{1\} + \dots$$

so that

$$\cos\left(a\, I_z\right) = \{1\}\cos\left(\frac{1}{2}a\right). \tag{A5.5}$$

# References

Abragam A. (1983). *Principles of Nuclear Magnetism.* Oxford University Press, Oxford.

Andrew E.R. and Bersohn R. (1950). Nuclear magnetic resonance line shape for a triangular configuration of nuclei. *J. Chem. Phys.* **18**, 159-161.

Andrew E.R. and Eades R.G. (1953). A nuclear magnetic resonance investigation of three solid benzenes. *Proc. R. Soc. Lond.* **A218**, 537-552.

Atkins P.W. (1990). *Physical Chemistry.* Fourth Edition. Oxford University Press, Oxford.

Aue W.P., Bartholdi E. and Ernst R.R. (1976). Two-dimensional spectroscopy: application to nuclear magnetic resonance. *J. Chem. Phys.* **64**, 2299-2346.

Bersohn R. and Gutowsky H.S. (1954). Proton magnetic resonance in an ammonium chloride single crystal. *J. Chem. Phys.* **22**, 651-658.

Blicharski J.S. (1967). Interference effect in nuclear magnetic relaxation. *Phys. Lett.* **24A**, 608-610.

Blicharski J.S. (1970). Interference effect in nuclear magnetic relaxation. III. *Acta Phys. Polon.* **38**, 19-24.

Blicharski J.S. and Nosel W. (1972). Interference effect in nuclear magnetic relaxation in liquid $^{10}BF_3$. *Acta Phys. Polon.* **A42**, 223-232.

Bloch F. (1946). Nuclear induction. *Phys. Rev.* **70**, 460-474.

Bloch, F., Hansen W.W. and Packard M. (1946). Nuclear induction. *Phys. Rev.* **69**, 127.

Bloembergen, N., Purcell E.M. and Pound R.V. (1948). Relaxation effects in nuclear magnetic resonance absorption. *Phys. Rev.* **73**, 679-712.

Bracewell R. (1965). *The Fourier Transform and its Applications.* McGraw-Hill, New York.

Brigham E.O. (1974). *The Fast Fourier Transform.* Prentice-Hall, Englewood Cliffs, NJ.

Carr H.Y. and Purcell E.M. (1954). Effects of diffusion on free precession in nuclear magnetic resonance experiments. *Phys. Rev.* **94**, 630-638.

*References*

Clark W.G. (1964). Pulsed nuclear resonance apparatus. *Rev. Sci. Instrum.* **35**, 316-333.

Cooley J.W. and Tukey J.W. (1965). An algorithm for the machine calculation of complex Fourier series. *Math. Comput.* **19**, 297-301.

Dickinson W.C. (1950). Dependence of the $F^{19}$ nuclear resonance position on chemical compound. *Phys. Rev.* **77**, 736-737.

Einstein A. (1917). Zur Quantentheorie der Strahlung. *Phys. Z.* **18**, 121-128.

Ernst R.R. and Anderson W.A. (1966). Application of Fourier transform spectroscopy to magnetic resonance. *Rev. Sci. Instrum.* **37**, 93-102.

Ernst, R.R., Bodenhausen G. and Wokaun A. (1987). *Principles of Nuclear Magnetic Resonance in One and Two Dimensions.* Clarendon Press, Oxford.

Feynman R.P., Leighton R.B. and Sands M. (1965). *The Feynman Lectures on Physics.* Addison-Wesley, Reading, Mass.

Fukushima E. and Roeder S.B.W. (1981). *Experimental Pulse NMR. A Nuts and Bolts Approach.* Addison-Wesley, Reading, Mass.

Gierer A. and Wirtz K. (1953). Molekuläre Theorie der Mikroreiburg. *Z. Naturforsch.* **8a**, 532-538.

Grant I.S. and Phillips W.R. (1979). *Electromagnetism.* John Wiley, Chichester.

Hahn E.L. (1950a). Nuclear induction due to free Larmor precession. *Phys. Rev.* **77**, 297-298.

Hahn E.L. (1950b). Spin echoes. *Phys. Rev.* **80**, 580-594.

Heine V. (1960). *Group Theory in Quantum Mechanics. An Introduction to its Present Usage.* Pergamon Press, London.

Homans S.W. (1989). *A Dictionary of Concepts in NMR.* Clarendon Press, Oxford.

Horowitz P. and Hill W. (1989). *The Art of Electronics.* Second Edition. Cambridge University Press, Cambridge.

Hubbard P.S. (1958). Nuclear magnetic relaxation of three and four spin molecules in a liquid. *Phys. Rev.* **109**, 1153-1158.

Jeener J. (1971). Unpublished lecture at the Ampère International Summer School II, Basko Polje, Yugoslavia.

Jeffries C.D. (1963). *Dynamic Nuclear Orientation.* John Wiley, New York.

Lösche A. (1957). *Kerninduktion.* VEB Deutscher Verlag der Wissenschaften, Berlin.

Margenau H. and Murphy G.S. (1956). *The Mathematics of Physics and Chemistry*. Van Nostrand, Princeton, NJ.

Marshall A.G. (1982). *Fourier, Hadamard, and Hilbert Transforms in Chemistry*. Plenum Press, New York.

Meiboom S. and Gill D. (1958). Modified spin-echo method for measuring nuclear relaxation times. *Rev. Sci. Instrum.* **29**, 688-691.

Mills, I., Cvitas, T., Kallay, N., Homann K. and Kuchitsu K. (Ed.) (1988). *Quantities, Units and Symbols in Physical Chemistry*. Sponsored by the International Union of Pure and Applied Chemistry. Blackwell Scientific, Oxford.

Pake G.E. (1948). Nuclear resonance adsorption in hydrated crystals: Fine structure of the proton line. *J. Chem. Phys.* **16**, 327-336.

Paliouras J.D. and Meadows D.S. (1990). *Complex Variables for Scientists and Engineers*. Macmillan, London.

Pauling L. and Wilson E.B. Jr. (1935). *Introduction to Quantum Mechanics*. McGraw-Hill, New York.

Pople J.A., Schneider W.G. and Bernstein H.J. (1959). *High-Resolution Nuclear Magnetic Resonance*. McGraw-Hill, New York.

Proctor W.G. and Yu F.C. (1950). The dependence of a nuclear magnetic resonance frequency upon chemical compound. *Phys. Rev.* **77**, 717.

Purcell E.M., Torrey H.C. and Pound R.V. (1946). Resonance adsorption by nuclear magnetic moments in a solid. *Phys. Rev.* **69**, 37-38.

Ramsey N.F. (1950). Magnetic shielding of nuclei in molecules. *Phys. Rev.* **78**, 699-703.

Redfield A.G. (1955). Nuclear magnetic resonance saturation and rotary saturation in solids. *Phys. Rev.* **98**, 1787-1809.

Redfield A.G. (1957). On the theory of relaxation processes. *IBM J. Res. Develop.* **1**, 19-31.

Richards R.E. and Smith J.A.S. (1951). Nuclear magnetic resonance spectra of some acid hydrates. *Trans. Faraday Soc.* **47**, 1261-1274.

Rojansky V. (1964). *Introductory Quantum Mechanics*. Prentice-Hall, Englewood Cliffs, NJ.

Slichter C.P. (1989). *Principles of Magnetic Resonance*. Third Edition. Springer-Verlag, New York.

Solomon I. (1955). Relaxation processes in a system of two spins. *Phys. Rev.* **99**, 559-565.

Torrey H.C. (1949). Transient nutations in nuclear magnetic resonance. *Phys. Rev.* **76**, 1059-1068.

Van Vleck J.H. (1948). The dipolar broadening of magnetic resonance lines in crystals. *Phys. Rev.* **74**, 1168-1183.

Werbelow L.G. and Grant D.M. (1977). Intramolecular dipolar relaxation in multispin systems. *Adv. Magn. Reson.* **9**, 190-299.

# Further Reading


Abragam A. (1983). *Principles of Nuclear Magnetism.* Oxford University Press, Oxford.

Abraham R.J., Fisher J. and Loftus P. (1988). *Introduction to NMR Spectroscopy.* John Wiley, Chichester.

Aitken A.C. (1967). *Determinants and Matrices.* Oliver and Boyd, Edinburgh.

Akitt J.W. (1973). *NMR and Chemistry: An Introduction to the Fourier Transform-Multinuclear Era.* Second Edition. Chapman and Hall, London.

Andrew E.R. (1969). *Nuclear Magnetic Resonance.* Cambridge University Press, Cambridge.

Andrew E.R. (1981). Magic angle spinning. *Int. Rev. Phys. Chem.* **1**, 195-224.

Arfken G. (1985). *Mathematical Methods for Physicists.* Academic Press, New York.

Atherton N.M. (1973). *Electron Spin Resonance.* Ellis Horwood, Chichester.

Atkins P.W. (1984). *Molecular Quantum Mechanics.* Oxford University Press, Oxford.

Atkins P.W. (1990). *Physical Chemistry.* Fourth Edition. Oxford University Press, Oxford.

Batchelor G.K. (1967). *An Introduction to Fluid Dynamics.* Cambridge University Press, Cambridge.

Bax A. (1984). *Two-Dimensional Nuclear Magnetic Resonance in Liquids.* Delft University Press, Delft/D. Reidel, Dordrecht.

G. Baym G. (1969). *Lectures on Quantum Mechanics.* Benjamin/Cummings, Reading, Mass.

Becker E.D. (1980). *High Resolution NMR.* Academic Press, New York.

Bloembergen N. (1961). *Nuclear Magnetic Relaxation.* W.A. Benjamin, New York.

Bracewell R. (1965). *The Fourier Transform and its Applications.* McGraw-Hill, New York.

Brigham E.O. (1974). *The Fast Fourier Transform.* Prentice-Hall, Englewood Cliffs, NJ.

Champeney D.C. (1987). *A Handbook of Fourier Theorems.* Cambridge University Press, Cambridge.

Cohen M.H. and Reif R. (1957). Quadrupole effects in nuclear magnetic resonance studies of solids. *Solid State Physics,* Ed. F. Seitz and D. Turnbull. Vol. 5, p. 321-438. Academic Press, New York.

Coulson C.A. (1965). *Electricity.* Oliver and Boyd, Edinburgh.

Das T.P. and Hahn E.L. (1958). Nuclear quadrupole resonance spectroscopy. *Solid State Physics,* Ed. F. Seitz and D. Turnbull. Suppl. 1, p. 1-209. Academic Press, New York.

Davies P.C.W. (1984). *Quantum Mechanics.* Routledge and Kegan Paul, London.

Debye P. (1929). *Polar Molecules.* Chemical Catalog Company, New York.

Derome A.E. (1987). *Modern NMR Techniques for Chemistry Research.* Pergamon Press, Oxford.

Dirac P.A.M. (1958). *The Principles of Quantum Mechanics.* Fourth Edition. Clarendon Press, Oxford.

Eckart C. (1930). The applications of group theory to the quantum dynamics of monatomic systems. *Rev. Mod. Phys.* **2**, 305-380.

Edmonds A.R. (1968). *Angular Momentum in Quantum Mechanics.* Princeton University Press, Princeton, NJ.

Ernst, R.R., Bodenhausen G. and Wokaun A. (1987). *Principles of Nuclear Magnetic Resonance in One and Two Dimensions.* Clarendon Press, Oxford.

Farrar T.C. and Becker E.D. (1971). *Pulse and Fourier Transform NMR. Introduction to Theory and Methods.* Academic Press, New York.

Feynman R.P., Leighton R.B. and Sands M. (1965). *The Feynman Lectures on Physics.* Addison-Wesley, Reading, Mass.

Freeman R. (1988). *A Handbook of Nuclear Magnetic Resonance.* Longman, London.

Fukushima E. and Roeder S.B.W. (1981). *Experimental Pulse NMR. A Nuts and Bolts Approach.* Addison-Wesley, Reading, Mass.

Fyfe C.A. (1983). *Solid State NMR for Chemists.* C.F.C. Press, Guelph, Ontario.

Gerstein B.C. and Dybowski C.R. (1985). *Transient Techniques in NMR of Solids. An Introduction to Theory and Practice.* Academic Press, New York.

Goldman M. (1970). *Spin Temperature and Nuclear Magnetic Resonance in Solids.* Oxford University Press, Oxford.

Goldman M. (1988). *Quantum Description of High-Resolution NMR in Liquids.* Clarendon Press, Oxford.

Grant I.S. and Phillips W.R. (1979). *Electromagnetism.* John Wiley, Chichester.

Haeberlen U. (1976). High resolution NMR in solids: selective averaging. Supplement #1 to *Advances in Magnetic Resonance.* Academic Press, New York.

Harris R.K. (1983). *Nuclear Magnetic Resonance Spectroscopy. A Physicochemical View.* Pitman, London.

Hebel L.C. Jr. (1963). Spin temperature and nuclear relaxation in solids. *Solid State Physics,* Ed. F. Seitz and D. Turnbull. Vol. 15, p. 409-491. Academic Press, New York.

Heine V. (1960). *Group Theory in Quantum Mechanics. An Introduction to its Present Usage.* Pergamon Press, London.

Heitler W. (1954). *The Quantum Theory of Radiation.* Oxford University Press, Oxford.

Hobson E.W. (1926). *The Theory of Functions of a Real Variable and the Theory of Fourier's Series.* Cambridge University Press, Cambridge.

Homans S.W. (1989). *A Dictionary of Concepts in NMR.* Clarendon Press, Oxford.

Horowitz P. and Hill W. (1989). *The Art of Electronics.* Second Edition. Cambridge University Press, Cambridge.

Ingram D.J.E. (1955). *Spectroscopy at Radio and Microwave Frequencies.* Butterworths, London.

Jeffreys H. (1967). *Theory of Probability.* Oxford University Press, Oxford.

Jeffries C.D. (1961). Dynamic nuclear polarization. *Progress in Cryogenics.* Heywood, London.

Jeffries C.D. (1963). *Dynamic Nuclear Orientation.* John Wiley, New York.

Kittel C. (1986). *Introduction to Solid State Physics.* Sixth Edition. John Wiley, New York.

Knight W.D. (1956). Electron paramagnetism and nuclear magnetic resonance in metals. *Solid State Physics,* Ed. F. Seitz and D. Turnbull. Vol. 2, p. 93-136. Academic Press, New York.

Krane K.S. (1988). *Introductory Nuclear Physics.* John Wiley, New York.

Landau L.D. and Lifschitz E.M. (1958). *Statistical Physics.* Pergamon, London.
Lévy-Leblond J.-M. and Balibar F. (1990). *Quantics. Rudiments of Quantum Physics.* North-Holland, Amsterdam.

Littlewood D.E. (1950). *A University Algebra.* Heinemann, London.

Lösche A. (1957). *Kerninduktion.* VEB Deutscher Verlag der Wissenschaften, Berlin.

Low W. (1960). Paramagnetic resonance in solids. *Solid State Physics,* Ed. F. Seitz and D. Turnbull. Suppl. 2, p. 1-193. Academic Press, New York.

Magnus W. and Oberhettinger F. (1949). *Formulas and Theorems for the Special Functions of Mathematical Physics.* Chelsea, New York.

Margenau H. and Murphy G.S. (1956). *The Mathematics of Physics and Chemistry.* Van Nostrand, Princeton, NJ.

Margenau H. and Murphy G.S. (1964). *The Mathematics of Physics and Chemistry.* Volume Two. Van Nostrand, Princeton, NJ.

Marshall A.G. (1982). *Fourier, Hadamard, and Hilbert Transforms in Chemistry.* Plenum Press, New York.

Marshall A.G. and Comisarow M.B. (1975). Fourier transform methods in spectroscopy. *J. Chem. Ed.* **52**, 6386.

Marshall A.G. and Verdun F.R. (1990). *Fourier Transforms in NMR, Optical and Mass Spectrometry.* Elsevier, Amsterdam.

Martin G.E. and Zektzer A.S. (1988). *Two-Dimensional NMR Methods for Establishing Molecular Connectivity. A Chemist's Guide to Experiment Selection, Performance, and Interpretation.* VCH Publishers, Weinheim.

Martin M.L., Martin G.J. and Delpuech J.-J. (1980). *Practical NMR Spectroscopy.* Heyden, London.

J. Mason (Ed.) (1987). *Multinuclear NMR.* Plenum Press, New York.

McConnell J. (1987). *The Theory of Nuclear Magnetic Relaxation in Liquids.* Cambridge University Press, Cambridge.

McLauchlan K.A. (1972). *Magnetic Resonance.* Oxford University Press, Oxford.

Mehring M. (1983). *High-Resolution NMR Spectroscopy in Solids.* Second Edition. Springer-Verlag, New York.

Mills, I., Cvitas, T., Kallay, N., Homann K. and Kuchitsu K. (Ed.) (1988). *Quantities, Units and Symbols in Physical Chemistry.* Sponsored by the International Union of Pure and Applied Chemistry. Blackwell Scientific, Oxford.

Munowitz M. (1988). *Coherence and NMR*. John Wiley, Chichester.

Overhauser A.W. (1963). *Dynamic Nuclear Orientation*. Ed. C.D. Jeffries. Interscience, New York.

Pake G.E. and Estle T.L. (1973). *The Physical Principles of Electron Paramagnetic Resonance*. W.A. Benjamin, Reading, Mass.

Paliouras J.D. and Meadows D.S. (1990). *Complex Variables for Scientists and Engineers*. Macmillan, London.

Pauling L. and Wilson E.B. Jr. (1935). *Introduction to Quantum Mechanics*. McGraw-Hill, New York.

Pines D. (1955). Electron interaction in metals. *Solid State Physics*, Ed. F. Seitz and D. Turnbull. Vol. 1, p. 367-450. Academic Press, New York.

Poole C.P. Jr. and Farach H.A. (1972). *The Theory of Magnetic Resonance*. Wiley-Interscience, New York.

Pople J.A., Schneider W.G. and Bernstein H.J. (1959). *High-Resolution Nuclear Magnetic Resonance*. McGraw-Hill, New York.

*The Radio Amateur's Handbook*. American Radio Relay League, Newington, Conn., 1991.

Ramsey N.F. (1953). *Nuclear Moments*. Wiley, New York/Chapman and Hall, London.

Roberts J.D. (1959). *Nuclear Magnetic Resonance*. McGraw-Hill, New York.

Rojansky V. (1964). *Introductory Quantum Mechanics*. Prentice-Hall, Englewood Cliffs, NJ.

Rose M.E. (1957). *Elementary Theory of Angular Momentum*. John Wiley, New York.

The Royal Society (1975). *Quantities, Units, and Symbols*. Second Edition. The Royal Society, London.

Saha A.K. and Das T.P. (1957). *Theory and Applications of Nuclear Induction*. Saha Institute of Nuclear Physics, Calcutta.

Sanders J.K.M. and Hunter B.K. (1988). *Modern NMR Spectroscopy. A Guide for Chemists*. Oxford University Press, Oxford.

Sanders J.K.M. and Hunter B.K. (1989). *Modern NMR Spectroscopy. A Workbook of Chemical Problems*. Oxford University Press, Oxford.

Schiff L.I. (1968). *Quantum Mechanics*. McGraw-Hill, New York.

Schumacher R.T. (1970). *Introduction to Magnetic Resonance*. W.A. Benjamin, New York.

Shaw D. (1984). *Fourier Transform NMR Spectroscopy.* Second Edition. Elsevier, Amsterdam.

Slichter C.P. (1989). *Principles of Magnetic Resonance.* Third Edition. Springer-Verlag, New York.

Spanier J. and Oldham K.B. (1987). *An Atlas of Functions.* Hemisphere Publishing Corporation, Washington.

Spiegel M.R. (1972). *Complex Variables.* Schaum's Outline Series. McGraw-Hill, New York.

Spiegel M.R. (1974). *Fourier Analysis.* Schaum's Outline Series. McGraw-Hill, New York.

Stothers J.B. (1972). *Carbon-13 NMR Spectroscopy.* Academic Press, New York.

Synge J.L. and Griffith B.A. (1959). *Principles of Mechanics.* Third Edition. McGraw-Hill, New York.

Tolman R.C. (1955). *The Principles of Statistical Mechanics.* Oxford University Press, Oxford.

Vetterling W.T., Teukolsky S.A., Press W.H. and Flannery B.P. (1989). *Numerical Recipes.* Cambridge University Press, Cambridge.

Wigner E.P. (1959). *Group Theory and its Application to the Quantum Mechanics of Atomic Spectra.* Academic Press, New York.

Wolfram S. (1991). *Mathematica. A System for Doing Mathematics by Computer.* Second Edition. Addison-Wesley, Reading, Mass.

Yannoni C.S. (1982). High-resolution NMR in solids: the CPMAS experiment. *Accts. Chem. Res.* **15**, 201-208.

# Index